The Green King

PAUL-LOUP SULITZER

The Green King

A NOVEL

Translated from the French by Denise Raab Jacobs

LYLE STUART INC.   SECAUCUS, N.J.

Published by Lyle Stuart Inc.
Published simultaneously in Canada by
Musson Book Company,
A division of General Publishing Co. Limited
Don Mills, Ontario

Queries regarding rights and permissions should be
addressed to: Carole Stuart, 120 Enterprise Avenue,
Secaucus, N.J. 07094

Manufactured in the United States of America

Library of Congress Cataloging in Publication Data

Sulitzer, Paul-Loup, 1946–
    The Green King.

    Translation of: Le Roi vert.
    I. Title.
PQ2679.U457R613   1984   843'.914   83-18103
ISBN 0-8184-0360-8

For my father
for my mother
for my sister Dominique
for my daughter Olivia

For Milly

For my friends J.-R. Hirsh
and J.-R. Rein

For my uncle Paul,
who was deported and killed

Some say he's mad; others that lesser hate him
Do call it valiant fury; but, for certain,
He cannot buckle his distemper'd cause
Within the belt of rule.

Shakespeare, *Macbeth*, V,2

Prologue

I hadn't been in Munich one hour when Captain Tarras informed me that advance units of the Seventh Army had just discovered another camp, in north Austria, near Linz; the place was called "Mauthausen." Tarras insisted that I leave right away; he had secured three seats in a military plane. He would join us in two or three days. I had many good reasons to obey Georges Tarras: he was a captain and I was only a first lieutenant; he had been, until the summer of 1942, my international law professor at Harvard; and, finally, it was he who, having accidentally run into me in Paris two weeks earlier, had recruited me to serve under him on the War Crimes Commission. If that was not enough, I liked him, although I had some difficulty in recognizing, beneath the olive-drab uniform, the sarcastic and brilliant professor who used to hold forth within the ivied walls of Harvard Yard.

Three of us left. I was accompanied by Mike Rinaldi, a sergeant, and by Roy Blackstock, a photographer. I had little in common with either of them. Rinaldi was from Little Italy in New York City, Blackstock was from Virginia. Although totally different physically—one, small, stocky, with a thin black waxed mustache; the other, six feet four inches of soft and still-expanding bulk—they seemed to share an impressive and cynical nonchalance I took as proof of maturity, of experience I had not yet acquired.

It was May 5, 1945. I knew little of the war then ending in Europe, except for the news of the taking of Berlin by the Russians, three days earlier, and the imminence of a total and official surrender of the Third Reich. The war was ending and I hadn't killed anyone and hadn't seen any fighting. Four months from my twenty-second birthday, I was like an adolescent entering a theater for the first time just as the curtain is coming down. Having returned to Europe for the first time in six years, I had seen my French grandmother again, in Paris. The fact that I had become an American, giving up my father's nationality for my mother's, had affected her ever so slightly; actually, she had barely reacted to the news, being too preoccupied with describing to me what had become of Paris and her Provence under German occupation. . . .

Once in Linz, Rinaldi managed to get us aboard a truck going to Vienna, where the Red Army had been since April 13. At about 2:00 P.M., we crossed the Danube at Enns. There, Rinaldi intercepted a Jeep and convinced the driver, an Italian-American like himself, to take us farther. We went first to the Mauthausen train station, and there we coerced the driver, with constraints bordering on pure and simple blackmail, to cover the last three and a half miles separating us from the camp.

There, for the first time, did my footsteps cross those of Reb Michael Klimrod.

Among the many clear memories I've kept of that day, there is, first, that lightness of the Austrian air, sunny and mild, balmy, with the perfume of a spring that seems eternal.

Only then came the stench.

It hit my nostrils when we were still two or three hundred yards from the camp. A large convoy of covered trucks forced us to stop, and our improvised chauffeur took this opportunity to proclaim with furious determination that he would go no farther. We had to get out and proceed on foot. The stench became more perceptible; it hung in the air in successive and unmoving masses. "Crematoriums," said Blackstock, with his Southern drawl. And the placid tone, the very accent, seemed to rid the word of its horror. We passed through the wide-open doors. Tanks had come, then gone, leaving fresh tracks on the ground. In their place, trucks kept arriving in a continuous flow, discharging supplies, medicine and bandages, bolstering the medical units already on the spot. But this flow, once inside the doors, lost itself instantly in the huge mute sea of living corpses, almost still, strangely, like a tide suddenly frozen. The arrival of the tanks, five or six hours before, had probably caused this sea to shudder, to become animated, but now, the excitement had dropped, the joy of freedom had dimmed, and the faces were rigid masks. It was as if they had entered a second stage, now that the end of the nightmare was accepted as reality. In the hallucinatory glances cast toward me, Rinaldi, and Blackstock, who used his well-fed mass to make a path, I could see a strange apathy, and a sort of resignation, but also hatred, an angry reproach: "Why didn't you come sooner?"

"And they stink," said Blackstock, "how they stink; it's unbelievable." With determination and without any gentleness, the giant pushed through the scarecrows in striped rags.

The American officer in charge of the camp wore gold maple leaves on his collar. He was short, stiff, had red hair, and was named Strachan. He told me that if there was anything at this moment that preoccupied him less than war crimes, he would like to know what it was. Right now he was trying to bring some order to this unspeakable mess. He had undertaken to separate the former prisoners into three categories: beyond help, critical, out of danger. Those beyond help were numerous. "Two or three thousand of them are going to die on me within the next few days, but at least they'll die free, and that's something." He stared at me with his brown, almost yellow, eyes.

"What did you say your name was?"

"David Settiniaz."

"Jewish?"

"No."

"What kind of name is that? Originally."

"French."

"Sounds Polish."

He had already turned away, barking orders. Rinaldi was gesturing at me. We entered a building that had served as offices for the SS detachment. "This room," asked Rinaldi, "or that one?" I chose the first one, which had a little waiting room furnished with three or four chairs. Blackstock had disappeared, off somewhere taking photographs. Rinaldi had found a piece of cardboard and was fixing it to the door. On it he wrote, going over the letters several times to thicken them: WAR CRIMES.

I stood there, overwhelmed by the stench and the strange and vibrant silence of Mauthausen, which was still populated by thousands and thousands of survivors. I felt such shame and de-

11

spair that, thirty-five years later, I can still relive it, experience again the nausea and the humiliation.

I had to get out, at one point. I can see myself walking through the dense crowd, which hardly opened in front of me. I went through one barracks, then another, and in the last one the medical teams had not yet arrived. There, a semidarkness reigned, yellowed here and there by the dusty spring sun. There were two-day-old corpses lying next to those who were still alive, three or four in each bunk. Skeletal shapes, heaps of old rags and bones, moved and crawled as I went by. The pestilence increased. I was brushed against, I was grabbed. I panicked and ran. I found myself outside, in the sunlight, shaken with spasms of nausea. I reached a narrow space between two buildings. I was all alone, or I thought I was. I vomited, and only then, in the same way you feel a burn, did I feel eyes staring at me. . . .

The grave was a few feet away. It measured only six by six feet. The earth that had been removed was neatly piled in a triangular hill, in which a shovel was planted. A few handfuls of dirt had been carelessly thrown into the grave, but the layer of quicklime placed there before had already corroded the mounds . . . as well as the naked bodies of the men they had tried to bury hastily. One could guess what had happened: the eight or ten naked bodies thrown into the ditch, pushed down with a gun butt or a heel to form an even surface. Then the quicklime, then the earth. But the dead kept rising to the surface. I could see hands, abdomens, penises, mouths, and nostrils charred and eaten away by the calcium oxide, the bones sometimes exposed and already rotted.

And right in the middle of the nightmarish tangle, I saw a face, frightfully drawn, covered with black spots of dried blood, in which a pair of light eyes shone with amazing sharpness. . . .

They followed me every movement as I drew away from the wall against which I'd been leaning. And I remember thinking of the steadiness of a stare frozen by death. I stepped closer to the grave. And a voice rose, in slightly accented French reciting Verlaine.

"Mon Dieu, mon Dieu, la vie est là, simple et tranquille . . ." (My God, my God, life is there, simple and tranquil . . .)

What happened then was out of a dream.

"Cette paisible rumeur-là vient de la ville . . ." (That peaceful

murmur comes from the town . . .) The verses came automatically to my lips, and it seemed I spoke them.

I know only that I went up to the grave. I crouched at the edge of it, put out my arm, and my fingers touched the large bony hand of the seventeen-year-old boy we would later call "The King."

The Photographer from Salzburg

1

The King said later that he opened his eyes and saw a soldier appear. He didn't recognize the uniform, which wasn't that of the SS, or the Volkssturm. It didn't resemble those of the Rumanian, Italian, or French contingents that had fought alongside the Wehrmacht in the last few years. And it certainly wasn't a Russian. He had seen Russians, either prisoners or shot by Obersturmbannführer Hochreiner, always looking to improve his personal score of men, women, or children shot in the back of the head. On May 4, 1945, the Obersturmbannführer was up to two hundred and eighty-three shot in the head, and an apparent sadness had shown on his face when he had announced to Reb Klimrod that he, Reb, would be his two hundred and eighty-fourth recorded victim, whatever regret that might cause either of them after having lived together, so tenderly, for the last twenty months.

The King said he had actually regained consciousness a few moments before he saw the soldier arrive. He doesn't know how long before. It was a slow, progressive awakening, marked at first by the extraordinary discovery that he was still alive. Then followed, in successive steps toward full consciousness, first, the last precise moment recorded by his memory, that of the Obersturmbannführer kissing him one last time full on the mouth before placing the barrel of the Lüger against his neck, then the still-unclear revelation that he was buried alive, his face almost free, covered only by a thin layer of earth. Then only, did he feel the pain: at the back of his head, but that was a dull pain, and in several places on his shoulders, his forearms, and his abdomen, everywhere the quicklime had bit. He realized he couldn't move at all, except for his head and his left hand. The rest of his body was caught in the tangle of naked corpses. Lying right across him, and having greatly protected him, was Zaccharius, the fourteen-year-old Lithuanian whom the Obersturmbann-führer had taken from the Grossrosen camp to join his harem of boys.

He moved his neck. Bits of earth and Zaccharius's arm slipped, just enough for him to see the sun. He didn't hear the soldier approach. Then he saw him, with his back turned and retching. His thinking was not clear enough yet to see a connection between this man in a foreign uniform, retching, and the sudden desertion, the previous day, if it was the previous day, of the Mauthausen camp by the Obersturmbannführer and his special team. It did not occur to him that the soldier might be an American. He simply sensed that the newcomer belonged to a foreign world. And for this reason only, he thought it best not to speak German. He chose, among the other languages he knew, French. He spoke, and the man answered—in fact, continued the recitation of the poem Reb had begun automatically, and it happened as if it were a prearranged signal, a key phrase to be exchanged between two men who had never seen one another until that moment, but were fated to meet. The man came close to the grave, knelt down, put out his hand, and touched Reb's left hand. He said something incomprehensible, then, in French: "Are you hurt?"

"Yes," said Reb.

He could see the soldier's face clearly now. The man was very young, blond, with wide-open blue eyes. Silver bars shone on his collar. He didn't seem to be carrying a weapon. He asked: "Are you French?"

"Austrian," said Reb.

The man was pulling him now, but to no avail. The mixed layer of earth and lime loosened a bit more, revealing Zaccharius's body, the buttocks and back entirely eaten away.

"Oh, God" exclaimed the man, beginning to retch again.

Reb's huge gray eyes followed his every move.

"And you, what is your nationality?" Reb asked.

"American," answered the young soldier.

His heaving had subsided. He managed to stand and meet the gaze of the amazing gray eyes.

"There are perhaps more survivors besides you . . ."

18

"I don't think so," said Reb. "They shot each of us in the back of the head."

His speach was extraordinarily slow and calm. He moved his left hand. "You will not be able to get me out alone," he said. "I am not lying flat. Actually, they buried me almost standing. Is there anyone else with you?'

"The United States Army," replied Settiniaz, without any sense of the absurdity of his answer and without the slightest intention of being humorous. He was bewildered and almost frightened by the man's calm. And, incredible as it seemed, he thought he detected a spark of gaiety in the light eyes.

"In that case, you might be able to get some help. What is your name?

"Settiniaz. David Settiniaz. My father was French."

Silence. The lieutenant hestitated.

"Go," ordered Reb Klimrod, with the same hallucinatory softness. "Hurry, please. I am finding it hard to breathe. Thank you for coming. I will not forget."

The gray eyes had an odd gleam.

2

David Settiniaz returned with Blackstock, a doctor, and two infantrymen. Blackstock photographed the grave as it was when they discovered it. These photographs were never published, or even put in any file. But they were purchased, thirteen years later, by the King, from Roy Blackstock and his wife. Blackstock is of the opinion that the boy survived not just because of a stupefying set of circumstances. The position of Klimrod's body, as they removed him, showed that he had begun a ferocious climb toward the surface as he was being buried. He had cleared a way through the corpses of his eight companions, the task made all the more difficult by the fact that he had been among the first thrown into the ditch and the top of it had been stamped down by SS boots before being covered with quicklime, then earth.

The grave contained nine bodies, all of young boys, ranging in age from twelve to seventeen, Reb Klimrod being the oldest and the only one to survive.

He was unconscious again by the time they finally got him out of the ditch. Settiniaz was astounded by the boy's height, which he estimated at six feet, and by his weight, about one hundred pounds.

He was twice wrong. On May 5, 1945, Reb Klimrod, four months away from his seventeenth birthday, measured six feet one and a half inches, and weighed eighty-six pounds.

He had been shot once in the back of the head, behind the left ear. The bullet had slightly grazed the lower lobe, had split the base of the occipital, and plowed the neck muscles above the nape, skimming the vertebra. In effect, the other wounds were more serious and probably more painful. Two more bullets were removed, one from the boy's right thigh, the other from directly above the hip. The quicklime had hit him in thirty other places. His back, hips, and lower abdomen showed traces of hundreds of lashes and cigarette burns, some of the scars years old. Only his face had been spared.

And this face moved not only Settiniaz, who was the first to see him, but also all those who were to see him thereafter. It wasn't that he was that handsome—his features lacked regularity—but he showed a dramatic, almost monstrous inner tension, together with total quietness. In no way was it, in a camp where expressions of death and hopelessness abounded, the face of someone who had given up. Mostly, you noticed the eyes, pale gray with green specks, looking at men and objects with a most impressive strength.

In the course of the next few days, he slept almost continuously. Yet he was the cause of an incident. A group of former prisoners came to Strachan to complain on behalf, they claimed, of all their comrades: they refused to share quarters with a "pansy of the SS." The word they used was much harsher. This demand did not stir the small red-headed major from New Mexico; he had other worries: the deaths continued at Mauthausen, hundreds each day.

As far as the boy was concerned, he told Settiniaz: "If not for you, I understand, he would be dead. Take care of him."

"I don't even know his name."

"Your problem," answered Strachan in his high voice. "From this point on, you figure it out."

This took place the morning of May 7. Settiniaz had the boy taken to the barracks where the *Kapos*, whose fate had yet to be decided, were assembled. He reproached himself for this. The very idea of attributing any wrongdoing to the young stranger revolted him. Three times he went to see him, finding him awake only once; he wanted to question him but was answered only by the serious and dreamy look.

"Do you recognize me? I pulled you from the grave. . . ." No answer. "At least tell me your name." No answer. "You told me you were Austrian. You must have family you want to get in touch with." No answer. "Where did you learn to speak French?" No answer. "I only want to help you. . . ."

The boy closed his eyes, turned toward the wall.

The next day, May 8, Captain Tarras arrived from Munich, along with the news of the German surrender.

Georges Tarras was a Georgian, not an American Georgian, but a Russian one. At Harvard, Settiniaz had learned that Tarras was an aristocratic Russian whose family had emigrated to the United States in 1918. In 1945, he was forty-four years old and had apparently given himself the task of convincing the maximum number of people from planet Earth to take themselves less seriously. He abhorred sentimentality, had a natural passiveness (or at least feigned it marvelously) when faced with the most extreme examples of human stupidity, and had sarcasm permanently on the tip of his tongue. Besides English, he spoke a dozen other languages fluently, among them, German, French, Polish, Russian, Italian, and Spanish.

His first task when he assumed command at Mauthausen was to cover the walls of his office with a selection of the most atrocious photographs taken by Blackstock at Dachau and at Mauthausen. "At least, when we question these gentlemen, who will lie to us through their teeth, we can show them the results of their pranks."

He quickly went through the few files that Settiniaz had started, leading the questioning himself.

21

"Small fry, Master Settiniaz. Anything else?"

Settiniaz told him about the boy who had been buried alive.

"And you don't even know his name?"

The information concerning the young man was sketchy. His name didn't appear on any German list; he had not belonged to any convoy dispatched within the last few months of 1944 and the early months of 1945, at the time tens of thousands of prisoners were being sent back toward Germany and Austria because of the Russian advance. As many witnesses had confirmed, he had been at Mauthausen for three months, four at most. Tarras smiled.

"The story seems simple enough. Some high-ranking SS officers—one officer could not have needed nine lovers, unless he was superhuman—turned back toward Austria to organize a last stand. They reached Mauthausen, where they gratuitously reinforced their garrison, and, at the approach of our Seventh Army, turned back again, this time in the direction of the mountains, of Syria, even of the tropics. All this not without having previously, with the characteristic attention given to order by this admirable race, neatly, beneath a few mounds of quicklime and earth, disposed of their now burdensome sweethearts."

At Harvard, a Gogol expert had given Tarras the not illogical nickname of "Boulba." Far from disliking it, he gloried in it, and used it to sign reviews as well as his comments on exam papers. Behind his gold-rimmed glasses, his bright eyes turned to the horror on the walls.

"Of course, my young David, we can always, all other matters notwithstanding, take an interest in your young protégé. All in all, we don't have more than a few hundred thousand war criminals feverishly awaiting the demonstration of our concern. A mere trifle. Without taking into account these millions of men, women, and children already dead, dying, or about to die."

He had a taste for peroration and a sadistic desire to nail in place with his sarcasm any person with whom he was speaking. Nevertheless, the young Austrian's story must have interested him. Two days later, on May 10, he went to see the boy for the first time. To the *Kapos* who were present, he spoke Russian, German, Polish, Hungarian. He cast a quick glance at the stranger.

22

It was enough.

He reacted as David Settiniaz had, with a sizable difference: he was similarly struck by him, but he knew why. He discovered a striking resemblance of the eyes of the survivor to those of a man with whom he had spoken briefly at Princeton, during a luncheon at Albert Einstein's house: the physicist Julius Robert Oppenheimer. Same pale irises, same impenetrable depth, opening onto a dream inaccessible to common mortals. Similar mystery, similar genius. . . ?

With the difference that this kid is at most eighteen or nineteen years old, he thought.

During the next few days, Georges Tarras and David Settiniaz devoted themselves to the task that had brought them to Mauthausen. Detective work most of the time, conducting investigations based on denunciations. They endeavored to make a list of all those who had, at any level, had any responsibility for the running of the camp. And gathered evidence to be used later, before a court-martial dealing specifically with war crimes in Dachau and Mauthausen. As the American troops approached, many of the former Austrian camp guards sought refuge in the immediate area, without taking any particular precautions, keeping their real names, hiding behind the virtue of obedience—*Befehl ist Befehl*—an order is an order—which for them justified everything. Lacking means and personnel, Tarras recruited former prisoners. One of them was a Jewish architect, a survivor of several camps, Simon Wiesenthal.

After some time, urged by Settiniaz (at least, this was the reason he gave himself), Tarras thought again about the boy who had been buried alive, whose name he still did not know. The little group of prisoners who had come to complain about him to Major Strachan had not appeared again, and three of its more ardent members—French Jews—had left the camp and returned to France. So the charges had in effect been dropped. Nevertheless, a file had been opened, requiring a decision. Tarras decided to handle the questioning himself. Many years later, facing the gaze of Reb Klimrod, but in far different circumstances, he would remember the impression left on him by this first meeting.

3

The boy was walking now, without a limp. You could not say he had gained weight—the expression would be grotesque applied to this kind of survivor—but at least his coloring had improved and he seemed less emaciated.

"We can speak German," Tarras said.

The gray gaze met that of the American and, with a deliberate slowness, circled the room.

"Your office?"

He spoke in German. Tarras nodded. He felt strange, almost shy, and this new sensation amused him.

"Before," said the boy, "this was the office of the SS commander."

"And you came here often?"

The boy was looking at the photographs on the wall. He moved closer to them.

"Where were the others taken?"

"Dachau," said Tarras. "That's in Bavaria. What is your name?"

Silence. The boy was now behind him, still examining the photographs. He's doing this on purpose, thought Tarras suddenly; he refuses to sit across from me, and now wants to force me to turn around, to show me he intends to lead this discussion.

Fine. He said softly: "You didn't answer my question."

"Klimrod. Reb Michael Klimrod."

"Born in Austria?"

"Vienna."

"Date of birth?"

"September 18, 1928."

"Klimrod is not a Jewish name, as far as I know."

"My mother's name was Itzkowitch."

"*Halbjude* then," said Tarras, who had already taken note of the two first names, one Christian, the other common in Jewish families, in Poland especially.

Silence. The boy started walking again, following the wall, going behind and, circling Tarras, reappearing at his left. He moved slowly, lingering in front of each photograph.

Tarras turned his head slightly and saw then that the boy's legs were trembling. A tremendous feeling of pity swept over him. This poor brat can hardly stand up! He watched Klimrod from the back, the bare feet in laceless boots probably too small for him, as were the pants and shirt, hopelessly short and floating on his thin, awkward body, which had been twisted time and time again by torture but which, still, by sheer strength of will, hadn't lost an inch of its height. Tarras also noticed his hands, long and fine, blotched by old scars of cigarette burns and quicklime; these hands hung alongside his body, unclenched, and Tarras knew from experience that this false nonchalance indicated a kind of self-control few adult men could achieve, himself included.

At that moment, he understood even more what had struck Settiniaz: Reb Michael Klimrod had a strange, inexplicable aura.

He retreated to his interrogation.

"When and how did you arrive at Mauthausen?"

"Last February. I am not sure of the date. Beginning of February." His voice was deep and his speech was very slow.

"By convoy?"

"No convoy."

"Who was with you?"

"The other boys who were buried with me."

"Someone had to bring you here."

"SS officers."

"How many in all?"

"About ten."

"Commanded by?"

"An Obersturmbannführer."

"Whose name was?"

Klimrod was now standing in the left corner of the room. Before him was an enlarged photograph taken by Blackstock of the open door of a crematorium; the flash had made the half-charred bodies especially white.

"I don't know any names," said Klimrod quietly.

One of his hands moved, upward. His long fingers touched the glossy paper of the photograph, as if to caress it. After that he swung around, leaning against the wall. He was impassive, gazing into space, blank. His hair, which was starting to grow in, was dark brown.

"What gives you the right to ask me these questions? Because you are American and have won the war?"

In God's name, thought Tarras, dumbfounded, for once in his life at a loss for words.

"I don't feel as if I've been defeated by the United States of America. In fact, I don't feel as if I've been defeated by anyone. . . ."

His eyes fell on a glass-fronted cabinet in which, next to stacks of files, Tarras had placed a few books. And it was the books he was looking at. . . .

"When we arrived here, at the beginning of February," said Klimrod, "we had come from Buchenwald. We were twenty-three before Buchenwald, but five boys were burned there and two others died between Buchenwald and Mauthausen. The officers who used us as women killed those two in the trucks and I buried them. They couldn't walk any more, they cried all the time, and they lost all their teeth, which made them less attractive. One was nine and the other was a little older, eleven maybe. The officers rode in a car and we were in a truck, but from time to time they made us get out and walk, sometimes run, holding us by cords tied around our necks. This was to make us lose the strength or even the desire to run away."

He pushed himself away from the wall with his hands. He was looking at the books with an almost hypnotic intensity, but he didn't stop talking, the way, thought Tarras, a school boy recites his lesson while looking at a bird outside.

"But before Buchenwald, where we arrived right after Christmas, we spent time in Chemnitz. Before Chemnitz, we were in the Grossrosen camp. Before Grossrosen, the Plaszow camp—that's in Poland, near Cracow and that was in the summer."

He moved completely away from the wall and began to walk slowly in the direction of the cabinet.

"But we stayed only three months at Plaszow, where some of the boys died, mostly from hunger. Six. I don't know their names. Before Plaszow, we walked for a very long time in the forest. . . . No, first we were at Przemyzl . . . but we walked before and after, for a long time. We were coming from the camp at Janowska. I was in Janowska twice. That time, in May of last year, and once before, in 1941, when I was twelve and a half."

His way of recounting was curious. He spilled out his memories backward, the way you rewind a film. He went three steps farther and was now directly in front of the books, separated only by a pane of glass.

"These books are yours?"

"Yes," said Tarras.

"The second time I was in Janowska, I was coming from Belzec. My mother, Hannah Itzkowitch, and my sister Mina died at Belzec on July 17, 1942. I saw them die. They were burned alive. May I open the cabinet and touch the books, please?"

"Yes," said Tarras, transfixed.

"My sister Mina was nine years old. I am absolutely positive that she was alive when they burned her. My other sister, Katarina, was two years older than I. She died in a railroad car that I was also supposed to get in. She climbed into a compartment meant to hold thirty-six people. They pushed in one hundred and twenty or one hundred and forty; the last ones in were lying on the heads of the others. On the floor, they had spread quicklime. My sister Katarina was among the first to go in. When they couldn't fit any more in, not even a child, they slid the doors shut, took the car to a siding and left it in the sun for seven days."

He read out loud: "Walt Whitman. Is he English or American?"

"American," said Tarras.

"He is a poet?"

"Like Verlaine," said Tarras.

The gray eyes touched his face, then went back to *Leaves of Grass*. Tarras asked a question, and thought he would have to ask it again, the answer was so long in coming. But the, boy shook his head.

"Not yet; only a few words. But I am going to learn it. And Spanish also. And maybe other languages. Russian, for example."

Tarras looked down, then up. He felt lost. Sitting behind his desk, he hadn't moved since Reb Klimrod had come in, other than to scribble. He said suddenly: "Keep the book."

"It will take me a while."

"Keep it as long as it takes."

"Many thanks," said Klimrod, looking at the American officer once again. He continued. "Before Belzec, we had been at Janowska since August 11, 1941. And before that, at Lvov, at the parents of my mother, Hannah Itzkowitch. We had gone to Lvov on Saturday, July 5, 1941. My mother wanted to see her parents again and had obtained passports for the four of us in Vienna. We had left Vienna on July 3, a Thursday, because Lvov was no longer occupied by the Russians, but by the Germans. My mother had great faith in passports. She was wrong."

He started to leaf through the book, but his gesture was mechanical. He leaned over so that he could read the other titles.

"Montaigne. I know him."

"Take it as well," said Tarras, emotion forcing him to speak. Of the twenty books he had brought with him, as refuge from the horror, if he had had to choose one, it would have been Montaigne.

"As for me," said Klimrod, "I survived."

Trying to regain his composure, Tarras reread his notes. He recited the list of camps, this time in chronological order: "Janoswska, Belzec, Janowska again, Plaszow, Grossrosen, Buchenwald, Mauthauser . . ." He asked: "You really went through all these places?"

The boy nodded indifferently. He closed the glass doors of the cabinet, holding Tarras's books against his chest, with both hands.

"When did you become part of this group of young boys?"

Klimrod moved away from the cabinet, took two steps toward the door.

"October 2, 1943. At Belzec. The Obersturmbannführer assembled us at Belzec."

"This Obersturmbannführer whose name you don't know?"

"That one," said Klimrod, taking another step toward the door.

He's lying, of course, thought Tarras, more and more disconcerted. Accepting the rest of the story as true—and Tarras believed it—it was inconceivable that the boy, who had such a fantastic memory, could forget the name of a man with whom he had lived for twenty months, from October 1943 to May 1945. He's lying and he knows I know. And he doesn't care. Nor does he try to justify himself, or to explain how he survived. Nor does he seem to feel any shame or hatred. But maybe he's in a state of shock. . . .

The last explanation was the least convincing to Tarras. He didn't believe it. Truthfully, during this first visit with Reb Michael Klimrod, a visit that didn't last more than twenty minutes, Tarras suspected that there was in this emaciated boy, who barely had enough strength to stand, a great aptitude for dominating any given situation. A superiority—that was the word that came to his mind. Just as he could feel, physically, the overwhelming weight of intelligence burning behind Klimrod's pale, deep eyes.

The boy took another step toward the door. His profile had a cruel beauty to it. He was getting ready to leave. So, the last questions asked by Tarras were meant mainly to prolong the interview.

"And who whipped you and burned you with cigarettes?"

"You know the answer."

"The same officer, for twenty months?"

Silence. Another step toward the door.

"You told me that the Obersturmbannführer formed the group at Belzec on . . .

"October 2, 1943."

"How many children were there?"

"One hundred and forty-two."

"Assembled for what reason?"

A slight movement of the head; he did not know. And this time, he is not lying. Tarras marveled at his own certainty. He asked more questions, hurriedly.

"How did you leave Belzec?"

"By truck."

"For Janowska?"

"Only thirty went to Janowska."

"And the other hundred and twelve?"

"Majdanek."

The name didn't mean anything to Tarras. He would learn later that it was another extermination camp, on Polish soil, on the order of Belzec, Sobibor, Treblinka, Oswiecim, Chelmno.

"And it was the Obersturmbannführer who chose these thirty boys? There were only boys?"

"Yes, to both questions."

Reb Klimrod took the last two steps that separated him from the door, stood on the threshold. Tarras could see his profile.

"I will return them to you," he said. His hands moved over the Whitman and the Montaigne. "The books. I will return them to you." He smiled. "No more questions, please. The Obersturmbannführer took us to Janowska. He started using us as women then. Later, when the Russians moved in, he and the other officers pretended to the German Army that they were on a special mission, to transport us. That is why they did not kill us, except when we couldn't keep up."

"You don't remember the names of any of these men?"

"None."

He's lying.

"How many children arrived with you at Mauthausen?"

"Sixteen."

"You were only nine in the grave where Lieutenant Settiniaz found you."

"When we arrived at Mauthausen, they killed seven of us. They kept only their favorites."

This was said in a calm and detached tone. He crossed the threshold, stopped one last time.

"May I ask your name?"

"Georges Tarras."

"T-a-two r's-a-s?"

"Yes."

Silence.

"I will return the books to you."

Austria had been divided into four military zones. Mauthausen was in the Russian zone. A large number of former prisoners were transferred to a camp for missing persons in Leonding, near Linz, in the American zone, in the buildings of a school on whose benches Adolf Hitler had sat, and across from a little house where Hitler's mother and father had lived for a long time. Georges Tarras, David Settiniaz, and their War Crimes unit went to Linz. Although the move put an added strain on their time, they didn't interrupt their search for former SS guards hiding in the area.

So it took several days for them to notice that young Klimrod had disappeared.

30

4

As of that morning, the presidency of the Innere Stadt, the Inner City of Vienna enclosed by the Ringstrasse, was in the hands of the United States Army, which was in charge of security for one month. On Kärntnerstrasse, in front of the well-lit door of the Military Police station, it was an MP from Kansas who sat down next to the driver. The three other members of the International Patrol—an Englishman, a Frenchman, and a Russian—squeezed in the back.

The car started for the fourth watch of the night, in the direction of St. Stephen's Cathedral, whose two towers were just becoming visible in the first light of dawn.

They drove slowly, in the middle of the empty street. It was June 19, 1945, and it was now 5:50 A.M.

The Jeep reached Franz-Joseph Quay. On the opposite bank of the Danube canal, beyond the half-destroyed Baths of Diana and the sea of rubble left by the war, they could see, against the pink sky, the black skeletal circle of the Prater's Big Wheel. They turned left, went along Gonzagagasse and then south. They could now see the baroque splendors of the Bohemian Chancellery.

They could also see the boy.

The Englishman saw him first but remained silent. He was sulking. He couldn't bear the bitter smell of the Frenchman's tobacco; he despised the American, who exasperated him with his never-ending stories of baseball games and feminine conquests made during his stay in London, before June of 1944; he detested the Russian, who wasn't even Russian, since he had slanted eyes, Mongolian features, and the intellectual vivacity of a pudding. As for the driver, who was Austrian, and, worse yet, Viennese, his constant cynicism and especially his refusal to consider himself a defeated enemy made him unbearable.

A few seconds later, the American looked up, and exclaimed. The five men turned, looking toward a small baroque house of three stories, six windows, with balconies across the first two, and a columned entrance.

All they saw was a silhouette, spread-eagled against the building on the top floor like a crucified figure. This image struck them. Everything conspired toward it: the incredible leanness of the tall body, on which floated pants and a shirt that were at the same time too large and too short, the bare feet, the emaciated face hollowed even more by two huge eyes, so light they seemed almost white in the beam of the searchlight, and the mouth, half open in a grimace of effort and suffering.

In truth, the scene lasted only a few seconds. Using the handle of a window, holding onto the ledge, the silhouette had moved. The light beam caught it one last time before it scaled the railing of a balcony. They heard glass breaking, the slight squeak of a window being opened and closed. Then silence.

"A burglar," said the Viennese phlegmatically. "But it was only a kid, in spite of his size."

The intent was clear. The International Patrol could intervene only in cases where a representative of the occupying forces was implicated. Ordinary misdemeanors were the responsibility of the Austrian police. The central police station was alerted. Ten minutes passed before the arrival of an inspector and two policemen.

This was enough time for Reb Klimrod.

For twenty, maybe thirty, minutes, two sorts of noises reached him in a strange superimposition.

First, the real noises, those made by the policemen entering the house and searching it from bottom to top, opening and closing doors, walking on the marble tiles of the ground floor and on the wood floors above, once so carefully polished. As he had expected, they followed the trail he had traced for them, using what energy he had left: they followed his bloody footsteps to the attic, found the small circular window open, concluded, naturally, that he had escaped that way, over the roofs, came back down, speaking louder, looked around one last time, left. . . .

Those noises, and then the others, the imaginary ones, spilling from his memory with an acuteness that made him tremble: Mina's lively footsteps running or skipping in the hallways, Katarina playing Schubert on the piano, their mother's voice, with that slight Polish accent she never lost, her calm voice, her soothing voice, which created a serenity all around her the way a pebble thrown into the water of a pond causes successive concentric circles, saying during the evening of July 2, 1941: "Johann, we will go to Lvov, the children and I, thanks to the passports Erich has gotten for us. We will arrive there on Saturday, and we will stay until Monday. Johann, my father and mother have never seen their grandchildren. . . ."

Reb Michael Klimrod had the eyes of his mother, Hannah Itzkowitch Klimrod, born in 1904 in Lvov, where her father was a doctor. She would almost have hoped to succeed him, but for the double handicap of being a woman and a Jew. She had instead studied literature in Prague, where the quota for Jewish students was less limited, and, using the vague pretext of an uncle in business in Vienna, had then gone there to study law. Johann Klimrod had been her professor there for two years. He was fifteen years her senior; the eyes that came from the steppes had caught his professorial gaze, and her exceptional intellectual sharpness and humor had done the rest. They were married in 1925, had Katarina in 1926, Reb in 1928, Mina in 1933. . . .

He heard the heavy front door slam as the policemen left. Then the muffled sounds of a discussion between the Austrians and the International Patrol, followed by the rumbling of engines starting up, whose noise then decreased. Silence returned to the house. Reb tried to straighten up. He had to twist himself, very slowly, inch by inch. A hundred times, as a child, he had hidden this way, curled up in this nook, deriving mysterious pleasure from this voluntary confinement, the first few times forced to fight an unspeakable panic and not resting until he had overcome it, forcing himself to press against the damp cold stone wall where whitish things crawled. At least he thought they were white; he had forsaken light in order to preserve the mystery and, mostly, the capacity to be scared, and, eventually, to dominate himself.

Under his fingers, the board finally gave way. He put out a leg, then one shoulder, and slipped through the opening. He found himself in the closet and, from there, in the room that had been his and was now empty of all furniture. He went into the hallway. To his right was Mina's room; further down, Kati's. Those rooms were also empty; there was nothing left. It was the same in what had been the game room, the conservatory, and what Hannah had given him as a study, him, Reb. . . .

And also the three guest rooms, the two rooms where the French governess lived, from which even the framed etchings of the Place des Vosges and the Pont des Arts in Paris, a view of the Loire near Vendôme, where Mademoiselle was born, another of an inlet in Brittany, and one of the Pyrénées had been removed.

On the next floor, only one of the servants' rooms seemed to be still lived in, or had been recently. He found two camp beds and some very neat packing. There was a slight aroma of mild tobacco in the air. Some khaki underwear had been hung to dry on a line in the bathroom.

He went back down to the second floor.

This was the floor where his parents had always lived. Hannah had turned the large hallway with the marble floor into a border, which neither children nor servants could cross without her express permission. On one side, the one whose windows faced the front, were the common rooms: the two living rooms, the dining room, lengthened at a right angle by a huge pantry and the kitchen and, at the other end, perpendicular to the serving rooms, the library, so large that it reached both sides and, in a way, united them.

He pushed open the doors to his right. This had been Hannah's private apartment, forbidden territory. Now completely empty. Even the tapestry had been removed, with great care. Hannah's large bed had been there, between these two windows facing the inner courtyard. Reb had been born in that bed, as had his sisters. Walking in a direction parallel to the hallway, he came to her boudoir. Empty. Then to her study, where, between his birth and Mina's, Hannah had prepared, successfully of course, a doctorate in philosophy. Empty also.

The next room beyond the connecting bathroom had been his father's. It was completely furnished. But he did not recognize the furniture. Also, the bed would not have suited his father; it was too high; the invalid could not have lain down on it without help.

He opened one closet, then another. Inside them, uniforms, many of them, similarly bedecked with stars and decorations. Underwear and shirts, meticulously ironed, were piled on the shelves. He saw shoes of all kinds, some low-heeled, with laces. On two coatracks, some unquestionably civilian clothes. He touched them . . .

. . . but his gaze was already on the last door, the one leading to the library.

He turned the handle, but didn't open it right away. For the first time since he had entered the house, his face showed some emotion. His pupils widened, his lips parted as if he were suddenly out of breath. He leaned his temple, then his cheek against the door frame and closed his eyes. His features clenched in despair. He could hear, probably more clearly than if the noises had been real, the smooth and familiar sound, hardly hissing, of the rubber wheels of the wheelchair belonging to Johann Klimrod, whose legs had been paralyzed by an attack of hemiplegia in 1931, in the spring when Reb Michael was not yet three years old. He could hear his father's voice talking on the telephone, or speaking to his associate Erich Steyr, or to one of the four assistants or one of the three secretaries. He could hear the clicking of the small elevator his father used to go from his ground-floor law office to the library and his private rooms . . .

. . . could hear his father saying to Steyr: "Erich, I am afraid of this trip to Lvov. In spite of these permits you have obtained for them . . ."

He opened his eyes, pushed the door, went in. The room contained the long polished oak table he had always known, an old carpet, a rickety chair. The walls, covered with garnet silk above the paneling, still bore outlines of the paintings that had hung on them. Some of the shelves accessible from an oak-railed balcony had been torn down. There remained not one of the fifteen or twenty thousand books collected by Johann Klimrod over forty years and, before him, by the four or five preceding generations of Klimrods, one of whom had been a high-ranking official under Joseph II, King of Germany and Holy Roman Emperor. Nor did there remain any part of the marvelous collection of madonnas in polychromed woods, slender, smiling, dressed in brocade, four and a half centuries old. . . .

In the ravaged library, fantastically resonant, daybreak began filtering through the closed shutters. He walked toward the elevator the way you go toward a last resource. . . .

To reach Vienna this dawn of June 19, he had traveled the almost one hundred miles separating Mauthausen from the capital on foot, moving only at night, sleeping during the day, stealing food from farms. He had covered the last twenty-two miles in one stretch.

Many years later, David Settiniaz asked him the reason for this frenetic, solitary rush—when he and Tarras would certainly have helped him return to Vienna—and he replied, in his faraway tone: "I wanted to find my father, and find him by my own means."

35

When the elevator had been built, in order to conceal it a tabernacle panel from some parish church in the Tyrol or Bohemia had been fastened to a simple wood panel, and that to the grille. It dated from the fifteenth century, and those who had ransacked the house hadn't missed it; the panel had disappeared, leaving only the ash one.

He opened it. The metallic cage was narrow, the exact size of the wheelchair. And the wheelchair was there, empty.

Reb Klimrod was certain that his father was dead. Standing before the empty chair, he cried.

5

The bookshop was on a curving street between the cavalcading statuary of the Daun-Kinsky palace and the Burgtheater.

One entered it by going down three steps, which have since disappeared. There were three arched rooms in a row, each lit by a small window. The man's name was Wagner, he was over sixty years old, and he had spent twenty years working at the Hofburg National Library before going out on his own. Not without reason, since he prided himself on being one of the foremost authorities on rare editions and the incunabula of Vienna.

He did not recognize Reb Michael Klimrod at first.

This was not surprising. More than four years had passed, and so many things had happened since last he had a visit from the child in short pants, with strands of hair hanging down his high forehead. The child came in almost every month, always on a Thursday during the school term. He would look through the shelves silently, examine the glass-fronted bookcases, usually leave without saying a word. Every so often, he would stop before a book, always one recently acquired by Wagner, with an infallibility that, after a time, ceased to amaze the bookseller. Then he would shake his head slowly, as if to say: "We already have

36

it." or he would ask about the origin of the book or manuscript, its date of publication, its price. Always ending with: "I will speak to my father about it. Could you please hold it until next Thursday?" Seven days later, he would return and announce the verdict in his soft, still high, but curiously distant voice, his eyes dreamy: Barrister Klimrod was or was not buying. When necessary, Wagner would call at the house to conclude the transaction with the invalid, whose fabulous library filled him with wonder.

The figure that now appeared before Wagner in no way reminded him of the child from years back. It was almost a foot taller, was wearing a British-looking tweed jacket, rust-colored pants—both slightly too short—magnificent low shoes, the kind you had not been able to find in Vienna for years. Wagner thought it was an Englishman.

At this point, Reb came down the last step and was no longer standing against the light. The eyes suddenly evoked something. Then the way the newcomer began roaming through the books accentuated the feeling of déjà vu.

Wagner asked, in English: "Are you looking for something in particular?"

"My father's books," replied Reb, in German.

At that very moment, he stopped before the thirty-two volumes of Voltaire edited in 1818. Wagner got up suddenly, then stopped, as if he realized he had shown too great a haste in his movement.

"You are young Klimrod," he said after a few seconds of silence. "Caleb Klimrod."

"Reb."

"You have grown incredibly. How old are you now?"

Reb moved away from the Voltaire and continued on his round. A little farther on, he stopped in front of, successively, the blue-leather-bound edition of Castelli's *Soldier's Songs*, Von Alxinger's *Doolin of Magenza*, Laclos's *Les Liaisons Dangereuses*, and the very rare Santa Clara's *Judas der Erzschelm*. On the edge of this last one, a *K* in fine gold was visible, though only to those who knew where to look or who had a magnifying glass.

He walked away.

"Why would I have any of your father's books?" asked Wagner. "I always sold to him, never bought."

"Recently?"

The question was asked quite naturally.

The bookseller's hesitation was clear, even though it lasted only two or three seconds.

"Not recently. Not at all, actually. Come to think of it, I haven't sold your father anything in three or four years. Almost as long as it's been since your last visit. You were away from Vienna?"

"I was traveling with my mother and my sisters," said Reb.

He turned around, smiling. "I am very pleased to see you again, Mr. Wagner. You still have beautiful books. I don't have the time right now, but I would like to come back, to speak with you. This evening perhaps?"

"I close at seven," said Wagner.

It was three in the afternoon.

"I will be here before," said Reb. "Or else tomorrow morning. But rather this evening. However, I wouldn't want to force you to remain open. Do not wait for me, if I'm late, please."

Wagner smiled back at him. "Come whenever you like. This evening will be fine. You never disturb me. And give my best regards to your father."

Reb walked down the street at his even pace. He didn't even have to turn around: reflected in the window of a watchmaker, he could see Wagner's furtive stance, half visible at the foot of the steps, after he came to the door to watch him leave. Reb walked out of sight, then doubled back to the Burgtheater, where he had a direct view of the entrance to the bookshop. He waited, thirty or forty minutes, and finally saw the men arrive. There were three of them, in a black car, totally unknown and not seeming the least bit interested in rare or old books. Besides, Wagner, who must have been watching for them, came out as soon as they appeared, talked with them, made gestures, some of which, even at a distance, were sufficiently explicit: he was describing Reb Klimrod to the men he had alerted by telephone. Two of the men entered the bookshop, the third parked the car and posted himself in the hallway of a building across from the shop. Watching.

Vienna in 1945 was no longer the Vienna of Johann Strauss, of the pleasure gardens of Grinzing; the famous Viennese golden heart no longer beat to the rhythm of a waltz. The town was half-dead, half-ruined, and, even under the June sun, gloomy. The Prater park was in the Russian zone, and the destroyed tanks there were just beginning to rust, slowly digested by the grass. Only a few blackened shells of buildings remained on Kärtnerstrasse, which had been the equivalent of the Rue de la Paix or Fifth Avenue, and where efforts to rebuild the upper floors were barely starting. Few people were where they had been; they were scattered throughout Europe, prisoners when they weren't dead, wounded, or on their slow way home.

Returning to the Klimrod house, finding it still standing but requisitioned by a British general, Reb Klimrod had not found any of the former servants. As a boy not yet thirteen, the age he was when he left for Lvov in 1941, he knew of most of them only that they lived on the top floor, knew of them what a child his age would know of his parents' employees.

He didn't go to the Austrian police, and certainly not to the occupying authorities. He had no identification papers, though that would not have been a major obstacle, even though he had committed a theft by stealing some of the British general's civilian clothing. Perhaps he thought that among the police he might find other Wagners.

David Settiniaz is convinced that Reb Klimrod knew right away that his father was dead and knew intuitively of the role played by Erich Steyr in his death. In June of 1945, Steyr was probably in Vienna, like so many war criminals who, when the war was officially over, simply went home; some, such as the notorious Mengele, reopened their medical offices from before the war. For Settiniaz, Reb's visit to Wagner was a revelation: the fact that the boy had chosen Wagner, and no one else, because of an old association he knew of between Steyr and Wagner. The result confirmed Reb's conviction; he saw in the appearance of the three thugs at the bookshop an attempt on Steyr's part to capture him and make him disappear.

But his main objective was to find a trace of Johann Klimrod. Reb spent two or three days in Vienna, hiding somewhere, in his former house or in a ruined building. On June 23, he found the woman from Reichenau . . .

. . . who led him to the photographer from Salzburg . . .
. . . and to the horror.

6

At Payerbach, he got off the wagon, which was drawn by a single horse. The peasant wasn't going any farther. Reb nodded his head, smiling.

"Thank you so much. And I hope your grandson will return home soon. I am sure that he will come home."

"May God hear you, my boy," answered the old man.

Reb went along the winding road. Straight ahead of him and to his right were peaks more than sixty-five hundred feet high. He was no longer wearing the clothes and shoes of the British general; he had sold them and, in exchange, besides a little money, had obtained a blue shirt and pants that almost fit him, as did the heavy, laced-up walking boots, one of which, the right one, was ripped several inches above the toe.

He arrived in Reichenau in the late morning of June 23. In Vienna, at dawn, he had been able to get a ride in a Jeep, which had left him on the square by the cathedral of Wiener Neustadt, where the war had left impressive traces. The peasant with the wagon had picked him up two and a half miles outside Neunkirchen, while he was walking along on bloodied feet.

Reichenau was only a village. At the first house, he was told where he might find Emma Donin. Having crossed a small mountain pasture, he came to a log house, raised by a stone subfoundation. Apparently it was large enough to sleep several people: three children, about two to six years old, with blond hair and blue eyes, were sitting side by side on the edge of a stone trough, strangely quiet and immobile, with their hands resting next to their naked knees, all three repulsively dirty. In the air, besides the smell of the humid spring earth, there was the smell of smoke. Reb smiled and spoke to the children, who didn't answer him, looking at him with the same frightened look.

He walked around the farmhouse and finally discovered the woman, who was very fat and massive, with powerful hands showing thick blue veins. She didn't react in any way when he told her who he was, Reb Michael Klimrod, of Vienna, the son of Johann Klimrod, the lawyer. Her thick, spatulate fingers continued husking corn, the grains falling into a cauldron already filled with water, a few potatoes, and some turnips. Standing in front of her, Reb could see the top of her half-bald head, where some sparse strands of yellowish-gray hair stuck with perspiration.

"You used to work in my father's house," said Reb. "I would like to know what became of him."

She asked why it was she he came to see. He explained that a wood seller from the street behind the Bohemian Chancellery had given him her name. She digested this information for the time it took her to finish stripping two ears, grasp the cauldron—refusing any help from Reb—take it inside the house, and place it over the fire. Finally she said:

"I never worked for a Mr. Klimrod."

"But in his house, yes. As of September 1941."

For the first time, she looked straight at him.

"You have come for the kids, right?"

"No."

"You have come for them. She complained again, that whore. She whores around in Vienna with the Americans, she gives me her kids to keep and almost no money, and she wants me to treat them like kings."

A slight noise of bare feet. Reb turned around. The three little boys had just appeared. One of them had a bluish bruise on a cheekbone; all three had whip marks on their legs.

"I have also come about them," said Reb. "She asked me to see how they were. Now will you kindly answer my questions, please."

She lowered her eyes first and said, with rancor: "I could put a little bacon in the soup."

"I was about to ask you to," said Reb, still looking at her.

He began to ask her questions. Who had engaged her, in September of 1941, as housekeeper in the Klimrod home? A man

41

named Epke, she said. This Epke, was he the owner of the house? No. In that case, who was above Epke and gave him orders? She couldn't remember his name. Reb smiled, moved his head. "Tttttt . . ." She really could not remember, she said. At least, not his name. But the man, yes. The boss.

"A very tall and very handsome man. Blond."

"In uniform?"

"In SS uniform," said the woman. "He was at least a general. He didn't come often."

And in September of 1941 were there still any servants in the house who had been there for a long time? For years? For example, a very old man with white hair whose name was Anton? "Yes."

And did she know where Anton was today?

"He is dead," she said. "Right before Christmas of that year. He was run over by a military truck."

And no one else from the former staff? No one else. She and the four other servants had been engaged at the same time. By Epke?

"Yes."

She had unhooked a piece of bacon from a beam in the ceiling, had cut off a slice, then, after a moment's hesitation, a second one.

"One more, please," said Reb. "One for each child. And I think they could eat three or four more potatoes."

And how was the Klimrod house furnished the day she had entered it for the first time? She did not understand the question. "Furnished? Yes, of course," she said, surprised.

"The potatoes, please," said Reb. "Not too small."

And did she remember the books, thousands of them? Yes. And the paintings? Yes, there were paintings, many of them, if you could call them paintings; and also things in fabric, hanging on the walls; yes, tapestries. And statues.

Reb moved. His last walk had drained his remaining strength. He was afraid that this exhaustion, showing on his face, might weaken his position with this woman. He moved to a darker area and, to make himself taller, raised his arms, grabbing the beam that held the bacon.

"In the library, where there were all the books, there was a small elevator. Do you remember it?"

She had just finished peeling the potatoes. Her fat hand that held the sharp knife, thumb pressed against the tip of the blade, stopped moving. She frowned, searching her memory.

"A thing like a dumbwaiter? Which was hidden behind a board with drawings on it?"

The "board" was the tabernacle shutter. "Yes," said Reb.

She remembered it. She had even opened it once, by accident, and had been shocked to discover the apparatus that no one had ever mentioned to her.

"When was this?"

"Before Christmas."

"Of 1941?"

"Yes."

"When exactly? In December?"

"Before."

"November, October?"

"November."

A few weeks after she was engaged. Reb's fingers tightened around the beam.

"Was there anything in the elevator?"

She said, right away: "A chair with wheels."

Had she looked at him at that moment, she would have realized how weak, how defenseless, and how despairing he was. But she was busying herself under the cauldron, rekindling the embers and adding wood. He walked out.

After a moment, he called the children and, when they had joined him docilely, he had them undress in front of the trough fed by a thin stream of clear water brought by a line of hollowed-out tree trunks. He washed them one by one.

"Do you have any soap, please?"

"And what else?" she sneered, in a tone that proved she was pulling herself together.

He cleaned the wounds as best he could, had them get dressed. He turned to the woman.

"When did you leave this employment in Vienna?"

"February. At the end of the month."

"And the furniture, the books, the paintings were still there?"

They had been moved out the night before she left, she said. Three army trucks driven by SS men had come and had taken everything away. At least, almost everything. The next day, secondhand men from Vienna had arrived and taken away the rest. Except for a table too big and too heavy to get through the doors.

"Epke was there?"

"He was in charge."

"Describe him to me, please."

She did. He could very well have been one of the three men who came to Wagner's bookshop after his own visit.

"And the one you called 'the boss'? The very tall and good-looking one?"

"He came that night in a car with a flag on it. He said to Epke: 'Take this and that,' and he told Epke to pay our wages and let us go."

"Where is Epke now?"

She shrugged her shoulders, a mean look of irony showing in her eyes. He almost had to push her aside when he went back into the house. Again he raised his arms and slipped his long fingers around the beam.

"You're no more than a kid," she remarked. "Why should I be afraid of you?"

He smiled. "You are afraid of me," he said softly. "Look at my face and my eyes and you will see that you are very afraid of me. And you are right to be afraid." His hand came down, holding the hook. "I will come back, Emma Donin. In a week or in two months. I will come back and I will examine the children. And if I find one whip mark, I will slit your throat and cut off your hands. First the hands and then the throat. . . . Did you speak with the old man with white hair whose name was Anton and who was run over by the army truck?"

She looked at the hook, and maybe even more at the large hand Reb held toward her, with terrified eyes. She nodded.

"Not often. He didn't speak much."

"I know," said Reb. "But maybe he said something to you or to one of the new servants about Johann Klimrod, my father. Try to remember, please."

The three little boys came in and sat down with the same furtive movement, their three faces looking from the hook to the frightened face of the woman without showing any interest in what was taking place. The presence, the attitude, the silence, the large, serious blue eyes of the three little boys in this farmhouse in the middle of the forest were reminiscent of German folklore stories, full of ogres and fairies.

"Once," said Emma Donin, "he spoke of a sanatorium."

"Where they might have taken my father between July and September of 1941?"

"Yes."

Near Linz, she said. Anton had said another name, but she didn't remember it any more. From under his shirt, Reb pulled out the official map stolen from the British general. It took some time; he read, one by one, all the names on the map, including Mauthausen, within a forty-mile radius of Linz . . .

. . . until the moment when she said yes, that was the name, Hartheim.

The castle of Hartheim.

7

Having left Reichenau, he spent the rest of the day and the following night in Payerbach, at the house of the old man with the barrow, whose invitation he had at first declined. And it was the only time in four years, since his departure for Lvov with his mother and sisters, that he slept in a real bed, ate at a table surrounded by a family. The old man's name was Doppler; three of his grandsons had been recruited into the German Army, two of them had already died, officially, and there was no word on the third one. Reb told Doppler about the children in Emma Donin's care and asked him to look after them.

He made a mistake when he returned to Vienna. Not in prowling around the Bohemian Chancellery, and even in going back into the house. But he asked too many questions concerning Epke.

In vain. The name didn't mean anything to anyone, as if Emma Donin had invented it.

In reality, the very fact that he had learned this name revealed the progress he had made. The same held true for the curiosity he showed concerning the exact circumstances of the death of Anton Hinterseer, "the old man with the white hair," who had been in the service of the Klimrods for over fifty years and had been killed by a military truck. If anything, Reb believed, he had simply been assassinated by Epke.

The tall, blond, and very handsome man in SS general's uniform described by Emma Donin was, of course, Erich Steyr.

And Steyr as well as Epke saw in Reb Klimrod's inquiries the sign that he was closing in on the dreadful truth.

Hartheim castle is on the road that runs along the Danube when you go from Linz northwest to Passau in Germany. The place is called Alkhoven. It is a small, quiet village, the kind you find by the hundreds in northern Austria. From Alkhoven to Linz is only a little over nine miles.

The castle is a large building, pierced by several blind windows, Renaissance-type, in the heavy and lugubrious German taste of Emperor Maximilian. A vast courtyard surrounded by rather nice colonnades does not succeed in diminishing the sinister impression of the whole place, which is dominated by four towers.

"It used to be a sanatorium," the red-haired man told Reb, reluctantly. "A kind of hospital, if you want. I went there twice, in 1942 and then the following year. They had a general short circuit and had me come."

He hastened to shake his head, already on the defensive. "But I didn't see anything unusual."

The red-haired electrician's shop was not far from the Trinity column in Linz. He had immediately recognized Reb Klimrod, the minute the adolescent's unending thin figure appeared on his doorstep. He remembered the boy the SS officers had dragged along with them, constantly, once on a leash, like a dog, in Mauthausen, to which he had gone several times in his capacity as electrician. Like all the men whose activity had dealt in small or great part with the camps, he knew that the search was on in full force, led by the section on War Crimes, and he was especially fearful of this Jewish committee recently organized in Linz. The Jews, now, were dangerous, terribly so. Twice already, in the streets of Linz, he had passed another former prisoner, Simon Wiesenthal, who actually lived close by. Sometimes, Wiesenthal's black, piercing eyes haunted his nightmares, although he considered himself to be completely innocent, unaffected: he was just an electrician, nothing more; for what could they blame him?

And yet, this boy who had just come in and was asking him questions about Hartheim was Jewish. The red-haired man clearly remembered the striped uniform on which the yellow *J* occupied the center of a reddish-yellow double triangle.

It was the red-haired man who gave Reb Klimrod the name of the photographer from Salzburg.

He had traveled from Vienna to Linz, hanging onto one of those open, almost completely demolished cars that the Austrian railroad had managed to put back on the tracks on certain lines. He arrived in Linz on June 30 and covered the distance to Alkhoven by foot and by military Jeep. The military willingly picked up civilian hitchhikers.

He never specifically told anyone whether he actually went inside Hartheim castle. Neither Tarras nor Settiniaz dared to ask him the question.

Reb Michael Klimrod was the first man—besides, of course, those who had worked there—to discover the true functions of Hartheim castle, which were only officially revealed in 1961, quite by chance, and on Simon Wiesenthal's initiative.

He arrived in Salzburg the evening of July 2 or the morning of July 3. More than two-thirds of the distance from Mauthausen he had done on foot, sleeping little, with the sole exception of his stop at Doppler's, in Payerbach, eating less yet, and, again with the exception of Doppler, without taking strength from any friendly presence. He was plunged in a desperate and dramatic solitude, driven by a unique obsession: to find out where and how his father had died.

The photographer from Salzburg was named Lothar.

"He is not here," said the woman with the gray hair cut very short. "He lives here but he doesn't work here. You can go to his laboratory."

She consented to give him the address—in a covered passage just behind the bell tower.

"Do you know where it is?"

"I'll find it," said Reb.

He left, trying to hide his limp. Crossing the square of the Old Market, he saw the ambulance for the second time.

The first time, it had been on the other side of the Salzach, when he emerged from the Linz road. He had noticed the vehicle parked at the entrance to the Staats Bridge, facing him. There were two men in the front seat, motionless, with that blank look of subordinates waiting for the order that will make them move again. The ambulance was painted khaki, with a red cross on a white background. There was nothing unusual about it, at first glance.

And now it was in the heart of old Salzburg, parked once again, with no one in it. But the license number was the same, and it had the same scratch on the front right fender.

Reb crossed the square, with a blank look on his face, but suddenly appearing rather awkward and limping more than before.

He was about two hundred and fifty yards from the bell tower.

He reached it twenty-five minutes later.

The passageway was dark and narrow; without even reaching, Reb could have touched the arch. He walked about thirty feet, going by dark shops, before he saw the painted sign, black on a white background, rather clumsy: K.-H. LOTHER—ART PHOTOGRAPHER. As he pushed the glass door, he set off the high-pitched tinkling of a small bell. He entered a low room, the walls and ceilings of which were uncovered stone. On either side of him were large wooden counters, but they were empty, as were the recessed shelves.

A voice, coming from a back room, said: "I am here."

All the way in the back, a cloth curtain covered the frame of a door. Reb drew it aside and walked into the next room. He found himself face to face with four men, one of whom immediately pressed a gun barrel against his left temple.

"Don't move and don't scream."

He recognized two of the men: the very ones who had been in the front seat of the military ambulance. He identified the third one from the description Emma Donin gave him at Reichenau: Epke. He had never seen the fourth one. They asked him where he had been and why it had taken him so long to arrive from the Old Market square, which, even if one was on foot and limping, was only two or three minutes away.

Reb Klimrod's face, as well as his whole manner, had changed incredibly. He seemed younger than his age, more fragile and exhausted than was possible. His eyes widened frantically.

"I was hungry and I got lost," he answered, with the whining voice of a child overcome by events. And terrified.

David Settiniaz received the phone call in place of Tarras, who had gone out, as he said, "to scour the country." The call must, of course, be from some military authority, because public telephones had not yet been fully restored in Austria. The man on the phone emitted an incomprehensible gibberish which was supposedly English.

Settiniaz identified the accent and said: "You can speak French, sir." He explained who he was and in what way he was capable of replacing Captain Tarras in almost all respects. Then he was quiet, listening with growing stupefaction to what the French occupying troops' officer was telling him, from Salzburg. In fact, he hardly took the time to think, but, in a move that was to have not a small effect on his life, told the first big lie of his career.

"Don't believe it," he said. "The boy is older and much more experienced than he looks. You can trust him completely. He works for the OSS, and he is one of their best agents. Do exactly as he tells you, please."

Only after hanging up did he ask himself the truly important questions, about what had led him to commit this foolish act, about what he was going to tell Tarras in order to justify the great lie, and about this extraordinary, and dangerous, situation in which young Klimrod had put himself.

The fourth man was, quite simply, Karl-Heinz Lothar. He was a heavyset, red-faced man, quite tall, with, as often happens, very small, almost feminine hands. In spite of the coolness produced by the stone ceiling, he was sweating profusely, and he was frightened.

Two Austrian photographers worked at Hartheim castle between the fall of 1940 and the end of March 1945. One of them is still alive, and lives today in Linz; Wiesenthal refers to him as Bruno Bruckner.

The other one was Karl-Heinz Lothar. For him, everything started in mid-October 1940. He was forty-seven years old. He was summoned by the *Gauleitung* of Linz, questioned as to his capacity to perform "certain special photographic tasks" and remain totally discreet concerning them. He was offered three hundred and forty marks a month. He accepted and was taken by car to Hartheim castle, which already had been baptized a "sanatorium."

The director of the establishment was, at the time, Captain Christian Wirth, who eventually, as a reward for the excellence of his work at Hartheim, was made general director of the Belzec, Sobibor, and Treblinka camps in Poland. Franz Stangl succeeded him as director of Hartheim, later also at Treblinka. The medical direction of the sanatorium was in the hands of Dr. Rudolf Lehauer of Linz, with the assistance of Dr. Georg Renno. (Lehauer killed himself in April 1945; Renno was arrested in 1963.)

Wirth explained to Lothar the sort of work they expected of him: he was to take the best possible shots of the sick people on whom the Hartheim doctors were performing experiments, at the rate of thirty or forty per day. These experiments consisted of determining the most effective way to kill people and of perfecting, in this field, truly efficient techniques, while establishing a scientifically exact graph of the degree of suffering a human body can withstand before succumbing.

Lothar was asked to photograph and film the subjects' brains, which had been carefully exposed by cutting away the skull, to focus on the eventual modifications visible at the moment of death.

That was the first mission of Hartheim, but not the most important one. The castle was in reality a school and a training center, reserved for "students" who, when their training was completed, could be assigned to the several extermination camps envisaged by Himmler during the Wannsee conference in January of 1941, but in fact planned before that date. Moreover, Hartheim was not the only establishment of this kind. There were three others.

Lothar was handicapped in his work by the fact that he often had to operate through a spy hole during experiments with gas; and he was rather inconvenienced at first by the vile odor of the crematoriums. All in all, he must have photographed at least two-thirds of the thirty thousand people killed at Hartheim.

One thing only really bothered him, perhaps: that the overwhelming majority of the thirty thousand subjects were Christians. They were Germans, Austrians, and Czechs who had been sent to Hartheim either because they were part of the program, established at the demand of Hitler and supervised by Martin Bormann, to exterminate the physically or mentally handicapped and the incurably ill, or because they were simply old people entering the category of useless mouths. Not a Jew among them; to die at Hartheim, Grafenegg, Hadamar, or Sonnenstein was an honor reserved only for Aryans.

"But of course, your father," said Epke to Reb Klimrod. "Your father really died at Hartheim. Is that what you wanted to know so badly?"

"I don't believe you," said Reb in a hollow and hesitant voice. "He is alive."

Epke smiled. Maybe Epke was not his real name: he was extremely blond, his eyebrows were almost white and blended into his very light skin, and he spoke German with the particular intonation of people from the Baltic states. He shook his head, with an expression of regret, like a professor who is not given the expected answer from a good student.

"He is alive," repeated Reb, more determined. "You are lying."

He looked exactly like a crazy adolescent. Even his size seemed to have decreased. He was half-collapsed against the wall, the barrel of the Lüger still pressed against his temple. His eyes darted from one man to another, stopping a little longer on Lothar, who was sweating more than ever. Behind Lothar was a small window, obstructed by two bars, with a dusty windowpane; not so dusty, however, that you could not see through it.

"Let's finish with this," said Epke.

"In the letter my father left for me . . ."

Reb stopped suddenly, as if he realized he had said too much. Epke's pale gaze had quickly returned to him.

"What letter?"

"My father is alive, I know it."

"What letter?"

Through the half-moon opening of the window people could be seen walking by in the street, from their shoes to their knees, even though the noise of the traffic was inaudible. The man wearing paratroopers' boots had already walked by once; he reappeared, and, just by the position of his feet, it was clear that he was facing, if not the window, at least the house where Reb and the four men were.

Reb lowered his head, defeated.

"I left it in Vienna."

"Where in Vienna?"

"I won't tell you." In the tone of a stubborn kid.

Epke was looking at him, uncertain. Finally, he shook his head and said, without turning around: "Lothar, can you find the pictures of his father?"

The fat man mopped his forehead and his whole face with his girlish little hands. "If I have the dates, yes."

Epke smiled at Reb. "August 1941. Around the twentieth." He smiled again. "And then you can tell me all about this letter, kid."

Lothar was kneeling in front of one of six iron trunks. He opened it. Inside, negatives and prints were meticulously arranged. His fingers ran over the aligned labels. Reb kept his head down. The silence continued.

"August 21, 1941," said Lothar.

There was a noise of riffled paper.

"Klimrod?"

A rough hand seized Reb by the face and forced him to look up. But he persisted in keeping his eyes closed, his features horribly tensed, this time without pretense.

"Open your eyes, kid. Isn't this why you went to Reichenau, why you came from Vienna to Salzburg?"

Reb put out his hand, took the photographs. There were three of them, showing the whole body, taken through a spy hole.

He saw his father, naked, with his atrophied legs, crawling on the floor, trying to scratch the cement with his nails. The photographs must have been taken at fifteen- or twenty-second intervals. They showed the progression of asphyxiation. In the last one, in spite of the black-and-white print, one could clearly make out the blood running from the mouth and the piece of tongue that the tortured man had ripped out himself.

The hand that was holding Reb let go. Reb fell to his knees, his chin against his chest. He turned slowly and rested his cheek against the cool stone wall.

"Burn this fucking stuff," said Epke.

The two other men, the false ambulance men, began pouring gasoline on the trunks after shooting off the padlocks.

"So, my dear Lothar," said Epke, very softly, "we wanted to start our own personal collection?"

The shot came almost immediately, hitting Lothar right in the mouth. The impact from the nine-millimeter fired point-blank threw the photographer backward. He fell on one of the trunks the men had set on fire.

"Let him burn with it," said Epke. "Now, your turn, kid. Why don't you tell me all about this letter?"

He raised the barrel of his Lüger and pressed it between Reb's eyes. That gesture probably cost him his life. Through the pane of the little window, the MPs misunderstood its meaning. They opened fired, with a machine gun. At least two blasts ripped through Epke, just when the yellow and blue flames of the gasoline vividly lit up the room. He collapsed on Reb, which explains, notwithstanding the hypothetical good aim of the marksman, the fact that Reb was not hurt except for a scratch on his right shoulder.

As for the other two men, one tried to escape and was shot down on the threshold of the door with the chimes. The other one fought back, after he had thrown against the window the can of gasoline he was holding, which immediately caught fire. Hidden by the thick smoke coming from the smouldering trunks, he managed to hold off, by himself and for several minutes, the arrival of the policemen.

For nothing, He reappeared in the form of a living torch, and was mercifully finished off.

Reb was dragged outside, roughly at first, but was shown a little more consideration after the intervention of a French officer. He was covered with blood, although the blood was not his. Questioned by the Frenchman and his Austrian interpreter, he gave only vague, meaningless answers, staring at them with his large gray hallucinatory eyes.

When he had gone to the Salzburg Military Police to request some help (the step that led to the phone call received by Settiniaz), he had pretended to be acting on the orders of Captain Tarras, in Linz, and spoke of war criminals whose traces he had uncovered. The fact that he spoke to a Frenchman was not just luck; at that time, of the three Western powers, the French were by far the most ardent pursuers of high-ranking members of the Third Reich.

Tarras arrived in Salzburg five hours after the shooting, having decided to cover up Settiniaz's lie, at the cost of a great discussion with Captain O'Meara, who was in charge of the OSS section in Linz. He handled the situation with his usual brilliant sarcasm. Besides, the circumstances lent themselves well: an investigation of Karl-Heinz Lothar's home revealed that the photographer, who had no woman in his house, had been taken away early in the morning by three unknown men, who had, at the same time, ransacked the house—undoubtedly looking for the contents of the trunks, which were found charred.

"Why are you complaining?" Tarras asked the military and civil authorities of Salzburg. "The situation is very clear. This Lothar had accumulated documents coveted by our dear Nazis, if only to destroy them. Which they did, quite adequately, I must say, executing Lothar for even further security. What could be simpler? Even policemen, even Military Policemen, by God, should be able to understand this. As for my young agent, he did indeed overstep the investigative orders I gave him. But you must understand his situation: his mother and sisters died in a camp in Poland and he is himself a most fortunate survivor. His zeal is understandable. And he is presently in a state of shock— that's quite obvious. Leave him alone, please . . ."

He brought Reb Klimrod back to Linz, had him hospitalized, and, in truth, also tried his hand at questioning him. But the boy remained prostrate, withdrawn into a now total silence. His physical state was disquieting; he was at the extreme end of his resistance, and, worse yet, the wild fire in his eyes, which had struck both Tarras and Settiniaz, had disappeared. In a delayed action, he seemed to have been affected by the camp syndrome suffered by a majority of the survivors. After the first few hours or the first few days, they were suddenly overwhelmed by the senselessness of a life thus rescued and fell into apathetic depression.

David Settiniaz also remembers going to Reb's bedside on two or three occasions after Salzburg, surprised by the interest he took in the boy. Reb still refused to speak. About his family, about his father, about the men who had almost killed him. It was as if he knew nothing. Nor did he speak of Erich Steyr or of the vengeance ripening in him.

8

Captain Eliezer Barazini (he held the rank from the British, with whom he had fought as a Commando in Libya), had come to Austria during the last days of May 1945. His mission was clear and simple: to recruit and organize, secretly, the transport to Palestine of former camp survivors, with a marked preference for young men and women, very young, who would be ready to use, in combat, the potentialities forged in the fire of the crematoriums. He was a small, thin man, extremely polite, born in Palestine.

He saw Reb Klimrod for the first time on July 5, 1945, and, in truth, didn't pay much attention to him. The surname Klimrod was not a Jewish one, and the boy, recently arrived from Salzburg, was in such a poor physical and psychological state that Barazini would, anyway, have put off for weeks, or months, the very idea of emigrating, especially clandestinely.

The representative of the Jewish Brigade had two other candidates in mind that day, one of whom was in a neighboring room. The other, whose name was, coincidentally, Reb, was Reb Yoël Bainish, a Polish Jew who had reached Mauthausen at the end of the winter of 1944–45. He had been part of a convoy of three thousand prisoners brought in February from Buchenwald to this camp in north Austria (a convoy that included Simon Wiesenthal and a Radziwill prince). Only a thousand arrived alive. In 1945, he was nineteen years old.

He was in the bed to the right of Reb Klimrod. He and Barazini spoke for a long time, in Yiddish.

Two days before the tanks of the U.S. Seventh Army reached Mauthausen, an SS man had broken Bainish's hip and his thigh with the butt of a rifle, and he had been taken to Room A, in Barracks Six, the "death barracks."

Barazini has no recollection of the sick boy lying right next to them, other than the fact that nothing he said to Bainish seemed to interest the stranger. Besides, even though he spoke fluent Hebrew and English, Barazini had enough trouble with Yiddish for it to occupy all his attention.

Bainish immediately agreed to the proposal made to him, with the understanding that he would leave as soon as his physical state would permit it.

Barazini announced that he would return in two weeks.
He did.

"I would like to speak with you."

The words had been in Hebrew. Barazini turned and at first didn't see anyone. The hallway of the hospital seemed deserted. Then he saw the long, thin figure huddled in the corner by a pillar, near the door he had just come through. The face didn't look familiar. The eyes, on the other hand, struck him by their extraordinary intensity.

"Who are you?"

"Reb Michael Klimrod. I am in the bed next to Yoël Bainish."

His Hebrew was absolutely pure but he spoke slowly, with an almost untraceable accent, like the French have. And he hesitated on certain words, in the manner of someone using an almost forgotten language. He must have seen the question in Barazini's eyes, for he added: "My mother was Jewish. Hannah Itzkowitch, from Lvov. She was at Belzec, as were my sisters. My father taught me French, she taught me Hebrew and Yiddish. I also speak Italian and a little Spanish. And I'm learning English."

He moved, very slowly, and his large thin hand appeared from behind his back, holding Whitman's *Leaves of Grass*. But his eyes hadn't moved and remained locked with those of the Palestinian, with a rather annoying steadiness.

Somewhat disconcerted, the first question that came to Barazini's mind was: "How old are you?"

"I will be seventeen in September. The eighteenth."

Barazini had a feeling at that moment that he couldn't describe.

"And what do you want from me?"

"I would like to leave with Bainish, and the others, if there are any."

Klimrod's youth didn't trouble Barazini. Seventeen was, for many of the fighters of Eretz Israël—the land of Israel—almost old, at least it was in the clandestine groups, Irgun and Stern. His discomfort was caused by something else. For a few seconds, he envisioned a British infiltration attempt—this had already happened—to hinder the massive exodus the London politicians feared.

"You were at Mauthausen?"

"Yes."

"I will check. Everything you say."

The gray eyes didn't even blink. "You would be wrong not to. And you don't have to answer me right away. I couldn't take someone seriously if they were to take me on in a few minutes. Besides, I'm not physically ready to travel."

"When will you be ready?"

"At the same time as Yoël Bainish. In two weeks."

Barazini conducted his investigation. He specifically went to see the people of the Jewish Committee in Linz, one of whom was Wiesenthal. The name Klimrod was not known to them. Only one man remembered having seen him at the camp—"made up like a woman and accompanying a group of SS officers."

He managed to find at least a dozen men and women who came from Lvov, and who were waiting in Leonding; none of them had met, in July of 1941, in Lvov, a Hannah Itzkowitch Klimrod accompanied by three children.

Around July 20, Barazini reported to his superior, future ambassador Asher Ben Nathan, who was in charge of assembling the Jews from the American zone of Austria. He told him of his hesitation.

"Something about this kid bothers me, and I can't figure out what it is."

"Is he intelligent?"

"Is he? I have the feeling when I speak with him that he is the adult and I am the child, with a mental age of three! He must think three or four times faster than I. I don't even get a chance to finish my sentences. He answers my questions before I ask them."

"That's probably what's bothering you," answered Ben Nathan, laughing. "That would bother me too."

The two men decided that Barazini should trust his instinct.

On July 30, he went back to see Yoël Bainish and Reb Klimrod. He announced his decision: they were to leave, together, the night of August 6.

Actually, Barazini had found a solution, which, in his eyes, settled everything. For a time, Bainish was to keep an eye on Klimrod. That was a first precaution. To this he added a second, reassuring, one: he sent a message to Tel Aviv, in which he particularly called Dov Lazarus's attention to Reb Klimrod.

Reb held his hand out to Bainish, whose leg and hip were still stiff. He pulled him up into the truck, where there were already eleven men and five women, mostly between the ages of eighteen and twenty-five. There was total silence. Someone pulled up the tailgate and locked it and also fastened the khaki cover, which cut out any kind of light. There was some whispering outside; then the engine was started and the truck pulled away. It was one o'clock in the morning, August 7, 1945.

To reach the rendezvous point, Reb and Yoël had left the hospital well before midnight. They had crossed Linz, avoiding the city's center, and reached the first rallying point, near a warehouse in the heart of the dock installations along the Danube. They had been joined there by two men and a young girl, but it was decided that they would not go on as a group. They had walked to the southern outskirts of the city. At no point was Reb aware of the rendezvous areas, of the time schedules, of the identity of his companions, of the conditions of the departure.

He made no effort to find out anything more during the next part of the trip. Out of Linz, they drove for over four hours, while one of the women occasionally sang softly, in Yiddish, her face hidden. There was a stop, a very short one, to satisfy natural needs. Day was breaking, and it lit mountains Reb couldn't identify—nor could Bainish, who didn't know Austria at all. But one of the men spoke in Polish about the Klamm Pass, which is to the north of Badgastein.

Bainish said, laughing softly: "He also speaks Polish, don't bother. . . ."

They rode for two more hours, the harsh early light of the Austrian summer filtering through the gaps in the canvas cover.

They spent the daytime hours of the seventh on an isolated farm not far from Igls. Back on the road at nightfall, they crossed Innsbruck around eleven o'clock, and Reb heard two men who must have been soldiers speaking French, one of whom had a melodious southern accent. After that, he knew the road they followed—the railroad tunnel of Mittenwald and the surging noises of the Inn, which he remembered perfectly. During the summer of 1938, his school (where he was two years ahead of his age group) had organized a trip to Saint-Anton.

He thought their final destination might be Switzerland, but at Landeck, the truck turned left. One hour later, it stopped. After discharging its human load, it turned around and began the descent.

They followed, on foot, a young boy who had appeared from the night and who, in German, told them to remain absolutely quiet. After what was perhaps a three-hour climb through the forest, they reached a barely illuminated inn. They didn't enter through the front door, but used a ladder, leading them to the large Tyrolian balcony on the second floor. A group of twenty other emigrants was already there, so anxious to be silent that they had removed their shoes, in order not to alert the guests below . . .

. . . guests who were also extraordinarily discreet. An hour after the arrival of his group, Reb, looking through a window, noticed a group of about fifteen men, some of them middle-aged. The newcomers had something military in their manner and in the way they were organized, in spite of their luxurious civilian clothing and their expensive suitcases. They kept quiet until they were inside, but their arrival set off a wave of exclamations, in German, which were quickly checked.

The staff of the inn shuttled between the two floors with perfect ease.

Yoël came up to Reb.

"Are you thinking what I'm thinking?"

Reb nodded.

Through the floor, they could hear the men settling down for the night. Had they wanted to, the two young men could have followed the whispered conversations by lying on their stomachs. A grimace of hatred disfigured Yoël's delicate features for a few seconds; he was a survivor of the Warsaw Ghetto. "Nazis on the run!" He wept with rage.

The entire day of August 8 was spent in this strange unnatural cohabitation.

And it is not impossible to believe that in this inn, near the

Reschen Pass, a few yards from each other, fed by the same innkeeper, and driven by the same smugglers, there were, simultaneously, survivors of Mauthausen and other camps and the very ones who had been their torturers.

Not Erich Steyr. Even Settiniaz finds that impossible. The dates don't match.

The trip, yes, of course.

They crossed the Italian border the following night. Two hours apart. First, the SS men, who had priority.

In Italy, a convoy of trucks was obviously waiting for Reb Klimrod and his companions, whose number, enlarged by numerous groups who had crossed the Reschen Pass during the preceding nights and had found refuge on Italian farms, had passed the one hundred mark.

Yoël Bainish had a natural cheerfulness and an almost amazing ability to make light of everything. At Mauthausen, he had risked immediate death twenty times by mimicking the gait or the tics of this or that guard. Coming down from the pass, he had hardly stopped singing, or, with a disrespect bordering on indecency, he had resurrected a certain Schloimele, the glory of his native village, near Lublin, who was a rabbi, or almost.

But when they discovered the trucks and the soldiers' uniforms, even Bainish was dumbstruck. The trucks and uniforms were unquestionably British. They belonged, they learned, to His Majesty's 412th Royal Transport Company. Thanks to them, they were all, notwithstanding the relentless blockades of Great Britain, going to reach the south of Italy and sail to Eretz Israël.

The 412th Royal Transport Company did not exist. It was the product of the fertile imagination of a man named Yehouda Arazi, leader of Mossad Aliyah Beth in Italy. Mossad, created in 1937 by the Haganah, a self-defense force of the Jewish colonies in Palestine, worked to strengthen these colonies by immigration.

While the British were actively looking for him in Palestine, Arazi had landed in Italy, right behind the Allied armies. And in these very armies were British units scattered within which were Palestinian Jews.

Four sergeants were among them, one of whom was Eliahou Cohen, known as "Ben-Hur," who founded, in the kibbutzim, the Palmah, a defense unit of the Haganah and the core of the future Israeli Army.

Arazi and the four sergeants had established a plan discreetly to use the material resources and the various supplies and provisions of His Majesty's forces. Arazi had also set up a communications system, running from Antwerp to Naples, through Paris, Marseilles, and Athens. A broadcasting station had been installed in a town about nineteen miles outside Milan; it maintained contact with the leaders of the Haganah in Tel Aviv.

In this partially occupied country, Arazi had trucks, men who spoke perfect English, noncommissioned officers in correct uniforms. He actually created a fictitious military unit, with false regimental rolls and real quarters: a large garage in the center of Milan, a garage that had been officially requisitioned by the British Army. He completed all this with a workshop of forgers in charge of drafting orders that could fool the Military Police, and also false papers for refugees who were in transit.

Thus was formed the 412th. And the strategem was discovered by the British only in April 1946.

On August 21, 1945, a group of thirty-five illegal emigrants embarked in Bari on a twenty-five-ton fishing boat, the *Dalin*— in reality, the *Sirius*, whose true port of call was Monopoli, twenty-six miles farther south on the Adriatic coast.

After seven days at sea, without the slightest incident, the first postwar clandestine boat arrived at Caesarea. Reb Klimrod and Yoël Bainish were aboard.

The Candlesticks of
Bogotá

1

Reb held the dagger in his hand, squeezing with his thumb to insure the direction of the weapon. At a distance of six feet he jumped, his right foot pressed against the hollow of the knee, his right hand hitting at eye level, while the other hand, the one holding the weapon, struck, from top to bottom. When he felt the blade thrust up to the guard, at the height of the epigastrium, his wrist executed an arclike movement. Slaughter. He had accomplished the series of movements with fantastic smoothness and rapidity.

He took two steps back, his arms falling to his sides. He had decapitated the dummy.

"Not bad," said Dov Lazarus, in his raspy voice. "Not too bad. Providing the sentry is deaf and also drunk. Moreover, if he were sound asleep, it would be even better. All these conditions being met, you would have one chance to slit his throat before his screams alerted the entire British Army within a two-hundred-and-fifty-mile radius. One chance, not two."

Under the short mustache he sported that day, his large white teeth shone as he smiled. The mustache seemed to have grown during the night. He didn't have it the day before. Dov Lazarus was nearly fifty; he weighed about one eighty-five and was only five seven. He had been born a little before the turn of the century in Petah Tikva—the Door of Hope—the first Jewish colony in Palestine. It had been established on the banks of the Yarkon by enlightened emigrants fleeing the Russian pogroms. His parents had been members of the Friends of Zion, and they had arrived, wearing babushka and boots to the knee, in 1882. He was, when not in disguise, very fair, almost strawberry blond. His massive round corpulence, his kind smile, his pleasant myopic gaze behind rimless glasses gave him the most misleading appearance. He was a man of violence and only that, driven all his life by a dark and exclusive passion. Yoël Bainish believes that Dov Lazarus lived for a while in Ireland, and fought in Collins's I.R.A., in the United States for several years, in South America, and even in the Far East. According to Bainish, many episodes of Reb Klimrod's life can be traced to contacts established by Lazarus in New York and Chicago between 1925 and 1930.

The change of direction in Lazarus's life came in 1933, when he met David Ben-Gurion for the second time. He had first seen Ben-Gurion in 1906, as a young boy in Jaffa, when the future Zionist leader had just arrived from Poland. The two met again in France in 1933, when Ben-Gurion toured Europe during an electoral campaign held in the heart of European Jewry. This "walking time bomb," as Ben-Gurion called Dov Lazarus, had finally found his place, working for a worthy cause. Lazarus idolized Ben-Gurion.

He said now to Yoël Bannish: "Your turn. Try to do better. Put the dummy's head back in place, and remember it's a man whose throat you are about to slit."

As Barazini had requested, Lazarus had personally taken charge of the new immigrants from Austria. His main function within the Irgun was to train newcomers to be shadow fighters. In the fall of 1945, the leader of the Irgun, created in 1937 as a non-terrorist movement, was a man born in Brest Litovsk who had come to Palestine only in 1942, Menachem Wolfowitch Begin.

"Pathetic," said Lazarus. "Unbelievably pathetic. Your only hope would be that the British sentry would have a great sense of humor. In which case, hilarity would kill him for sure."

He got up, moving like a shadow, and went to stand next to the dummy.

"Try it on me, Yoël. Try to slit my throat. Start when you like. Take off your shoes. And really try to kill me."

Bainish removed his shoes, hesitated. The knife in his hand was as sharp as a razor and the blade was nine and a half inches long.

"You have one minute to kill me," said Lazarus, with his back turned. He was facing the white wall of a house on a narrow street between the Jewish and the Armenian sections of Jeru-

salem, near the Tower of David. Yoël looked at Reb, who nodded.

Bainish jumped . . .

. . . and three or four seconds later, the knife was pointed at
his own throat, grazing ever so slightly the skin below his Adam's
apple, and a terrible pain flashed in his left arm and shoulder.

Silence.

Klimrod asked: "Can I try?"

Their eyes met. Bainish remembers the silence that followed.
Dov Lazarus smiled.

"No," he said.

The two young men from Mauthausen participated in their
first real operation on September 28, 1945. They had learned,
among a hundred other things, how to make nitroglycerin, by
pouring, drop by drop, preferably without trembling, glycerin
into equal parts of nitric acid and sulphuric acid at a seventy-
degree Baume concentration; and to make the classic black pow-
der from saltpeter taken from the walls of stables and cattlesheds,
sometimes even from catacombs. They learned to handle military
explosives, usually obtained by commando raid on British quarters: trinitrotoluene, C-4 melinite, and others.

In the beginning, Yoël Bainish showed remarkable abilities as
a preparer, his specialty being, without doubt, an incendiary ex-
plosive made from three parts of potassium chlorate to which
was added one equal part of pine resin and one part of powdered
sugar. (This last ingredient delighted him; it reminded him of a
cooking recipe.)

In the beginning only. When it came to real action, he turned
it over to Reb Klimrod. Reb's total lack of fear in all circumstances
was obvious from the start. In all the teams trained by Dov Lazarus, whether for Irgun or Stern, there was never a lack of courage, sometimes bordering on recklessness. Reb was different. And
not only in his complete indifference to danger. Many members
of Begin's Assault Force were camp survivors, often the only
surviving members of their families. They were not intimidated
by death, and this fighting was sometimes their only way to remain sane, by giving them a reason to live. Reb was just like
that then. But there was something else: he never took part in
any discussion of the Jewish state. In this respect, he was like

Dov Lazarus. For Lazarus, politics were an abstraction, and he lived only for action. This wasn't the case with Reb, of course, but from the start, there was between them a surprising, but real, rivalry and complicity.

The mission of September 28, 1945, consisted of the ambush of a small British column on a road seven and a half miles northeast of Ascalon. Fifteen men took part in it, under the command of a man known to Bainish only as Eliahou. The orders were to give priority to the destruction of equipment over the execution of British soldiers, and to break away at the first signal. It was essentially a movement of harassment, aiming, according to Begin's expression, to give the British the feeling they were "sitting on a nest of scorpions."

There were five trucks, preceded by a Jeep. As planned, Eliahou's machine gun fired first, raking the column on its right. The incendiary chlorate grenade that was to have blown up the Jeep bounced on the hood with no result. It was a simple contraption made of a whisky bottle filled with chlorate, powdered sugar, and resin, sealed with a round piece of felt, completed by a small flask made of thin glass that held the sulphuric acid. Before throwing it, one had to break the flask so that the acid filtered through the felt. Then, it was better not to waste any time.

Yoël saw Reb get up thirty feet to his right. At no time did he seem in a hurry; his movements were always accomplished in what appeared to be detached nonchalance. He reached the road in four big steps. He jumped over the low embankment and went directly toward the head of the column, across from the Jeep. The machine gun was still firing, and the path of its bullets must have passed very close to him. In his large left hand, he held four or five grenade bottles by the neck, the way Grinzing waitresses served new wine. A few yards from the Jeep, he shattered a flask of acid, patiently counted to three, and threw a grenade at the center of the grille, between the headlights. The vehicle rapidly caught fire. Reb had already dodged it. He tackled the first truck, blew it up in the same way. Then another, and another, while all the machine guns were still firing.

He wasn't even hit. The action didn't last long. From the first shot fired by the machine gun to the breakaway signal given by Eliahou, no more than two minutes elapsed. The withdrawal of the commando team took place as planned. Four hundred yards from the road and the burning vehicles, where the British were still shooting, just in case, a regrouping took place, only to disband. Bainish and Klimrod were relieved of their precious arms.

Then they were suddenly alone, or rather, three, trudging through the reddish sand. The third man was Eliahou, who normally would not have accompanied them. They walked together for two hours, until they were in sight of Telashod. Eliahou stopped.

"We are going to separate here," he said. "You have certainly been told where to go and how to get there."

He hesitated. Much smaller than Klimrod, and even smaller than Bainish, he was staring at Klimrod's face in the semidarkness. He finally shook his head.

"I could have killed you ten times, with my machine gun."

"You didn't," answered Reb.

"Two steps further to the right or left, or forward, and you would have been in my direct line of fire. Did you know?"

"Yes."

Eliahou shook his head again. "And I believe you; that's what amazes me the most. How old are you?"

"About a hundred years old," said Reb. "Give or take a few weeks."

"Who taught you to use a grenade like that? Dov Lazarus?"

The gray eyes, very light in the night, looked down.

"I don't know anybody by that name."

Eliahou began to laugh. "O.K." He started to walk away, stopped, turned around.

"Try not to get killed right away."

"I'll try," said Reb. "You have my word."

He and Yoël left together. A truck from a kibbutz came for them, as planned, at four o'clock in the morning, to take them, as planned, to the north of Ashod. They were in Tel Aviv before sunrise, having crossed many checkpoints without trouble, eating fruit they had picked during the night.

In October and November of the same year, 1945, they took part in a dozen missions, one of which took them into the desert and lasted six days. The objective was to blow up, in as many places as possible, one of the British-Iranian pipelines.

69

Apart from these missions, they lived in Tel Aviv, where the Irgun had found them housing and official work to serve as a cover. Yoël Bainish became a shopkeeper, selling knickknacks in a booth on Allenby Road. Reb Klimrod was a waiter in a coffeehouse on Ben Yehouda Street. The place was frequented mostly by lawyers. His progress in English was spectacular, and fascinated Yoël, who was himself quite talented when it came to learning languages. Besides Yiddish and Hebrew, Yoël spoke fluent Polish, German, and Russian, and he too would soon be speaking English. At that time, whenever he had a free moment, Reb went to the movies, where American films in the original language were usually being shown. Bainish remembers that the tall Viennese would sit through twelve or fifteen consecutive screenings of *Citizen Kane, Bataan Patrol, Objective Burma,* the Marx Brothers' *Go West,* and *My Darling Clementine,* and he could do a perfect imitation of Bogart in *The Maltese Falcon* and suave Cary Grant in *Philadelphia Story.* Even the indescribable nasal sound of Groucho Marx. He still read voraciously, but now it was mostly in English.

And there was an undeniable relationship between this bulimia for reading—through the lawyers he served each day at the coffeehouse he had obtained access to special libraries—and the change that took place at the end of November. The partnership of Klimrod and Bainish was dissolved. Each of them had become an excellent explosives specialist, and to let them work together was redundant. Begin's Assault Force was beginning to intensify its activity as the Irgun was becoming better organized, following the example of the French Resistance. Leaflets from that period refer to the British as the "occupying force," and members of the Irgun were, it was said, no more terrorists than were members of the French Resistance: "The situation is the same as that which existed between the French maquis and the German invaders."

At the end of November, Reb Klimrod was given a new assignment. First, he completely changed both his identity and his work. He was given papers that identified him as Pierre Hubrecht, born in Paris in 1926—an assumed name he was to use at least two more times. The curriculum vitae given him specified that his mother was Jewish and had disappeared in Paris in 1942, and that his father, a career officer who had chosen to fight on the side of the Free French, had been killed in Syria, where he had been joined by his son, after a detour in Spain. Although all of these biographical details were perfectly authentic, they had nothing to do with Reb Klimrod; but they did explain his knowledge of French and rudimentary Arabic.

As for his new work, these papers gave him access to a bank in the business center of Tel Aviv, the Hakim & Senechal Bank, whose central office was in Beirut. He started as a runner. One of the Hakim brothers was a silent partner funding the Irgun, but that was not the only reason Reb was soon promoted; he was simply a little too bright to be a runner. Around mid-December, he was working as a money broker. He was only seventeen, although his passport said he was twenty.

Another change marked his separation from Bainish. The latter had left Tel Aviv for Jerusalem and now specialized in attempts against the railroads and pipelines of the Iraqi Petroleum Company.

Reb, on the other hand, because of his physical appearance—light-brown hair, light eyes, fair skin—and because of his employment at Hakim & Senechal, which justified his traveling and his absences, was more and more used by the Irgun for infiltration of British circles, and, on a military level, for urban terrorism.

From this point on, too, he was almost always teamed with Dov Lazarus.

2

The Jeep was driven by a man named Harmond. He had changed the original *e* of his name to an *a* in order to anglicize it. He had fought in the British Army in Africa and in Italy. He had, in fact, been part of the four-hundred-man detachment that had for ten straight days held off the Italian Ariete Division near Koenig's Free French at Bir-Hakeim, at the cost of seventy-five percent of their number. The uniform he wore was truly his: that of the Sixth Airborne Division. Officially, for his British superiors, he was on leave.

Dov Lazarus was at his side, wearing the insignia of a major. Behind them was Reb Klimrod, also in uniform, with corporal's stripes, his feet resting on canvas bags containing explosives. A truck followed the Jeep; on board were fifteen men plus the driver and an officer who had a beautiful red mustache. Among the men, ten had handcuffs on their wrists and were dressed as Arabs; the other five, in combat uniforms and helmets, served as guards.

Two hundred yards before reaching the police station, at a signal given by Lazarus, Harmond slowed down and stopped the Jeep. But the truck kept going.

The place was called Yagur and was halfway between Haifa and Nazareth. The police station was a two-story square building, surrounded by a double fence of barbed wire. Four sentries were posted at the entrance and four others were on the roof, protected by a rampart of sandbags. Inside, there were probably twenty more soldiers, plus policemen, out of uniform perhaps, but certainly armed. It was three o'clock in the morning, March 1, 1946.

"One minute," announced Lazarus.

From the Jeep, parked in the shadows, they had a direct view of the entrance. They saw the truck approach, stop. The officer with the mustache got out, had a discussion with the sergeant in command. He must have been convincing, since the sergeant seemed agreeable. The truck entered the defensive perimeter of the station. The false guard made the false Arabs prisoners get down, prisoners who were concealing Sten and Bren machine guns beneath their robes.

The whole group went into the building.

"Two minutes," said Lazarus.

Harmond had a general idea of what was taking place inside the police station. The commando was neutralizing the British, those on the ground floor and then those on the floors above, one by one. All very quietly, so as not to alert anyone, especially the sentries posted on the roof, with their ready machine guns. Then they would empty the arms store, free the prisoners, the false officer with the mustache would appear at the door, give the signal by removing his hat, and he, Harmond, would drive the Jeep up to the entrance quite naturally, to drop off the two

72

men with him. He learned their names only later, but he did know that they carried with them enough explosives to blow up half a town.

"Three minutes. We're running late. . . ."

Lazarus sounded amused. Harmond, his hand on the gearshift, ready to pull away at a second's notice, glanced at him quickly. Then, in the rear-view mirror, he looked at the thin, blank face of the other man. He remembers how amazed he was by their absolute calm, and by the disparity, on all counts, of this team: one, short and stocky, already old; the other one, very young and very tall, with pale eyes lost in a dream.

"Watch out . . ."

The warning, uttered in a surprisingly quiet tone by Lazarus, came one second before two events that were to upset all the plans. One was the appearance of two half-tracks, one hundred yards to their right, on the road to Nazareth; right after, from inside the station, a scream, the sounding of an alarm, gunshots. After that, everything happened quickly, as always. Harmond's orders had been very clear: in the event of a serious incident, he was to retreat immediately, and leave. He shifted into reverse, preparing to turn around.

"Wait."

Lazarus's hairy paw came down on his wrist.

"Listen, ducky," he said, smiling. "The half-tracks are going to block their way. They won't even be able to leave."

And right then the two armored vehicles suddenly accelerated and took up positions at the entrance to the station, where shooting had reached a peak. Harmond saw one of the false Arabs run out of the building, but he was stopped short by a burst of gunfire.

"Completely blocked," said Lazarus, smiling even more now. "Reb? Are you coming with me, kid?"

"I didn't have the slightest idea what they were going to do," Harmond said later. "Even if I had, I'm not sure that I would have had the courage to go with them. But they were both extraordinarily calm. It was only later that I understood that they were, in a way, trying to outdo each other. And that they were crazy."

Harmond stopped the Jeep exactly between the two half-tracks. "That's fine," said Lazarus, getting out and nodding appreciatively to the men in the armored trucks, who were looking at him, not without surprise, wondering where the hell he had come from. "Good work," he said, with a slight Irish accent. "You fucking well stopped them, those bastards. Keep that door in your line of fire and don't let any of them get out. I'm going in to see if I can get them alive. It's alive that I want them." He seemed to discover then, almost at his feet, one of the outside sentries, who had fallen to the ground upon hearing the first shots and was waiting, with his machine pistol aimed.

"Is this any time to take a nap, my boy? Why don't you get up and take your position at that angle. As far as I remember, there is another door there, through which those bastards might try to escape. Cover it. Who is the officer on duty tonight?"

"Lieutenant Parnell," answered the young soldier, crushed by this outburst of sarcastic authority.

"Another Irishman!" commented Lazarus. "What would the Empire do without us." He half turned, and as he gestured amiably to the sentries posted on the roof, their machine guns searching for a target, he said to Reb: "And you, Barnes, what are you waiting for? Why don't you get your ass out of that Jeep and come with me. . . ."

Very slowly, he walked through the first wire entanglement and advanced toward the building, where automatic firearms were still cracking. As sometimes happens, there was a sudden pause in the shooting, and Lazarus took advantage of it.

He screamed: "Parnell! We've got them blocked off here, but I want them alive! Do you hear me, Parnell?"

In answer, a spray of bullets hit the ground less than a yard from his feet, but without touching him. And Harmond understood two things: first, that the burst of gunfire had come from his Irgun comrades, who were stuck on the ground floor, and, second, that they had recognized his voice.

A head appeared on the second floor, that of a young officer in shirt sleeves, disheveled, holding a regulation pistol. Lazarus smiled at him broadly.

"Lieutenant Parnell? I am Major Connors. God bless Ireland. We've got the bastards. The trick is to get them to talk. I'm going to speak to them in their gibberish. Would you ask your men to stop shooting, please."

He went on, in Hebrew, in a loud and resonant voice, marked

now more than ever by a heavy Irish accent. He wasn't taking any risks, just in case there should be someone in the British contingent who might understand him. Addressing the men from the Irgun, he suggested they give up, on the spot, and put down their arms. He told them he was coming in, that they didn't stand a chance of getting out alive, except as prisoners, in which case he would personally guarantee them status as political prisoners.

Reb Klimrod had reached his side, carrying two heavy satchels. Silence fell suddenly, after one final shot. And in the silence they all heard the rumbling of an arriving tank, followed by several trucks filled with perfectly authentic paratroopers. These reinforcements deployed themselves, encircling the building. Lazarus glanced at them and nodded, looking more satisfied than ever.

"Not a chance," he repeated in English, then in Hebrew. "I'm coming in."

And he went in—they went in, he and Klimrod. Harmond, dumbfounded at the wheel of his Jeep, saw them disappear inside the station, and experienced "rather serious concern," as he put it, feeling the tight line of paratroopers closing in around him.

Inside, one Englishman had been killed, three others wounded, while the losses on the side of the Assault Force were two dead and three wounded, one in the stomach.

Later on, Harmond learned that the commando had lost time for the idiotic reason that no one could locate the key to the arms store.

One or two minutes went by, in eerie silence. And then Lazarus spoke again.

"Parnell? You can come down. They give up. And tell those valiant reinforcements who came to rescue us that the battle is over."

Behind Harmond, the line of helmeted soldiers opened. A captain and two civilians, all from the dreaded C.I.D., moved forward. They walked by Harmond and into the station.

Lazarus smiled at the newcomers, and at that moment must have realized that at least one of them had recognized him, or was going to any second. He took Parnell by the arm and went toward them. Without turning around, he said: "Show them, kid."

Klimrod, with his left hand, opened the two satchels revealing the packages wrapped in oiled black paper, with wires hanging from them.

"Thirty-four pounds of TNT in each bag," explained Lazarus. "And the thing the kid is holding under his arm is an electric pressure-sensitive detonator. You'll notice that he keeps his right arm pressed very close to his body. Should he move his arm away from his body, even to sneeze, bam, we would all go up in smoke. I can guarantee you the total destruction of your station . . ."

Klimrod said, in his impersonal voice, his eyes drifting: "We are in an enclosed space. The power of the deflagration would be further strengthened. . . ."

"Exactly," approved Lazarus, beaming like a teacher whose favorite student has just given the correct answer. Through his rimless glasses, his pale-blue eyes shone mercilessly, leaving no doubt about the incredible violence in him. He went on. "In short, it would not be unreasonable to count on forty or fifty dead. Go stand close to that guy with the blue shirt, kid. He's from the C.I.D. and I think he has recognized me. . . ."

Only then did he reveal his immediate plans.

The same truck that had brought the commandos took them back. They left behind only their two dead, after checking to see that no paper or personal effect that could permit rapid identification had been left on them. They took the road to Haifa, and, as planned initially, met, three miles farther to the northeast, with three men whose task it was to cover their withdrawal, and who were ready with cans of gasoline they would have used to water down the road and build a wall of flames in case of a pursuit.

This did not occur.

As for Harmond, he took advantage of the circumstances, a few minutes after the C.I.D. men arrived, to slip quietly away. He rapidly lost himself in the streets of Yagur, exchanged his uniform for civilian clothes, and still remembers, with a wince, the exhausting bicycle trip back to Nazareth, where, officially, he was on leave with his family. Later, he rejoined his unit, on time, in Port Said. For a long while, he did not know how the incident ended, and learned it only much later.

76

James Parnell had seen the line of paratroopers open up to let through the truck that had carried the commandos. Before their departure, the terrorists—in his eyes, they were terrorists—had been careful to burn all the documents found in the offices of the police station. But, according to the terms of the transaction, they hadn't touched any of the arms he had there. This was his only source of satisfaction. None of the other events did anything to boost his spirits. He found himself designated, along with the two C.I.D. representatives and five other men, all policemen, no soldiers, as hostage for so-called Major Connors and his young companion.

At no time did Parnell question the authenticity of the explosives (the doubts came after, and the answer much later). Toward the older one, whose Irish brogue was so perfect, he immediately felt a violent antipathy, and fear. But the other one, the tall young boy with the amazing eyes, in a certain way scared him even more; that bottomless gaze frightened him.

Parnell, who eventually became a journalist and returned many times to Israel, was forced to climb into the back of the truck and lie down, hands crossed behind his head, just like the other hostages. The terrorist with the glasses sat next to the driver, Gammon grenade in one hand, Smith & Wesson in the other. With a disquieting psychological ability, he had chosen the driver himself: a civilian policeman in his fifties, the last man capable of conceiving and carrying out a desperate action.

His young accomplice climbed into the back, impassive and silent, one arm pressed against his body, a sten machine-pistol in his other hand.

The paratroopers once again let them pass. The truck pulled away rather slowly. They want to make sure they're not being followed, thought Parnell, who couldn't see a thing. They started toward Nazareth. Parnell was hopeful: there was an army barricade a few miles farther south. But after three or four minutes, the vehicle changed direction, going along a dirt path for half an hour. Then it stopped. He heard the voice of the man with the glasses.

"Everybody out. Except for the two aces from the C.I.D. and my favorite Irishman."

They drove on, leaving the freed men in the middle of the desert, with Parnell at the wheel this time and the two C.I.D.

men lying in the back with their wrists in handcuffs and their ankles in shackles. They rode for an hour, on a practically impassable road.

Again they stopped. Parnell was tied to the front fender. He knew some Hebrew, enough to follow the discussion—the argument—that then took place betwen the two terrorists. The older one wanted, at all costs, to kill the two men from the C.I.D. on the spot. After which, he'll kill me, too, he thought. Oh, my God, why am I Irish?

A rainy dawn began to appear over Galilee. Parnell expected to hear shots at any moment. But the tall, thin boy came around to him, leaned over to unfasten him, and said, in a surprisingly soft and calm voice: "Don't try anything, all right? Otherwise, I won't be answerable for your life."

"All right," said Parnell, sincerely and extraordinarily relieved. "And thank you. Thank you so much."

The gray eyes passed over him, unfathomable.

They arrived in Saint John of Acre at six-thirty in the morning. Parnell was alone in the cab of the truck. Twenty minutes earlier, his two adversaries had moved to the back, right behind him, the younger one warning him not to turn around and breaking the rear-view mirror so that he could not see what was happening behind his back.

When he reached the square of Han-el-Amdam, near the Inn of the Columns—his assigned destination—he slowed to a stop, reassured by the continued silence.

And, of course, the truck behind him was empty, except for the two C.I.D. men, enraged, but alive.

3

Reb Michael Klimrod arrived in Cairo during the last days of March 1946. He and Lazarus traveled separately, but they met in the Egyptian capital.

According to Yoël Bainish, who is the most precise and constant witness of that period of the King's life, Klimrod and, especially, Lazarus were among the terrorists most wanted by the British in Palestine. The Yagur incident had a great deal to do with this. The C.I.D. men had had a good chance to study their faces, and Klimrod's height would make him easy to spot.

The attack on the Yagur station had been only one episode in a much larger offensive carried out by both Irgun and Stern. A general attack had been ordered on March 1, and Lazarus's mission was only one part of it. There had been attacks on barracks in Haifa, Rehovot, Pardess-Hana, and on main arteries in the districts of Jerusalem, Tel Aviv, and Petah-Tikva. Even the area under the Sixth Airborne Division in Jerusalem had seen fire.

As for the reasons that led to Klimrod's and Lazarus's departure for Cairo, and eventually for Europe, Bainish is certain concerning Lazarus. An organization like the Irgun, which wanted to be only clandestinely military, had some misgivings about this former member of the I.R.A. and friend of North American gangsters; they frowned on his almost gratuitous violence, which sometimes went against their political purposes.

As for Klimrod then, Bainish knew nothing of his motivations. One thing was certain: it was at his own request that he left Palestine. "At one time, I even thought he had received new orders, perhaps from Mossad in Europe. It was only in August or September that I learned that that was not the case, that he had left on his own. I was disappointed, and even worried. Just the fact that he had teamed up with Dov didn't predict anything good. I was only half wrong. . . ."

In Cairo, Nadja Hakim lived in a villa on the island of Gezireh, a residential neighborhood. A former member of the British Army's ATS, she had married one of the sons of the Hakim Banking family. Her change in status had in no way affected her commitment to the clandestine Zionist movement.

She was advised of the arrival of two men and was asked to help them, first during their time in Cairo, then to reach Europe. She had Lazarus and Klimrod stay in her former apartment, behind the American Embassy, and obtained passports for them—an Irish one for Lazarus and a French one for Klimrod-Hubrecht.

She booked ship passage for them, and on March 30 the two men reached Marseilles.

On April 8, Reb Klimrod was in Nuremberg, alone.

"*Nakam*," said Bunim Anielewitch. And he asked, in German: "Do you know what that means?"

"Revenge, in Hebrew," answered Reb.

They were walking in the suburbs of Nuremberg, between a double row of demolished houses, under a fine, icy rain. They were almost the same size—the advantage going to Klimrod by two or three inches. Anielewitch was twenty-eight years old, with large black eyes, deep, sad eyes, permanently veiled in a way that dimmed them.

"I don't like your companion," he said after a while. "First of all, he's too old. The oldest among us isn't yet thirty. But mostly because he has a professional look. He looks like an American gangster."

"He's extremely effective. More than I am. For the time being."

"I appreciate efficiency. There is nothing I hate more than these Talmudic discussions on the one hundred and twenty-seven reasons to do or not do something, whether it be to open or to close a door. But for what we are about to undertake, what we have already begun to undertake, efficiency comes second in the qualities we require. I don't want any professional killers, Reb. I want, most of all . . ." He hesitated, and then said almost timidly, ". . . purity. We are going to kill although hating to kill. Revenge is the weapon of the weak, they say, but what can we do? It is not so much to punish these men as it is to ensure that their crimes will not be forgotten. People are already forgetting. Some of them are on trial, right here and now. The newspapers are talking about it. But for how long? The whole world has to know that such an abomination cannot be forgotten in two or three years. And for that there is no other solution but to kill. Do you really want to be one of us?"

Reb nodded rather vaguely, his large hands shoved into the worn pockets of his jacket.

"I have been checking up on you. Our organization is widespread with agents all through Europe. And, what's more, I have friends, reliable friends, in Warsaw and in Moscow. Personal friends, I mean. They disapprove of us in Tel Aviv; the Haganah would like to control us, maybe even destroy us. The Talmud, time and time again; speechifying for hours instead of acting. As far as you're concerned, we have checked everything. One of our members was in Belzec; he remembers your mother and sisters, and he will answer for you."

"But not for Dov Lazarus."

"Not for Lazarus. However, we can use him. We are going to need money, a lot of money, and none of these sanctimonious rogues from Haganah, Mossad, Irgun, or Stern want to furnish us with any. We are on our own. We have a network that deals with the smuggling of gold and drugs. . . . I know: there is a contradiction between this purity we seek and the illicit traffic. But, here again, we don't have any choice. If need be—but I'm against it—Lazarus could work in that area of our organization. I have seen his file: in the States, he met a good number of those people they call 'the Mafia,' he collaborated with Jewish gangsters in New York, and he still has many contacts among them and their Sicilian friends. But let's talk about you. It's too late for you to participate in our next mission. At least in a primary role. But you speak French, and very well, I understand. As soon as this mission is over, its participants are supposed to withdraw to France. I would like you to take care of this withdrawal, to go to France and prepare refuges for them. Can you do it?"

"I'll need some money."

"You'll get it. But look at this."

Anielewitch had stopped him by putting a hand on his arm. Reb looked up and saw what he thought to be a factory, protected by policeman and a barbed-wire fence. But Anielewitch shook his head.

"No. It's an industrial bakery. Inside, they make two sorts of bread, delivered each morning, and luckily you can't make any mistake: the white bread goes to the American, English, and Polish soldiers. We won't touch that, of course. The loaves of black bread are reserved for the prisoners. These prisoners are in what used to be Stalag XIII. There are thirty-six thousand of them, all SS against whom the Allied Military Police have gathered proof. We hope to kill at least a third of them. With arsenic."

The mission took place during the night of April 13, 1946, and that night was marked by a violent storm, which explained its partial failure. In the weeks leading up to it, though, all precautions had been taken. Two men from the Nakam group, not mentioning the fact that they were Jewish, had been able to find work within the stalag, one as a chauffeur, the other as a warehouseman. Chemists in the organization had perfected an arsenic-based mixture that, when applied to the bottom of a loaf of bread, had the exact consistency and color as the flour with which German bakers dust their products. Other men had succeeded in finding work within the bakery itself, where they had dug, in secret, under the floor of the warehouse where the bread was kept before it was shipped, a hiding place for the poison and the tools. They brought the poison in by concealing it in hot-water bottles slipped under their clothing.

At the end of the afternoon of April 13, three men stayed behind in the hiding place, coming out only after nightfall, when the employees had all left. Wearing gloves and protecting their faces, they began to coat the loaves, in a strange stormy night. The wind became so violent it broke one of the windows of the warehouse. Alerted, policemen arrived. Not finding anyone there, they concluded it had been a robbery attempt, not unusual in these hungry times. Their routine investigation, the following day, forced Nakam to cut short the operation.

On the sixteenth, Nuremberg newspapers reported the discovery of the hiding place by the police, and the poisoning of five thousand SS prisoners.

Of these, four hundred died.

Accompanied by a French Jew by the name of Mayziel, a sometime member of Nakam, Reb Klimrod had succeeded in finding a large apartment in Lyon. For ten days he harbored four of the men who had engineered the Nuremberg affair. They were still mourning their failure, having poisoned only two thousand loaves instead of fourteen thousand.

Anielewitch himself came to Lyon one week later and met with Mayziel and Klimrod. He asked the latter to accompany him as guide and interpreter on a trip that would take them to Belgium and Germany. Mayziel saw them leave on April 26, at dawn, in an automobile they had bought for the organization. Almost five months were to pass before he saw the tall young man again. Klimrod had left behind in the apartment in Lyon his only worldly goods at the time: two books, Montaigne's *Essays*, in French, and Whitman's *Leaves of Grass*, in English.

Reb Klimrod reappeared in Lyon in mid-September, with Dov Lazarus.

But, before that, there was the Paris episode.

Two hours earlier, the telephone had rung. A stranger had asked to speak to David Settiniaz. The servant told him that he was not in Paris, or in France. Luck had it that Suzanne Settiniaz was in the room. She took the phone, explaining that she was David's grandmother. "Are you a friend of my grandson?"

"Not really," answered Reb Klimrod in his slow, serious voice. "We met last year in Austria, and he did me a great favor. I would have liked to see him again."

In 1946, Suzanne Settiniaz was sixty-five. She had been a widow for more than ten years, and had no other child than David's father and no other grandchild than David. Although the fortune left to her by her husband kept her more than comfortable, she suffered from loneliness. She loved David, to the point where she had decided, although she didn't speak a word of English, to spend the preceding spring in Boston. She had returned to Paris on September 9, after having spent her summer, as usual, in her house in Aix-en-Provence. She suggested to the man on the phone that he come visit her, "since you are a friend of David's." Reb accepted.

He looked around him, and his eyes stopped on a small painting hung between two sections of a bookcase of carved mahogany, above a meridienne. The canvas had been painted in oil and tempera, probably in the early nineteen-twenties; it showed mostly undefinable objects, except for two sienna-colored fish on a flat blue background.

"Paul Klee," he said. "We had an almost identical one."

"We?"

"My father and I. We lived in Vienna."

He smiled, and suddenly his entire appearance changed. Up to this moment, his features were not impassive, but he had the expression of someone absorbed in contemplation, an impression accentuated by his light eyes, his huge, deep pupils. But he smiled, and everything changed.

He said: "You have a magnificent apartment. My father would certainly have spoken of a jewelcase worthy of the pearl it contains. He liked to pay that sort of compliment, probably to justify his Viennese nationality."

His accent was slight, and he could have passed for a French-man from the East.Like her own grandson and Georges Tarras before her, Suzanne Settiniaz felt disconcerted. She, too, was affected by the disparity between the physical appearance of her visitor, whom she assumed to be about twenty-one, when he was not yet eighteen, the rusticity, the actual poverty of his clothes, and the feeling of immensity that came from the eyes, the voice, and the whole person of Reb Klimrod.

She asked him questions about her grandson, asked him how they had met. He answered that David and he had met "near Linz, in Austria," soon after the arrival of the victorious Allied troops, and that, at a time when he, Reb Michael Klimrod, was in "a difficult situation" (these were the words he used), David had helped him. And they had become friends.

At no time did he speak of camps, or death. In answer to the only question she asked him, hesitantly, for fear of being indis-creet, about his family, he said he no longer had one, his father having been "killed" during the war. So Suzanne Settiniaz imag-ined a rather normal situation. She assumed that the father of her visitor had, as had most Austrians, fought in the armies of the Third Reich, that he must have died in combat; and she thought that even Reb himself must have taken part in the hos-tilities in a German uniform, since she was mistaken about his age. When, later on, David revealed to her the actual circum-stances of his meeting with Klimrod, she was doubly horrified: by the facts themselves and, maybe even more, by her own mis-taken judgment. She cried over it.

He changed subjects easily and began talking about the six or seven trips he had made to France, the last one in April of 1938. He said he had learned to speak French from a governess who came from the area around Vendôme, and had perfected it during a summer in Paris, and other vacations, in Deauville, Biarritz, and on the Riviera. Yes, he knew Aix-en-Provence; he mentioned the Granet museum, "where there is a Rembrandt and two Cranachs." His knowledge of art dazed Mrs. Settiniaz, who knew the name of Klee only because her husband had bought one of his paintings.

She told Klimrod that David had been demobilized and that he had just resumed his law studies at Harvard. She gave him the address in Boston where David would be at this time of the year unless he was still at the family summer home.

"Shall I make a note of the addresses and phone numbers?"

He shook his head, smiling.

"That will not be necessary. I have rather good memory."

He stood up to leave, in a calm and courteous manner. She realized then that he was probably alone in Paris, and in France, maybe even completely without friends or family. Not daring to offer him money, she tried to think, almost desperately, of how she could help him, and impulsively she invited him to have lunch with her the following day. She saw him hesitate, but he finally said yes, he would come "gladly." He remained a few moments longer on the threshold, looking at her fixedly and gravely with his surprising gray eyes. She suddenly felt a strange timidity come over her, which she pushed away with a feeble joke.

"And I promise not to try to seduce you."

"It's too late," he said with a sparkle in his eyes. "As my father would have said, once again, you have already made my fortress crumble."

He brushed the old woman's hand with his lips and left.

The following morning she received a note, along with a rose. In small, tight handwriting, with elegant but strongly defined downstrokes, he asked her to forgive him for not being able to accept her invitation; he had to leave Paris that very day.

"I met," she wrote to David one week later, "the most disconcerting boy, the strangest and yet also the most extraordinarily intelligent boy I've met in sixty-five years. If there is anything that you can do, with or without my help, for Reb Michael Klimrod, do it, David. I had the feeling he was in a rather miserable situation at the moment, although he said nothing of it to me. . . ."

The news of Reb Klimrod's reappearance, and especially the fact that he had turned up at his French grandmother's house, stupefied David Settiniaz, who had been certain that he'd never hear of the man again. By return mail, he told his grandmother that he, too, had been strongly affected by the fellow and he asked her, "should he appear again," to try to find out where he coud be reached, because he, too, would like to see his "Austrian friend" again.

4

Dov Lazarus sat back with a peaceful sigh in one of the wicker armchairs of the Café de Paris, on Place de France in Tangiers. "Martini?" Reb shook his head. Lazarus ordered a rosé martini for himself, a drink he had recently switched to, and a mint tea for his companion. He began to speak about gold, in Yiddish. Gold was beginning to abound in Tangiers, he said; it came from all over Europe, even from Switzerland—after all, the Russians were in Vienna and who was to say that they would always be stopped by Swiss neutrality? Besides, the gold markets in Paris and London were closed, and inflation . . .

"Do you know what inflation is, kid?"

"Yes," said Reb indifferently.

He had turned eighteen aboard the *Djenné*, between Marseilles and Tangiers. When they had arrived, Lazaus had booked two rooms at the Hotel Minzah. Reb had then walked along the Boulevard Pasteur alone while his companion was at a meeting. He had stood on the observation deck from which one can see the magnificence of the Straits of Gibraltar and Malabata Point, and had wandered into the Gran Socco.

"Are you listening to me, kid?"

"Yes."

"You don't look like you are. Reb, there is money to be made. In the Legislative Assembly of the International Zone, there are three Jews. I've met one of them. They are shortly going to decide to extend to gold the benefits of an undeclared deposit; that is to say, anyone, resident or not, will be able to deposit any amount of gold without paying taxes. In France alone there are thousands of guys dreaming about gold, because of the inflation. Do you know what the difference is between an ingot of gold in Zurich and the same ingot in Lyon, for example? Two hundred thousand francs. We could, using Tangiers as a base, deliver gold in small planes, using the old fields of the French Resistance . . ."

"I don't know how to fly a plane."

A waiter who was at least seventy-five years old and, it turned out, spoke eight or ten languages brought them their drinks and the package of cigarettes Lazarus had also ordered. Lazarus kept his shiny little eyes glued to Reb's face.

"You in a bad mood, kid?"

The silence continued. The gray eyes turned to meet his gaze. Lazarus smiled.

"You don't have a dime, you have no family, no place to go. Without me, you'd probably starve. I've taught you everything. I even brought your first woman to your bed. Right?"

"Right."

"Did you kill anyone with Anielewitch?"

Before meeting Dov, Reb had strolled through the markets, coming back through Rue du Statut to the entrance to the Mendoubia, which overflowed with hibiscus and where there were dragon trees thought to be eight hundred years old. He had seen the man and had recognized him instantly, despite his civilian clothing, despite his mustache and his longer hair. With his jacket over his arm, mopping his neck with a handkerchief, the man was talking pleasantly to some British sailors who were arguing with a moneychanger. It wasn't Erich Steyr, or Hochreiner. Reb, who had a "rather good memory," had seen him only once, four years earlier. It had been at Belzec, on July 17, 1942. This man had walked through the rows of Jews who had just been brought from Lvov, and, in almost perfect Yiddish, had asked them all to write a letter to their families, to reassure them and tell them that they were not being mistreated, and that their deportation had not, in fact, been so terrible. . . ."

"You didn't answer me," said Dov.

"No."

"You didn't kill anyone?"

Reb smiled, shaking his head.

"I didn't answer you."

Lazarus picked up the pack of Philip Morris the waiter had brought with the mint tea and the martini.

"I was talking to some people in the market. In Italian, they call this *U fumu*, the smoke. They say you can make a lot of money with this also."

It was Dov Lazarus who financed the first operation, which took place in the second half of October. Then they did ten more, with the same destination: Spain. The system was easy, provided you could get a boat: the mild cigarettes that came from the United States were officially in transit in Tangiers, where their cost was thirty francs per pack, and in order to take them out, legally, you had only to indicate a port of destination where tobacco imports were legal, usually Malta. They would agree with Spanish buyers from Valencia to a meeting place at sea, outside territorial waters, since otherwise the Spanish ran the risk of meeting up with Franco's customs men. There were almost no risks, and the profit was quite satisfactory: one could resell for between fifty and sixty francs the pack bought in Tangiers for thirty. And since they sometimes carried fifty cases a trip, that is, twenty-five thousand packs, the profit from just one expedition could reach five or six hundred thousand francs—or, with the dollar then at one hundred and twenty francs, between four and five thousand dollars. It was not surprising, therefore, that there were fights over the business, which had not yet fallen into the hands of vagrants; former officers of the Royal Navy, a future French minister, British and Italian aristocrats, and even a crew made up entirely of lesbians, who sailed under a pink flag, were elbowing each other among an assortment of other smugglers.

After the first six trips, Reb was in a position to reimburse Lazarus for his initial investment.

"You don't have to do that," said Dov. "I didn't ask you to."

"I prefer it this way," answered Reb simply.

A man was present during this exchange, a Frenchman named Henri Haardt, who dreamed of adventure and had come from Nice to Tangiers only for that purpose. Haardt and Klimrod had met accidentally, standing in front of the shelves in the Librairie des Colonnes bookstore. The man from Nice, who was a history scholar, was the first to strike up a conversation—about the book this tall fellow was looking through. It was Spengler's *Decline of the West*, which Reb had almost succeeded in reading entirely. During the prolonged conversation on the terrace of the nearby café, the revelation that this young Spengler reader was only eighteen amazed Haardt, who was thirty, but the fact that he was dealing in cigarettes greatly intrigued him. He himself had a few new ideas on the subject, and could even imagine a "boulevard of cigarettes" going from Tangiers to the French and Italian coasts, where one could sell a pack of Philip Morris or Chesterfields for up to one hundred francs. . . .

"And if, instead of fifty cases per trip, we carried five hundred or one thousand, even more—it's a simple question of boats—

the profits would soon be fabulous. One million dollars a year would not be too far-fetched."

Haardt was surprised at his own continued obstinacy in wanting to convince a kid to team up with him. A kid who was hesitating, visibly. Certainly not for lack of nerve or ambition. There was something else.

"Is it your Irish friend? Because of him?"

"Not really."

"If you want," Haardt finally said, "we could all three get together. Although . . ."

He did not like Dov Lazarus (whom he knew only as O'Shea, a pseudonym he used the whole time he was in Tangiers) and actually was frightened of him. On two or three occasions, he had heard him in heated conversation, in English, with some rather suspicious-looking Italian-Americans, mentioning names like Hymie Weiss, Meyer Lansky, Lepke Buchalter, Lucky Luciano, the way former soldiers speak of their commanders. Haardt had a frantic desire for adventure, but within reasonable limits. A Lazarus–O'Shea seemed off-limits to him, just as the ill-matched duo he formed with young Hubrecht did. Ill-matched and dangerous.

All in all, Haardt was behaving like an older brother. And wondering why.

He couldn't do anything about the Langen incident. He was only a witness to it, and not even a direct one.

"They are Dutch," said Lazarus. "One is named Langen and the other one De Groot, or something like that. One of them has a license as a master mariner, and we need a real captain, right? We are talking about crossing the Mediterranean this time, not just going to wave at the *señoritas* along the Spanish coast. De Groot is the guy we need. As for the others, as crew, there will be one Maltese and three Sicilians."

"And us," said Reb.

"And us. Eight in all. We won't be enough to carry nine hundred cases. But there will be a team to help us when we get there."

"And we would be going to?"

"Sicily. To a bay to the west of Palermo. You have something against it, kid? Perhaps you thought we were going to continue

89

to play like children? We are going to get serious now. Come. I want you to meet these Dutchmen. . . ."

Henri Haardt was already at the Café de Paris, sitting with a friend of his, a Corsican customs officer who was dispensing much advice, as an expert, on the thousands of ways to use to maximum advantage the pleasant provisions of Tangiers's international status. He saw Klimrod and Lazarus arrive and sit down a few feet away, next to two men in their mid-thirties, whose backs were toward him. He could see the brutal steadiness of Klimrod's gray eyes, which at one moment widened for a few seconds; he noticed Klimrod's curious gesture—leaning down, with his head almost entirely under the table, to adjust a shoe-lace that didn't need adjusting, before sitting up, his face once again impassive. And, glancing at Lazarus–O'Shea, Haardt realized that he too had noticed something. Twenty or thirty minutes went by, after which the two strangers got up and left. . . .

Dov said in Yiddish and in a low voice: "Don't play the distant princess with me, kid. I saw your expression. Do you know one of those guys?"

Reb was stretching his fingers over his thighs, and seemed fascinated by them. He finally said: "At least one of them is not Dutch."

"Which one?"

"Langen."

Dov's eyes shone behind the lenses of his glasses like cold blue diamonds. He threw a bill on the table and got up.

"Let's get out of here."

Two months earlier, he had bought a two-toned Packard, a convertible. He took the wheel and started driving toward Malabata, with Reb at his side. They didn't exchange a word, but when they approached the lighthouse, Lazarus cut the engine, got out, and walked to the terrace from which you could see Tangiers, the Atlantic, and Spain.

He moved so quickly it was as if he hadn't moved, but the Colt .45 was now in his right palm, which was resting on his left hand. He shot once, and the seagull was brought down, killed in mid-flight. Dov was smiling.

"I asked you a question when we arrived in Tangiers. Whether you had killed anyone with that crazy Anielewitch. You didn't answer me."

With the same startling rapidity he had shown a few minutes earlier, he was in a shooting position again, with another seagull in his line of fire. But this time he didn't pull the trigger.

"Do you want to kill this Langen, Reb?"

"I don't know," said Reb quietly.

Dov's hand moved; the Colt was back in place under his jacket, tucked in his belt behind his right hip.

"Let's go back, kid. We'll go on that cruise to the coast of Sicily with De Groot and your friend Langen. I would be surprised if even this De Groot guy turned out to be Dutch. He's probably one of them, too, Reb. Langen can say he's Dutch in Tangiers, but do you think a real Dutchman would let himself be jerked around? Or else he's involved in a different way. They had SS there, too, even in Holland. . . ."

For the first time since they had been together, he touched the boy, putting his arm around his neck, leading him back toward the Packard.

"In any case, you couldn't kill him in Tangiers, kid, believe me. We've been seen together, him and us, and Tangiers is not very large. On the other hand, in Sicily one gets killed easily. . . ."

He started the car and smiled.

"You'll kill him over there, Reb."

5

The boat was called *Wild Cat*. Made of oak, it was eighty-five feet long, had a gross tonnage of seventy, a Marconi rig, and a one-hundred-and-eighty-horsepower Diesel engine. It was carrying six hundred and sixty cases of Philip Morris, two hundred of Chesterfields, and sixty of Camels. It left Tangiers on January 17, 1947, and sighted Cape San Vito, at the western end of the

Gulf of Castellammare, about thirty miles from Palermo, at nightfall on the twenty-third. None of the little speed boats of Italian customs was less than fifty nautical miles from the spot. Besides, the manifest and the bills of lading were in order and listed the exact cargo, giving Corfu as the port of destination.

According to instructions, De Groot cut the engine and waited. Around eleven o'clock, a triple yellow light on the shore indicated that the coast was clear. *Wild Cat* headed toward shore, then stopped again at another signal. Soon they heard the lapping of waves as a flotilla approached, a dozen large fishing boats. The fishermen began the transshipping, assisted by two or three customs officers, accomplices because they earned a thousand lire per case. Two trips back and forth were enough, and during their final boarding, the boats brought barrels of Greek wine, if you believed their trademark. One of the Sicilians tore up and burned the manifest and bills of lading and presented new ones that certified that *Wild Cat* was returning from Corfu, where it had taken on its cargo.

At seven o'clock the following morning, they entered the port of Palermo. They asked for a free stay; that is, a stopover without any movement of cargo. They had been at sea almost eight days without the slightest hitch; the deal was clinched.

"And our Italian clients are so pleased with us, they have invited us all to lunch," announced Dov Lazarus.

He glanced sharply at Reb. And he was smiling, of course.

From Mondello, outside Palermo, they followed the winding road up Mount Pellegrino. Well before the belvedere, they turned onto a small path, bordered by eucalyptus, on which was a white house with blue shutters. There were two cars, both American; Dov Lazarus, Langen, and an Italian-American named Sal Mancusa, through whom this part of the story came, were in one; in the other were Reb Klimrod, De Groot, two of the Sicilian sailors from *Wild Cat*, and the driver.

The cars stopped at the foot of a flight of stairs. The drivers remained in the cars, and the sailors lingered to talk. The others went up onto the terrace, probably shaded in summer by a large wisteria, which is still there, and from which there is an admirable view of the Bay of Palermo.

And it was probably then that the two so-called Dutchmen realized what was about to happen.

There was no meal ready at the house. Instead, two men were there, blank-faced, dressed in black except for their white shirts, worn without collar or tie. Each was holding a *lupara*, the Sicilian gun used for hunting wolves. But they didn't interfere; nor did Mancusa, who remained in the background.

The Colt .45 appeared in Dov Lazarus's hand as if by magic, and he said: "Langen? The kid and I have been wondering about something since Tangiers: what's your real name?"

Langen answered that that *was* his real name, that he *was* Dutch, nothing else, and that he didn't understand. Lazarus shook his head.

"Come, come . . . there is one thing I know about the kid: he has a fantastic memory, absolutely fantastic. He never forgets anything, a name, a face, figures, or a book. It's incredible, Langen: he reads a book once, only once, you hear, and that's it; he has it in his head forever. It's the same with faces. So if he says he saw you in Treblinka . . ."

"Belzec," corrected Reb in a hollow voice, looking down.

"Sorry, kid. Belzec, O.K. Langen, when the kid says he saw you in Belzec, in your SS uniform, at the time you killed his mother and sisters, when he says that, he is not mistaken. It's impossible, and no one . . ."

"It's not true. I could be wrong," said Reb in a whisper.

"And no one, not even the kid himself, will make me believe it. Get on your knees, Langen. Get on your knees or I'll blow off your little Nazi *schlong*, your cock, in one shot. And tell me: how do you say 'It's a nice day today' in Yiddish? Langen? Do you really want to suffer a lot before you croak?"

"*Sara sheyn veter haynt,*" said Langen.

"Doesn't he have a good accent, kid?" exclaimed Lazarus.

He pulled out another Colt and at the same time must have noticed the second so-called Dutchman start to move, behind him, for he said, good-naturedly, without even turning around: "One more step, De Groot, and I'll shoot your ass." He smiled at Reb.

"You are going to have to kill him. And *now*, please; we are not going to spend all day on this. It's not worth it. Take it, kid, take this .45. *Take it!*"

The gun changed hands.

"And don't shoot him right in the head. Right in the mouth, rather. He should see your finger on the trigger, you understand? Look, you do like this. . . ."

He guided Reb's hand, and the barrel of the gun went deep into Langen's mouth.

Suddenly, he screamed in Yiddish: "*Do it, Reb! He killed your mother and your sisters! What did he do to them, Reb? He burned them alive, right? KILL HIM! Fucking shit, KILL HIM!*"

Silence.

"O.K., kid, move away," Lazarus said softly, in English this time. "Just move away, and leave that thing where it is."

Then, a few seconds later: "Suck it, Langen . . . Suck the gun as if it were a nice fat Jewish *schlong* . . . There, that's right . . . Very good, Langen . . ."

The shot went off after the last word. He wheeled around and, with his other weapon, held in his left hand, killed De Groot with one shot in the head, right in the temple.

Dov Lazarus and Reb Klimrod reappeared in Austria, in Linz, at Landstrasse 36, Simon Wiesenthal's home. Henri Haardt, who was worried about them, was told by a certain Sol Mancusa, who was now in command of *Wild Cat*, that, having quarelled with the Dutchmen, they had lingered on a while in Italy.

Wiesenthal asked Klimrod whether he belonged to any organization, and he answered no, he was acting alone.

"And the other man?" asked Wiesenthal. "The one who is waiting in the street?"

"A friend," Reb said simply.

The names of the men he was interested in were Erich Joachim Steyr and Wilhelm Hochreiner.

Neither of these names was familiar to Wiesenthal, who didn't have them on his lists. But in the beginning of 1947 very little was known about the men who ran the extermination camps or what had happened to them since May of 1945. In February 1947, Wiesenthal was just drawing up a list of Adolf Eichmann's close collaborators, and he had no way of knowing if he was still alive. As for the ODESSA network, an intricate channel set up in 1947 to facilitate Nazi escapes, it was totally unknown to him.

"I have some Steyrs. But no Erich Joachim, born in Graz on what date . . .?"

"April 14, 1905," said Reb. "Son of Joachim Steyr, also born in Graz, on November 6, 1879, and Martha Silvernagel, born October 23, 1883, in Klagenfurt. Which makes him forty-two years old. He's five feet ten. Blond, blue eyes, very good-looking, with a star-shaped scar on his right palm. Before the war, he was a lawyer in Vienna. He speaks English and a little French. He is very interested in art, especially in painting. His favorite painters . . ."

He recited the facts in a slow, detached voice. It happened often, and it was to happen even more often, that people who were total strangers to Simon Wiesenthal, as was this tall boy with the dreamy expression, would come and tell him stories. Often these stories would shed new light on his research. Names and facts would suddenly fall together. So he made a note of the names of Steyr and Hochreiner.

"War criminals?"

"Yes," said Reb.

"I would need facts. If you agree to testify and to . . ."

"And what would happen if I testified?"

"These men would be sought. And, if the proof is sufficient, provided they are found, they would be arrested, tried, and sentenced."

The boy smiled.

"I see," he said. "I will think it over, and perhaps I'll come back to see you."

He got up.

Wisenthal asked: "There is between you and these men a personal matter, is there not?"

"In a way," answered Reb, giving his curious slow smile.

"Do you want to tell me about it? I myself have lost eighty-five members of my family."

The boy shook his head politely. "Another time, perhaps. And thank you for your kind welcome."

Wisenthal saw him go out, pass by number 40, where the offices of the OSS were located, and join the other man, who was much smaller, older, broader, with very wide shoulders and rimless glasses.

He never saw Reb Klimrod again.

In 1932, Erich Steyr had joined a firm of lawyers headed by Johann Klimrod. He assumed official control of it in 1941, but had been running it de facto for more than six years, on the basis of a trusteeship document signed by Klimrod, who couldn't maintain his practice because of the hemiplegia that had forced him to move about in a wheelchair. Steyr did not reappear in Vienna, or anywhere else, at the end of the war. And in February 1947, before the Graz tribunal, his wife filed a petition for a *Todeserklarung*, a legal declaration of death, for her husband, basing her request on the testimony of a man who swore he witnessed the death of Erich Steyr, killed by a Soviet machine-gun blast in Prague. The court granted this request easily, since this was a classic procedure. The name of Steyr disappeared from, if ever it had appeared on, the list of Nazi criminals.

Steyr's career was rather well documented. His participation in the failed coup of 1934 was established in a police report, which mentions an intervention by Johann Klimrod in his favor. His enrollment in the Nazi party dated from February 1938, card number 6.330.372. As of that date, he became a recognized legal specialist in the "Jewish problem." Appointed legal counsellor to the Central Bureau for the Emigration of Jews, he participated in the arrest, internment, and expulsion, for a ransom of several million dollars, of Baron Louis de Rothschild. In 1940, he worked on the legal aspects of the Madagascar Project, which foresaw the deportation of all European Jews and used for the first time the term "final solution to the Jewish problem." The following year, as ordered by Reinhard Heydrich, he made several trips to the Low Countries as an administrator of assets and pensions belonging to the one hundred forty thousand Dutch Jews, of whom only five thousand survived. At the same time, he continued to manage, in his own way, the Klimrod office.

In 1943, having joined the Waffen SS, he left for the Eastern front, returning in March 1944 for hospital treatment. As of October 1944, his official activities decreased. Less and less is known about him after that, until his complete disappearance in April of 1945.

That was the official Erich Joachim Steyr. David Settiniaz offers a more complete version of the life and accomplishments of this man.

The discretion with which Steyr's career was conducted within Nazi Germany was deliberate. Steyr used current events for strictly personal ends, with a cynical and impressive effectiveness. His aim: getting possession of all the worldly goods belonging to the Klimrod family, as well as those entrusted to Johann Klimrod, the crippled but honest lawyer, by his clients, in those already dark years from 1938 to 1941. Steyr had also counted Hannah Klimrod among his objectives. As a result of an investigation conducted at his urging in 1982, David Settiniaz has a photograph of Hannah Klimrod, taken on August 7, 1937, on the Lido beach in Venice. She is standing in the middle of a group, with her three children; she is looking at the lens with her extraordinary light eyes, which Reb inherited from her; her beauty is breathtaking, a serious, calm, yet radiant beauty. Steyr is standing about six feet from her not looking at the lens, but looking at her. He did not succeed in obtaining this possession, more precious than all the others. He lucidly sent them to Lvov, she and her three children, with the passports he had obtained for them, with all the guarantees he could give them from his position as a high-ranking Nazi . . .

. . . with, also, the certainty that he was sending them to a death he had probably planned himself.

And Settiniaz believes that Johann Klimrod's arrest, carried out so discreetly, and his consignment to Hartheim castle, to be used as a guinea pig for the future torturers of the extermination camps, was all the handiwork of Steyr, who completed his personal *Anschluss* by laying off the former servants and killing Anton Hinterseer, the old butler.

As for what Erich Steyr did after April of 1945 . . . He found refuge, at first, in an American prison camp, using a false name, waiting for the moment when he could reappear officially. When Reb Klimrod had shown up once again—now more dangerous than he would have been two years earlier—Steyr realized that his security was seriously endangered . . .

. . . which explains what happened in the Austrian mountains . . . and Steyr's flight to South America in March 1947.

For Settiniaz, there is no doubt: of all the possible channels, Steyr used the one known as "the Route of the Monasteries."

6

At 8:10 A.M., a tall man, rather corpulent but still cutting a
pleasing figure, came out of a private house on Zeppelinstrasse,
in Munich, near the Isar. He raised the fox collar of his coat,
adjusted his smart suede gloves, and opened the door of his garage. The Mercedes, his pride, was there, sparkling clean. He
sat down behind the wheel and reveled in hearing the engine
purr softly. He put the car in gear.

"Don't move, please."

The voice was so soft and so courteous that he felt no fright.
Then, turning, he recognized the eyes, and a blazing terror overtook him.

"It can't be!"

"I'm afraid so," answered Reb. "I know that your children are
going to come out and that you have to take them to school.
There will be no change in the program. There better not be. I
would be forced to kill your children, also, and I would rather
not. Now, drive normally, please."

"Michael . . ."

"Drive, please."

The Mercedes backed out of the garage and pulled up slowly
in front of the house. The two children walked out, bundled up
in red and blue wool scarves. They showed some surprise at
seeing a stranger next to their father, but Reb smiled and said
to them: "Your father and I are old friends. He took care of me
almost like a father for twenty months. Come, get in; we are
going to drop you at school."

The children smiled at him and asked questions. He told them
his name was Michael, or, rather, that their father called him
that because he did not like his other name. And what was this
name? Oh, he said, something very foreign and strange, and they
could ask their father what it was.

They arrived at the school, and Reb said to the driver of the
Mercedes: "You should kiss your children. They are charming."

The children went into the school, and the car pulled away.

"Michael, my God . . ."

"We are going to Dachau," said Reb. "Please. Mauthausen is
too far and we would have to cross the border. Dachau will do."

"Michael . . ."

"My name is Reb," said Reb, smiling. "Slow down a little, please. I wouldn't want us to have an accident. And I would like you to be quiet. To hear you speak . . . only increases that great anger I feel. Do you understand?"

They drove in silence. The camp appeared, still intact after twenty-three months.

"We are not going inside. It's not necessary. Just follow the wall until you can see the crematoriums."

Two minutes went by.

"There. Stop now, please. And get out of the car."

Reb also got out. He was holding a can in his left hand and a weapon in his right.

The former Obersturmbannführer asked in a hollow voice: "Would you really have killed my children?"

"I think so," said Reb. "But I'm not sure. I am very angry but I don't know whether I would have gone as far as to kill them."

He handed him the can.

"Open it and drink, please."

The former Obersturmbannführer unscrewed the cap and immediately recognized the smell. He said in a strangled voice: "It's gasoline."

"Yes," said Reb. "I remember a young Frenchman you forced to drink, three years and four days ago, at about the same time. For him, it was sludge. Probably because you did not have enough gasoline. He was ten years old. he was born on July 23 in Bordeaux. I remember him very well. It took him ten hours to die. I think you will drink this gasoline because you will hope until the very end that I will not kill you. And it's true that you have a chance. Not a big one, but you have one. But, before you drink . . ."

From the pocket of his jacket, he took a small object wrapped in paper.

"A present," he said.

The man removed the paper. He found a lipstick.

"I would very much like you to put some on your face, on your lips especially . . ."

Time went by.

"There. The cheeks, also, please . . . Very good. Now you can drink the gasoline. . . . The can is yours, in case you did

99

not recognize it. And this letter will be found in your pocket. It was written by a young Lithuanian named Zaccharius. You'll tell me he's dead. But is that reason enough? He describes in it what you did to the children, of which I was one. . . . Drink a little more, please . . ."

He shot from very close, under the right cheekbone. Then he placed the weapon in the still-warm hand of former Obersturmbannführer Wilhelm Hochreiner and, with the dead man's own fingers, pulled the trigger once again, this time shooting into a bush.

He waited until he was far away before throwing up. In fact, Dov Lazarus had to stop his car two more times so that he could throw up again.

"Watch it," whispered Dov.

The woman had just reappeared, this time with two men.

"Don't you recognize one of them, kid?"

Reb nodded. The smaller of the two men was German, and three weeks earlier, right after Hochreiner's execution near the crematoriums of Dachau, he and Dov had seen him driving one of the trucks that delivered *Stars and Stripes* between Salzburg and Munich. The Military Police never searched those trucks, other than to take a few copies with a smile, so that during almost every trip Nazi fugitives traveled, hidden behind stacks of newspapers. As for the woman, with short gray hair and a cold expression, she was the one who, on July 3, 1945, in Salzburg, had told Reb he could find the photographer named Lothar at his laboratory near the bell tower and had in this way sent him into the trap laid by Epke.

The woman had been the first step in the hunt undertaken by Reb Klimrod. (The search for Hochreiner had been easy, because the former Obersturmbannführer had simply, at the beginning of 1946, returned to running his textile mill.) Reb had found her less than a hundred hours after he returned to Austria from Munich, and on this day, March 23, 1947, he and Lazarus, together or separately, had been on her trail for forty-three days.

"There are other guys in the chalet, kid. At least three men."

"Four," said Reb.

It was about 10:00 P.M. and it was going to be a cold night. Below the small wood where they were lying in wait, they could see the lights of Althaussee. It was in the heart of the Dead Mountains, and the lakes there are deep and dark, set between high, often almost vertical cliffs. Sixty thousand civilians loaded with loot from all of Europe had sought refuge there during the last months of the war.

"Four men and another woman," said Reb. He had started with the hypothesis that, working with Epke, she might have been at the house near the Bohemian Chancellery. He was right: Gerda Huber, as described by Reb, had been identified by two shopkeepers in the neighborhood. They had also revealed her name and her origin. She came from Graz, Erich Steyr's hometown. The rest had been easy. The woman worked for the Austrian Red Cross, helping displaced people. As such, she had access to all sorts of passes.

"Something's up."

A third man came out of the chalet, and Dov as well as Reb recognized him.

"Arni Schaide," said Dov, "my old pal Arni, who likes so much to visit the Franciscan monasteries between here and Rome."

On two occasions already, Dov had tracked Schaide, who each time had led him to Rome, to the very door of the Vatican. From there, each time, Schaide had come out alone, having obviously entrusted to the Roman Curia the fugitive he had escorted. Schaide also worked for the Red Cross.

"Dov?"

For a long time, Reb had focused his binoculars down toward the first curves of the little road leading to the chalet.

"Two automobiles, Dov. But they have stopped, both of them, and they have just shut off their headlights. They are three hundred yards away."

In the dark, they looked at each other.

"Cops?"

"I don't think so," said Reb.

The two large Mercedes-Benzes certainly did not belong to the Austrian police, or to any of the occupation authorities. No, it was something else, and Dov must have thought the same thing. He left his post, retreated, and also focused his binoculars.

After half a minute, he said: "Ten days ago, when I returned from Italy for the second time, right behind Arni, I saw an identical Mercedes. With the same back left door handle broken. It was in Innsbruck. Three men inside looking like crack shots. Arni got in with them. I remember the licence plate number. . . . Wait for me, kid."

He slipped down, disappeared.

Less than a minute later, the phone in the chalet rang and was immediately picked up. Three more minutes, after which there was some commotion around the chalet. Reb saw the men who until now had been talking leisurely jump up. One of them rushed outside, two others spread out, weapons in hand. They've just been alerted, he thought.

After a pause there was an almost imperceptible sound. Reb hid behind a tree, his finger on the trigger.

A whisper: "Kid? Don't shoot me, please." Dov appeared about fifteen feet away, out of breath.

"Same car and same guys. Except there are eight or ten of them. And more coming. It looks like Stalingrad all over again, my boy. And I'll bet you a rabbi for a doughnut that it's us they're after."

He smiled.

"And I wonder who the hell is in that fucking chalet. Are you sure it's not Adolf Hitler?"

A quarter of an hour later, they had proof that it was, in fact, a roundup: all around them, in a semicircle of which they were almost the center, flashlights were turned on.

"But they ended up losing, in Stalingrad," said Dov.

He and Reb were moving along the eastern bank of the little lake of Althaussee, and were already more than a thousand yards from the chalet. They were not running, yet. They went along under the trees, not really worried. Their intention, since the descent toward Altaussee was cut off, was to reach another little village, more to the east, called Grundlsee. From there, they intended to go either to Bad Aussee or for help, even to the police. But Reb, who was walking ahead, suddenly stopped. Another line of flashlights had appeared, to their right. The circle was closing in, or almost.

They had no choice but to continue straight ahead, tripping halfway down an increasingly abrupt slope.

They increased their speed, and in the clear night they could see before them the snowy peaks of the Dead Mountains. "We'll never get through," said Dov. "At least not me. I don't have your young legs, kid." He was ready to mount a counteroffensive, which was in his nature, but Reb pressed him to keep going. The concentric line of flashlights was now one hundred yards from them as they moved on. They had to pass to the northeast of Grundlsee, and for an instant they saw automobiles, with their headlights on, stationed along the little road that leaves Grundlsee and ends in a cul-de-sac two and a half to three miles farther on. There were men lined up there, also, in the light of the headlights, all armed, some with rifles, their faces turned in their direction. "All the survivors of the Third Reich are here," remarked Dov, laughing.

He had already fallen twice and had lost his glasses. In the dark, he could hardly see at all. Reb must certainly have helped him. The flashlight carriers were on their heels and closing in.

More lights appeared to their right, those of Gossl. They had now been running for two hours. They were in sight of Toplitz Lake. Dov could go no farther. He screamed, adressing himself to those chasing them, that he was Dov Lazarus in person and that he was ready to fight them. . . .

They answered with six or seven shots, the dry, light clicking of .22 Mausers, entrusted during the war to the sharpshooters of the Wehrmacht. Neither Dov nor Reb was hit. Again they were climbing, a more and more abrupt cliff, and soon Dov refused to go any farther or any higher. The lake was beneath them, almost vertically down. Dov said that he was going to stay right there, in this hollowed-out rock on a kind of platform "from which you have a magnificent view," and he shook his head quietly, probably smiling in the dark. He was going to remain there, he said, and he intended, even without his glasses, to prevent this Nazi army from coming too close. "Think, kid. And, anyway, I'm sure you thought of it before me, with that head of yours: we won't make it this way, by running. They run faster than we do. So, you stay calm, kid, you stay sharp. And listen to that fucking brain of yours that is so extraordinary and is telling you that that's our only chance . . ." He would hold out long enough for Reb, with his young goat's legs, to climb through the Dead Mountains and maybe get some help.

"I won't move, Reb. What are you going to do? Carry me? I weigh a good one ninety-eight, from all that beer. Beat it, kid, please. Find that guy you're looking for and put me on his bill."

. . . And, of course, when Reb Klimrod agreed to leave him behind and began his climb, he heard, a few minutes after his departure, the first shots. He also heard Dov singing as loudly as he could—"My bonnie lies over the ocean, my bonnie lies over the sea."

He was two hundred yards farther up, after a mad climb in the night, when he heard the thudding sound of a mass tumbling down the mountainside and falling into the icy black water of the lake. He thought Dov was already dead. But shortly after, he could hear the sound of the two .45s firing calmly and the Irish-accented voice singing again.

But it was finally interrupted, by one ultimate round of fire.

At around 3:00 A.M. he was back in sight of the chalet. There were no guards visible, but he could see a light. He climbed to the balcony, and at the sound of his footsteps someone asked in German: "Did you get them?"

"Only one," answered Reb.

The guard appeard at the threshold with a double-barreled shotgun under his arm. As soon as he saw Reb, he started to reach for the gun. Reb's bullet pierced his throat.

He went into the chalet, where he found another man, un-armed, and one of the two women, not Gerda Huber.

"Do not move, please," he said to the terrified couple.

With the barrel of his gun toward the floor, he checked to see that the other rooms were empty. The man was looking at him fixedly; he had a thin face and a hooked nose and was balding.

He asked: "Who are you looking for?"

"Erich Steyr."

"I knew an Erich Steyr who was an attorney in Vienna."

"That's the one."

"I have no idea where he might be. He may even be dead." His shiny black eyes gave him a somewhat Jewish appearance.

"Who are you?" asked Reb.

Just then, he heard, through the door he had left ajar on pur-pose, the sound of the engines of at least two automobiles.

"Who are you and why are you being so protected?"

"You are mistaken," said the man. "The one who was being protected left this very evening. I am only the owner of this chalet. And I never knew the name of the man who was hiding here."

Klimrod took the papers the man had on him. At that time, he had never heard the name Adolf Eichmann.

Yoël Bainish saw Reb Klimrod in Rome around April 10, 1947. Luck had nothing to do with the meeting of the two young men, who had not seen each other for almost eighteen months. Bainish was in Italy on behalf of Haganah, to handle emigration channels. (Three months later, he was to play an active part in the embarcation of four thousand five hundred and fifteen people, on an old American cargo ship, the *President Garfield*, which became the *Exodus*.)

He and Klimrod met in front of the Castel Sant' Angelo, at the end of the morning.

"How in the world did you know that I was in Italy? I found your message at Bertchick's just in time. I'm leaving Rome tomorrow."

Klimrod explained that he had gone to Bertchik's "to talk to someone about Mossad or Haganah" and that, in order to make himself known, he had to give the names of men who would answer for him.

"Yours was one. And Bertchik told me that you were in Rome. Do you have two hours to spare? I would like to show you something."

He took Bainish into a little street leading to the Via Crescenzio, right next to Saint Peter's Square, and showed him a plaque, in Italian and German.

"The escape route leads to this place. They leave Germany through Lindau and Bregenz on Lake Constance, or by the Reschen Pass, which you and I took, two years ago. They travel by car, sometimes by bus, and spend their nights in Franciscan monasteries. I've made a list for you. One of the men who arranges the convoys is named Arni Schaide. There is also a woman, Gerda Huber. There's also a list of them. In Rome, they are taken in charge by Monsignor Heidemann, a German, who runs an official organ of the Vatican. Heidemann furnishes them with passports from the Red Cross. Some of them are even given cassocks and false papers belonging to Jesuits. They leave Italy through Bari or, mostly, Genoa. Some of them go to Spain, Syria, or Ethiopia, but many embark for South America. Hundreds have already escaped this way."

Bainish was stunned.

"Why this sudden avalanche of information?"

"I found out about all this while looking for something else. I had to tell someone about it."

That last sentence implied that he had no superiors or organization to whom he had to answer. Bainish (whose career was progressing: it had finally been recognized that he was too intelligent to be a dynamiter and he was being assigned more delicate missions) knew that his former road companion had severed all ties with the Zionist organizations. Someone had spoken to him about a certain Klimrod who was working for "those crazies in Nakam."

He asked: "Are you still with them, Reb?"

"No. Not for a long time."

"And Lazarus?"

"Dead."

Nothing else. They were walking along the Tiber. Bainish examined Klimrod and found him changed. Not so much in size or weight, though he might have grown a little more and gained a few pounds. But he still had the silhouette of a daddy longlegs, that same apparent slowness of step, and the same depthless gaze. The change was elsewhere: there was a greater hardness and an apparent certainty of a destiny.

"Did you find what you were looking for, Reb?"

"Almost."

Silence.

Then Bainish said suddenly: "I've always felt a great friendship for you. Really. If there is anything . . ."

"Thank you, nothing."

And again silence.

To fill it, Bainish began to talk about this country that was being born on the banks of the Tiberias and the Jordan, where they would finally have their place, he and Reb and so many others who had come or were coming. He was getting excited talking about the great adventure to be lived, even in the Negev desert, which they were begining to conquer.

The answer came, slowly but definite.

"Without me," said Reb.

"You are almost as Jewish as I am. To be Jewish can also be a choice."

"I am nothing. Nothing."

Bainish took down the list, needing almost twenty pages, even with his small handwriting, the names, the monasteries, the relay stations, all the information Reb had gathered while "looking for something else."

Strangely uncomfortable, Bainish started to laugh.

"It's as if you were giving us a farewell gift."

"In a way," said Reb.

And then a warm, friendly look came into his eyes, and he began to smile. He wrapped his large hand around Bainish's shoulder. "Thank you, thank you for everything." He left and crossed the Tiber.

In Tangiers, Henri Haardt also saw Klimrod again, around this same time, "mid-April, I think."

"He came to see me as if he had seen me the night before, asked me if I would agree to carry out a few operations with him. He had some money, about six thousand U.S. dollars, and wanted to invest it all in a single trip, in a sort of double or nothing.

"He looked about twenty-two or twenty-three years old. His second stay in Tangiers lasted four months, and during this period we made four trips together, all successful. Not counting expenses, that left us with a profit of a little more than fifty dollars per case. One hundred and twenty cases were his during the first trip, and after that he had two hundred each time. The calculations are simple: he netted close to thirty-five thousand dollars.

"As for his departure from Tangiers, it was as simple as his arrival. He merely told me that our collaboration had been 'both extremely pleasant and agreeable'—he really spoke like that, slowly and softly, with an almost old-fashioned courtesy—but that the time had come for him to leave. I told him of my regret and that I had a great feeling of friendship toward him, almost affection. And I also told him that we could have made a fortune together. He smiled at me and told me that that did not interest him.

"I don't know where he got it, but under his arm he was carrying a small painting, unwrapped, which he showed me, asking me whether I liked it. I have never been an authority on painting and all I could see were spots of color. I told him so, and he started laughing, but the laughter never reached his eyes, which widened ever so slightly.

" 'The signature belongs to a man named Kandinsky, who died three years ago,' he said. 'A very great painter. One can kill for a painting, Henri, but one can also be killed by it. . . .'

"On Boulevard Pasteur, he bought a cloth bag the exact size of the painting. And, as far as I know, that was the only baggage he took with him when he left Tangiers, at the beginning of August 1947, for a destination unknown to me. That painting and those two books that he was always dragging around with him . . ."

7

At the time, Arcadio Almeiras was fifty-six years old. He had dreaded becoming a painter, but had been one for five or six years in the early nineteen-twenties with Emilio Pettoruti. He had gone as far as Berlin to meet Klee. As for Kandinsky, he remembered very well the three or four times he had visited him in Weimar. That was when he hoped to have a little, a very little, bit of talent. "Not even a little bit. The Gobi desert."

He asked: "And whose is it, in your opinion?"

The tall young man shrugged his shoulders.

"A name like Kondinjki. But it's worth a lot of money, I'm sure. At least a thousand dollars."

His Spanish was perfectly correct, although he spoke hesitantly.

"French?"

"Belgian," said the young man.

Almeiras took the painting to the door to his shop and held it up to the pale daylight of the Argentine winter. He examined it closely. As often happened, the *s* in Kandinsky had been made by the painter to look like a *j*. He smiled at a very pretty young woman who was walking by his gallery in Buenos Aires, then-turned around.

"It's a Kandinsky, a Russian painter who died recently in Paris. And you are right; it is worth a great deal. More than a thousand dollars, at any rate. You are really interested in selling it?"

"I need money. And I did not steal it."

He presented some documents, which it turned out, were not worth much, establishing that the painting had been legally purchased in Madrid a year earlier, from a man named Maurer, and legally taken from Madrid to Buenos Aires.

Almeiras said: "There is mention of other paintings. . . ."

"Four others," said the young man. He took a little notebook from his pocket, opened it, showed the page to Almeiras, who read: "July 3, 1946, Madrid. Five paintings bought from Gunther Maurer, of Berlin. Klee, F. Marc, Kondinjky, F. Marc, A. Macke. 1200 U.S. dollars."

"You really paid twelve hundred dollars for these five paintings?"

"He wanted five thousand, but he was in a rush."

Almeiras closed his eyes. "Twelve hundred dollars for a Klee, two Marcs, one Kandinsky, and an August Macke! These Europeans have really gone crazy! And are you considering selling all of them?"

"I don't think so," answered the young man quietly. "Or maybe later . . ."

"Or if you are made an interesting offer."

The young man's thin face, rather impressive with those light eyes that pierced it, softened noticeably when he smiled.

"I guess."

They decided that Almeiras would keep the Kandinsky for a few days. He would have liked to see the four other paintings, if only for his personal pleasure, but the young man told him he did not have them with him, that they were not in Buenos Aires, not even in Argentina. He had left them with his brother, in Bogotá. Yes, he had family, his father, his mother, and three brothers in Bogotá. And he would be going back there shortly.

"Do you speak German?" asked Almeiras

Just the usual words, he said. "*Jawohl!*" and "*Kommen Sie mit mir*" and so on. He laughed, very pleasantly.

"*Der Blaue Reiter*," said Almeiras. "The Blue Rider. That was the name of a group of painters before the Great War of 1914. Kandinsky, Marc, Macke, and Klee were part of it. A collector would certainly be interested in the purchase of your five paintings at the same time. It's already a collection in itself. You understand?"

"I understand," said the young man.

"Especially Argentines of German origin. We have many Germans in Argentina, especially of late. Franz Marc and August Macke both died during the 1914–18 war. Their paintings are much in demand by collectors. They died and did not have time to paint very much. And for people of German origin, to buy these paintings is almost like—how shall I put it?—like making a patriotic gesture.

"I understand," repeated the young man. "I am agreeable to a complete sale, then, if the price is interesting. And thank you for your honesty. I will not forget it."

No, he couldn't furnish an address in Buenos Aires, but he would return to the gallery. His name was Henri Haardt, he said, in answer to the question put to him by Almeiras.

After a seventeen-day watch, Erich Steyr appeared.

Diego Haas was an Argentine, born in that country of a father from Carinthia and a mother whose name was—and she never failed to point it out—de Carbajal and a Thousand Other Things. He was a chubby blond young man whose small size was inversely proportionate to his cynicism, which was considerable, and he exhibited an insolent cheerfulness that bordered on pure folly. Speaking German and English, besides Spanish, he had studied law for a while and had recently been engaged as secretary to an extremely rich German immigrant named Erich Steyr. It was not September, and five months of employment had already taught him the essential facts concerning his employer: Steyr, Erich Joachim, was quite rich, quite intelligent, quite handsome, quite learned, quite elegant and refined, but if he wasn't the world's most despicable worm, he wasn't far from it.

Diego smiled graciously at Steyr.

"I have never heard of this Kandinsky, *señor*. But I am prepared

110

to find him admirable." He glanced casually at the painting and exclaimed: "Admirable!"

After that he left the gallery and went outside to ogle the *señoritas*. Nearby were Steyr's car, Steyr's chauffeur, and Steyr's bodyguard. Steyr did not live in Buenos Aires. As soon as he arrived in Argentina, he had acquired, through Diego, a beautiful *estancia* near Córdoba, and less than a week after the purchase, the crates had arrived, innumerable, concealing the treasures of Golconda. Even Diego, who prided himself on his lack of culture, had marveled upon seeing such treasures. At the same time, Steyr was setting up his Argentine, even South American, future: he was going to establish himself as an investment counsellor, especially to those unfortunate compatriots of his who had been chased from their native country by the forces of international Jewry. "*Jawohl,*" Diego had said, imperturbable, unaffected by this false exaltation. Steyr, he thought, was far too intelligent to take this nonsense seriously; he was a piece of garbage and that was that. They had traveled through Argentina and to neighboring countries, as far as Venezuela and Chile, and had already been to Bogotá, in Colombia.

In truth—and he recognized it himself when he spoke to Georges Tarras—Diego Haas had no particular recollection of that day in September 1947. From the start, he was aware of Steyr's passion for the arts, painting especially. The Almeiras Gallery was therefore an almost compulsory stop; it was the finest in Argentina, and thus the visit to the Kandinsky was not of an unusual nature. It was not until Diego's own meeting with the King and particularly, the hallucinatory scene in Bogotá two months later that he made the connection. . . .

For it took several weeks for the "Kandinsky Affair" to achieve real proportions. During that period, Steyr returned many times to the gallery, apparently conducting a slow negotiation.

On November 5, Almeiras informed Steyr that the owner of the five paintings he wanted to acquire had finally decided to say yes.

Steyr left for Colombia with Diego, using a business meeting as a pretext, and hoping to kill two birds with one stone.

They arrived in Bogotá on November 6, 1947.

111

"I hate Bogotá," said Diego Haas. "What's more, I also despise Santiago, in Chile. And Lima. And La Paz and Quito. I barely tolerate Buenos Aires. Not to mention Asunción, which I abhor, and Caracas, which I positively loathe. In fact, besides Rio, although they don't speak Spanish there . . ."

"Would you be kind enough to shut your big mouth," said Steyr, as always without raising his voice. Seated in the back of the car, he was reading, deeply engrossed in some business matter. A Colombian driver who looked like a turtle was at the wheel, with the bodyguard to his right, a man named Gruber, whom Diego judged to be a little less astute than a cow, and he didn't think much of cows. Diego was seated in the back, next to the lawyer.

"I don't know Europe very well," continued Diego, completely unaffected by the rebuff. "Except for a few petticoats here and there. I had almost convinced Mamita—that's my mother—to offer me one or two years in Paris when you Nazi guys started your own excursions there. In my own way, I am a victim of the Third Reich."

One hour earlier, the plane from Caracas had brought the three men to Bogotá.

"Haas, one more of your stupid jokes and I will ask Gruber to beat you up. Which he will be delighted to do."

They were approaching the center of the city, which they reached a little after 4:00 P.M. It was raining, a very fine cold rain, explained probably by the very high altitude. They went directly to their hotel, near San Carlos Palace, where Bolívar had lived. At the reception desk, a message was waiting for Steyr. It was written in Spanish and signed by Henri Haardt. Digeo translated.

"He writes that if you want to buy his paintings, you can find him every day after six in the evening at Carrera de Bacata, 8, in the Chapiñero section. *Olé!* The '*Olé*' is mine."

Steyr decided to put it off until the following day. But then, driven by what Diego thought was his feverish haste to see these paintings he had been waiting for for two months, he decided to go that very evening. Diego sets the time as 8:15 when they arrived at 8 Carrera de Bacata. They found a brand-new building, which looked as if it was not yet lived in, but as soon as they reached the door, a man appeared and told them that one apartment, on the fifth floor, was occupied. By Señor Henri Haardt, precisely, and that Señor Haardt had just come in; therefore he was at home.

After entering, there was a narrow hallway, through which there was access to the cellar and the caretaker's rooms. It led to a straight staircase, whose first flight ended on a landing. To the left, five or six steps led to a second hallway, where there were two elevators and the service stairway.

As always, it was Gruber who opened the door, and thus arrived first at the elevators. He preceded Steyr by two or three yards and Diego Haas by much more, because Diego had stopped to have a few words with the caretaker, whom he thought rather "bizarre."

Diego heard three shots, but, at the moment, did not know who was shooting. He had just reached the top of the first flight of stairs and was about to step onto the landing. He hesitated, not knowing what he wanted to do: go see what was happening or "get the hell out as quickly as possible while pretending that I had gone for help." Events did not give him the choice. A very tall figure appeared above him and calmly gave him an order in Spanish.

"Call the caretaker, and tell him to come here. There has been an accident."

Diego did not have to call; the caretaker had also heard the shots. (But not the Colombian driver who had brought Steyr and his two companions, because the door of the building had been closed.) Diego, in a way reassured by the calmness of the stranger, climbed the last steps.

He reached the second hallway. Gruber was lying crouched against the metal door of one of the elevators, as if he were listening through the door, with his cheek pressed against it. But blood was beginning to run down his neck.

Erich Steyr was a few feet away, unharmed, hands above his head, with a look of terror on his face.

"On your stomach," Diego was told. He complied immediately, as did the caretaker, who had just arrived, breathless. A large hand appeared in Diego's field of vision and proceeded to search him.

"No tickling, please. I can't stand it. And I am not armed, thank God. Handy as I am, I could maim myself with nail scissors."

"It is not you I am after," said the deep voice of the stranger. "Nothing will happen to you if you remain quiet."

"I will be as quiet as a mouse," answered Diego with as much conviction as he could muster. "I had actually intended to spend the evening on my stomach."

The man also searched the caretaker, without result. There was a moment of silence, and when the stranger spoke again, it was in German.

"Do you recognize me, Erich?"

"Reb Klimrod," said Steyr. "You have grown a lot."

Silence.

"She died in Belzec, Erich. Just like Mina and Kati. Did you specifically request Belzec, or did you leave it up to the SS in Lvov?"

"I did not have any particular camp in mind. Reb, that young blond man you had lie down understands everything we are saying. In other words, you will have to kill him also."

"And I went to Hartheim castle."

"I asked Epke to show you the pictures, if he could find them, before killing you. Did he?"

"Yes."

Silence again.

"I am not afraid, Reb. No matter what you do to me."

"Good."

"How did you find me?"

"The postcard you sent to your wife from Buenos Aires, to tell her you had arrived safely. I searched her house one night. I almost missed it. And then I remembered that play you had written, the one that took place in Venice. One of the players was named Tarantello, like the signer of the card."

"That's the price one pays for having literary aspirations. Do you really have a Klee, a Marc, and a Macke?"

"No. Anyway, not since you robbed us. Go into the elevator, Erich. The one on the right."

"Everything is in Córdoba, Reb. Absolutely everything. Given time, I could arrange it so that it would all come back to you, legally."

"Get in."

"If I die, you'll lose everything, Reb. All the things that belonged to your father that you loved so much."

The fourth shot made Diego Haas look up. He saw Steyr grimacing from pain and standing on only his left leg; the bullet had mangled his right knee.

"Do not try to force me to kill you this way, Erich. You won't succeed. Go into the elevator."

Steyr moved, hopping on his good leg and leaning against the wall for support.

"Do you really speak German?"

For a few seconds, Diego did not understand that the question was being asked of him. He didn't even think of lying. "Fluently," he said. "But the only reason I went to Europe was to look under women's skirts there." For the first time, he saw the face of the man Steyr had called "Reb Klimrod." His features were frozen in a terrible grimace of hatred and disgust. But the voice remained fantastically calm.

"Please get up and go look."

Diego did. He discovered an elevator that seemed perfectly ordinary. Then he realized that the sides were made of sheets of shining steel, as if someone had forgotten to finish them.

And there were three photographs lined up at eye level, all three showing the same man crawling on the floor of what appeared to be a cave, mouth open, at the height of suffering.

"My father, Johann Klimrod. Look at him well, Erich. You'll have plenty of time to do so."

Steyr had collapsed in a corner of the elevator. He tried to say something, but the steel panel closed shut and the noise of the lock muffled the sound of his voice. In the door that had just shut, there was a little window, not larger than two hands placed side by side. Quickly, Steyr's face appeared behind it. Diego could see the lips moving but there wasn't the slightest sound.

"What is your name?"

"Haas. Diego Haas."

"Move back. I don't want you to get hurt. Go sit back there, with the other man. He is not a caretaker and not responsible for anything. He had no idea what I was going to do. Don't move, either of you."

With that, Klimrod got to work. From the stairwell, he brought a cloth bag and an entire network of electric wires. For one second, he seemed to hesitate; his pale eyes had widened and his

115

lips were quivering, as if he were about to cry. But he plugged in all the connections. Only then did Diego notice the blood running down the back of his right hand, and the bloody tear in his jacket, above the elbow: one of Gruber's shots must have hit him.

Nothing seemed to be happening since he had plugged in the wires. There were no sparks, or anything else visible. Klimrod took a step back, staring into the little window. After a few minutes, he brushed the steel door lightly with his fingers. A gesture that he repeated many times during the following minutes, in total silence.

Until the moment when he said to Diego without even turning his head, in German: "Come feel this."

Once again, Diego obeyed. He put out his hand, which was trembling, and pulled it back immediately. The steel was very hot.

"And that's nothing," said Klimrod in a distant, almost dreamy voice. "In one minute the metal will start turning red. . . ."

Then only did he press the button. There was that hollow noise characteristic of elevators beginning to function, but the steel cabin started to rise with infinite slowness, almost imperceptibly, maybe one inch per minute.

From the cloth bag, Klimrod took eight silver candlesticks and as many candles. He lined them up in front of the elevator, the steel of which was actually beginning to redden slightly. Diego did not dare look through the little window.

"Eight candlesticks, eight lights," said Klimrod. "Two for each member of my family. . . ."

He lit the candles one by one. Through the window, Steyr's face seemed to be melting in pain; his eyes looked as if they were burning. Diego thought that maybe, at that moment, he should say something. Klimrod took a step back and, in a language Diego did not immediately recognize, began to recite something.

When he was finished, above the yellow flames of the candles, below the elevator, which was now red, there was an empty space. The elevator was still rising, the steel more and more incandescent. Diego was chilled with horror, and looked away.

"Please get up. Both of you."

The order had been given in Spanish.

He made them go down the short flight of stairs, then the full staircase. They were halfway down it when the Colombian driver saw them.

The two shots fired by Reb Klimrod went high over the man's head, but he nonetheless felt like a target and disappeared from the doorway.

"This way."

They went into the quarters of the caretaker, two rooms in a row.

"Come in here, please," Klimrod ordered the caretaker. He closed the closet door on him and locked it. Diego Haas, on the other hand, he pushed ahead of him. They reached a door, to which Klimrod had the key, and found themselves in a little street where a Volkswagen was parked.

"Please drive. My wound would encumber me. I hope you know how to drive."

They heard footsteps behind them: the driver was running toward them. One of his bullets crashed through the rear window and hit the right edge of the windshield. Klimrod answered with two shots, apparently not wanting to hit his target.

"Let's go, please."

The car was hit two more times, but one sharp turn taken at full speed by Diego put them out of reach. They quickly got to Avenida Caracas.

Diego asked: "And we are going to?"

"The airport.

"The driver is going to warn the police. And Señor Steyr had some very powerful friends here."

"The airport."

"Straight ahead."

He was pulling himself together, recovering some of his friskiness, even if he was still horrified by the scene he had just witnessed.

He asked: "What was that you were reciting, in front of those candlesticks?"

"The *Kaddish*, the Jewish prayer for the dead."

"Because you are Jewish?"

"Not any more, but I was, a little, at one time," said Klimrod . . .

. . . who suddenly yelled, "STOP!"

The Volkswagen had just reached the vast esplanade of the Campo Eucharistique, and two military police vehicles were about to close in on them.

"Turn around. Quickly, please."

"Call me Nuvolari," said Diego.

But he turned at furious speed, as if his life depended on it. And it probably does, you big fool! he thought. If this big guy with the soft, frightening voice and light eyes doesn't kill you himself, the *policía militar* certainly will; they shoot anything that moves. He went full speed toward the Techo race track. He was living the most exciting hours of his life.

Because other cars appeared, from the left and the right, and from behind, he now was really involved, and, with an incomprehensible cheerfulness, he did his best to avoid them, going into a wild saraband . . .

. . . until the moment when, at an order given by Klimrod, he stepped on the brake to stop. He didn't even have time to understand ("Everything was ready and waiting, I assure you"), but found himself at the wheel of a truck this time, driving west, driving by the same police cars that were chasing the Volkswagen.

A short time after, the road began to descend vertiginously; it became a path, one of the muddiest, hardly visible through pouring rain. The headlights, at each turn, lit either the wall of a forest-covered mountain or the frightening gap of a precipice. At least a dozen times, having clumsily used the brakes, Diego felt the truck, carried by its own inert force, begin to slide in the yellow mud, directly toward the abyss. Each time, miraculously, he had managed to pull out of it. I couldn't stop even if I wanted to, he said to himself. This is the final fall, Dieguito!

It was only after several hours of this mad descent that they came in sight of a tiny esplanade. Diego hit the brake with all his strength, standing on the pedal, which didn't stop the truck from crashing into a rock.

But they had finally stopped.

They both stepped out at the same time. In a corner of the rock, there was a niche, and in it stood a light-blue-and-gold Virgin, at whose feet some flowers had been left in a can, as well as votive offerings, thanking the Madonna for watching over truck and car drivers through their harrowing descent.

"Ah, that explains it," Diego said cheerfully. "I am not such a bad driver after all. . . ."

He turned around and saw Reb Klimrod, his forehead pressed against the rock, crying.

After this stop, and one more that they made to get some gasoline, they had to drive four more hours to reach the little town of Villavicencio, which is, in altitude, not distance, a bit more than a mile lower than Bogotá. By this time, a rather strange accord had developed between Klimrod and Haas.

After they left Villavicencio, going east, Klimrod asked Diego where they were, and what was ahead of them. Diego burst out laughing.

"I was never very good at geography. No more than at history, Spanish, foreign languages, physics and chemistry, and mathematics. And I was always excused from gymnastics with the help of Mamita. That, under those circumstances, I was able almost to complete a law degree is, certainly, one of the most nauseating scandals of worldwide university history. Anyway, to put it simply, to the right, there is nothing; to the left, it's completely empty. As for straight ahead, it's even worse."

"Which means what, exactly?"

Diego pointed, thinking, This smacks of being a historical moment, what you are about to do, my chubby little Diego.

He said: "You walk straight ahead for fifteen hundred or two thousand miles and, at one point, you turn right. That will be the Amazon. There, you start rowing and, theoretically, after another six hundred or so miles, give or take a month, you reach the Atlantic. From there you can go back to Austria."

He looked up and was chilled by the incredible emotion he could see on that thin face.

"They will be after you," he said, suddenly regretting his lightheartedness. "Just in my country, in Argentina, they have invested more than one hundred million dollars. There are men like Steyr everywhere, throughout the continent, and I have heard talk about a network that is going to send even more of them over here. They can't let something like what you have done to Steyr go by; it could give others ideas. The caretaker of the building . . ."

"He was not the real caretaker. I paid him to play the part, but he knew nothing else. He thought it was a joke. Please exonerate him."

"Did he speak German?"

"No."

"Therefore, he could not have understood anything you and Steyr were saying." He smiled, his yellow eyes sparkling. "I am actually the only witness, the only one to know your name. . . ."

He took Klimrod's hand, forced it to take the .45 from his belt, and pressed the barrel of it against his own temple.

"Boom!" he said gaily. "But I don't mind telling you that that would annoy me."

They drove by a place called Puerto López, and there, because a small plane flew over them twice, they suddenly changed direction, in the ocean of llano grass in a silence that was buzzing in the heat. They went south, for no other reason than that they had stumbled onto a new road that was hardly visible and obviously old. They had been gone from Bogotá for more than forty hours when they went through San Carlos de Guaroa, and they reached the Chaffuray rancho on the morning of the ninth. Beyond that, there was one more registered rancho, and that was La Horqueta, which they reached after one last stretch that lasted fourteen hours of driving time. After that, the road ended.

Although Diego tried to go farther in the truck, he finally had to capitulate before a river where there was no bridge, and where, after a long search, they could find no ford.

"That's it," siad Diego, worn out.

When he shut off the engine, the silence bounced back at him, overwhelming in its force. Moreover, he had the feeling that an irreparable folly was about to occur. That wild descent from Bogotá, for hours, on that winding road where they should have been killed twenty times, had nothing premeditated about it; it was simply the continuation of their escape from the Chapiñero. Then, the trip east, going deeper and deeper into a world that was less human, had been a kind of game, like moving up inch by inch to the edge of a bottomless pit. . . .

"Now, we have come to the final point. . . ."

He climbed onto the running board and from there to the roof of the truck. It was not so much what he saw—jungle ran along a yellow river and sometimes obscured it completely—as what he imagined beyond it: an absolute immensity, unknown, glaucous and gluey, for hundreds of thousands of square miles, swarming with beasts and . . . It gave him goose bumps.

"Listen," he said suddenly, with a seriousness that surprised even him, "this is madness. You can't possibly be thinking of going on, alone, straight ahead. . . ."

"There is one thing I would like you to do," said Klimrod softly. "This truck we have been using—I rented it from someone who did not know what I was going to do with it. This man, whose name and address you will find inside the truck, might have some problems because of me. Try to convince the police of his innocence as well. And compensate him, please."

He had on only the boots, pants, and cotton shirt he had bought in Villavicencio five days earlier. He pulled the Colt .45 from his belt and put it on the hood.

"Take that, too, or throw it away. As for money . . ."

He turned the cloth bag from which he had taken the candlesticks and candles in Bogotá upside down. Out came two books, three passports, and a bundle of bills. He took only the books, which he put back into the bag, and swung it over his shoulder.

"And thank you. I will remember you, Diego."

The next minute, he had walked away.

Diego Haas remembers yelling after him, two or three times, imploring him to come back, torn by an inexplicable despair. But at no time did Klimrod seem to hear. He went straight into the jungle, which rapidly, avidly, engulfed him.

Two days later, on November 11, 1947, having returned to civilization, Diego Haas was arrested by soldiers, who hit him a little on the head, as well as on other parts of his body. He was taken back to Villavicencio and from there to Bogotá, where he was questioned with a meritorious determination. He nevertheless stuck to his own story: he had been an innocent victim, forced by the madman, threatened by a huge gun and twelve grenades, to drive a car, then a truck, to the very ends of the llano, to which, had he been alone, he would never have thought of going. No, the madman said nothing about his name or the reasons that had made him burn Señor Steyr alive, "my-dear-boss-whose-tragic-death-has-overwhelmed-me-with grief. *Olé.*" (The final "*Olé*" had been *in petto*.) Of Señor Steyr, after the elevator had been opened by a blowtorch, there was left only a rather repugnant mass of well-done meat.

What did the madman look like?

"He is about thirty-five," said Diego. "I would estimate his height as five feet six, black hair and very dark eyes, a scar on the left cheek. And he is missing part of the little finger of his left hand. Oh, and I almost forgot: he limps. Yes, he speaks German, but with a heavy Russian accent. No, no, not Polish, Russian. I know some Russians, you see! There is no way he could be a real German. At one point, he spoke of Caracas and of Venezuela. But my guess is that he is headed toward the border to the south."

They hit him a few more times, because his description of the madman didn't agree too well with the one given them by the caretaker, who was not even the real caretaker but a chance substitute. Diego said that was not surprising, because the substitute caretaker was clearly myopic and an alcoholic (which was true).

After that, his mamita, in Buenos Aires, who had high connections and big means, was able to intervene and explain that her only, and crazy, son was anything (a loser in particular) but a criminal who might serve as an accomplice to a "Polish Jew or a Russian Communist." As soon as he was set free, Diego found the owner of the truck, who had not been too worried (they had knocked out only a few of his teeth); he was compensated for his misfortune with part of the twelve thousand six hundred and twenty-five dollars Klimrod had left Diego. The caretaker-who-was-not-the-real-caretaker was given the rest, after he got out of prison with no greater damage than the loss of three fingers.

Stirred by a textile magnate from Medellín, who was offering a twenty-thousand-dollar reward for the madman's capture, the search went on for four weeks, covering a wide area stretching from Nunchia in the north to the border in the south.

To the east, two columns of soldiers and three planes took part in the search. They even found the last spot the truck had reached, and there they searched through the llano for dozens of miles. Without much conviction, for, as crazy as he might be, the madman could not be crazy enough to have gone straight ahead.

The King, in the meantime, was on his way to his future kingdom.

Guaharibos

1

The King himself said one day to David Settiniaz that he was absolutely incapable of retracing the itinerary he had followed. In fact, had Settiniaz not insisted, Reb probably would not have bothered coming back this way to retrace his steps. But Settiniaz did insist and got his way. In March of 1969, he and the King, in a huge helicopter, flew over the region, equipped with numerous maps.

The river before which Diego Haas had had to stop the truck was the Manacaccías, or one of the large streams that feed it. The Manacaccías, after one east-southeast meander, actually runs to the north; it flows into the Meta, itself a feeder of the Orinoco. The King did not follow its path. He simply crossed it and went in a south-southeast direction. That's when he must have come across the Rio Ariari. He told Settiniaz about a path half eaten by the forest, which Settiniaz identified as the one traced in 1942 by Rubber, an American company that was exploiting the heveas of the Colombian region of Guaviare at the time.

And the King spoke also of an isolated hut near the village of Puerto La Concordia, where the Guayabero meets the Ariari to form the Guaviare, another large feeder of the Orinoco.

The King never gave any other explanation for his fantastic trip. He more or less followed the course of the Guaviare, reached the small agglomeration of San Fernando de Atabapo, in Venezuelan territory, around the beginning of February 1948, after walking for one hundred days.

From San Fernando, the young man could easily have gone down the Orinoco and reached Guyana or Caracas and the Caribbean Sea.

But he chose to go to the east, deep into what was really Amazonia, always going straight ahead, toward the unknown upper Orinoco, which flowed between the Capitales des Formes of the Serra Parima, vertiginous and incomprehensible cones that surge like monstrous organ pipes from the humid jungle, the highest reaching five thousand feet.

Settiniaz flew over the region alone during the year that followed his first journey with the King. At San Fernando de Atabapo, he discovered a small town of perhaps a few thousand inhabitants, where low houses were grouped around the inevitable Plaza Bolívar, a town that had been practically abandoned fifty years before, when it had been the capital of Amazonas, and the point of departure of the *seringueros*, who were trying to keep alive the great rubber adventure. In a helicopter that had taken off from Puerto Ayacuch, he flew over the Orinoco, first to La Esmeralda—the Emerald—which at the time Reb was there was the farthest outpost of Venezuelan administration. Beyond that, Settiniaz entered a forbidden zone, passing three Catholic missions, recently established, the oldest of them dating only from 1951. He landed at the third and last one, Platanal, where he was graciously welcomed by a Salesian missionary, an Italian named Bartoli.

Settiniaz continued his aerial ascent of the Orinoco. He went beyond what Humboldt had called "the Columns of Hercules of South America"—in reality rapids that were two to three hundred yards wide, depending on the season, the rapids of Guaharibos—and convinced his rather nervous pilot to enter the narrow valley where the river officially begins. They came in sight of the pass and the border with Brazil. To this day, it remains one of the wildest and most mysterious places on earth. Settiniaz imagined it inhabited by hundreds of thousands of crawling and flying animals. He was not disappointed: there were mosquitos, millions of them per square yard; *jejenes*, little gnats whose bites take a week to heal; hundreds of assorted insects that come to suck on the slightest scrape; *niguas*, a sort of chigoe flea which lays its eggs under the skin; bats; trap-door spiders which could jump almost eight inches to reach their victims, and are horribly venomous; ants, red and otherwise; termites, capable of devouring a wood chest in one night; snakes, of course, for whom Amazonia is a favorite resort; and jaguars, crocodiles, electric fish . . .

126

. . . and the Indians.

In Caracas, and this was in 1970, twenty-two years after Klimrod was there, Settiniaz had been warned: the place where he was going, luckily by helicopter, was the territory of the Yanomami, who twenty years before were still being called the Monkey Men. "Very dangerous, *señor.*" The Yanomami were the last great Amazonian tribe to refuse contact with civilization.

It was among them that, in April of 1948, the King arrived, after a solitary odyssey of over one thousand five hundred miles.

He had already met Indians, often, before reaching the banks of the Orinoco, at San Fernando de Atabapo, and even more after that, while he was following the course of the immense river. Several times he had been able to climb into one of their canoes, sometimes for a few days. Those Indians occasionally spoke broken Spanish, and the sight of a white man did not seem to surprise them.

Then there had been those famished-looking *seringueros*, with whom he had traveled for a good week. They had warned him: the Maquiritares were generally peaceable; they were sometimes thieving, but that was all. The Guaharibos, on the other hand, "they will kill you, *muchacho*, and you won't even see them kill you. . . ." And they would start telling frightful stories about the ferocity of the Monkey Men, who had settled between Venezuela and Brazil.

Without any identification paper or passport, Reb Klimrod had crossed, either on a raft or by swimming, the Colombian-Venezuelan border, and therefore the Orinoco, at the height of San Fernando. He had not appeared in the tiny town, nor at any of the ranchos that he might have passed after that. He did the same at the mission of La Esmeralda, waiting for night before skirting the few buildings there. He must have reached the rapids of Guaharibos around the end of March.

The meeting took place about twenty days later.

It must have been close to midday, and yet the light was dusk-like, the slightest ray of sun being completely obscured by a ceiling of trees, leaves, and lianas, several dozen yards thick. Some of the lianas were almost three feet wide and in this murky light, a submarine light, they looked like monstrous snakes, which sometimes they were. On the ground, a fetid humus thickened by rotting leaves was swarming with a disquieting larval life. It was like walking inside the stomach of a legendary animal, dark green and palpitating.

He stopped, to catch his breath rather than out of fear. He held a machete in his right hand, for which at some point he had exchanged his watch. And Diego Haas probably would not have recognized him: he had become thinner, but at the same time his body had changed; the signs of adolescence had forever disappeared. He had reached his final height, six feet two, and the figure, the slim shape, David Settiniaz would always know. His skin was tan, that golden color that would always seem so shocking next to those light irises; his beard, which was never very full, had grown, giving him that mystical look of Mexican Christs. When he located the Indian camp, he had just completed six hours of uninterrupted walking, in heat of one hundred twenty degrees to one hundred thirty degrees Fahrenheit, with incredible humidity, which had not stopped rising during the last seven days.

After a moment, when his breathing had resumed a normal pace, he went on. Without causing the slightest movement to the leaves, he slipped through the vegetal wall and after a few more feet arrived at a cleared patch almost two hundred feet long.

There were three huts in this artificial clearing. They were triangular, just as the *seringueros* had described them, and the palm trunks of which they were made had not been cut down by any mechanical instrument; they had been uprooted and broken by torsion, according to the Guaharibos's technique. There was no sign of life except for a small fire burning in the humidity-laden air.

He remained still for a long while at the edge of the open space, shaded by the dark green of the forest, which would suddenly yellow and, at the tops of the trees, turn a scintillating white. Then he moved forward, slowly. He neared the hearth, put down the cloth bag, began undressing, removing even his boots. Of these, and of his clothes, he made a straight pile, right next to the rising smoke, and on the top of the pile he placed his machete, with the blade facing himself, in other words, offering the handle.

Taking three or four steps back, he stopped again, his head tilted slightly backward and looking up at the minuscule opening in the ceiling of foliage, which permitted one still to believe in the sun. His entire body was the same golden-bronze color as his face and hands, and perspiration further defined his fine long muscles. He waited. It was a few minutes before he heard once again the indistinct rustling sounds he had previously perceived, over the breathing of the forest.

They all appeared at the same time, five men, extricating themselves from wherever they had taken cover when they heard him approach, with a reptilian ease and without the slightest noise. The tallest of them was five feet three, but they were all young, athletic, and naked, a smooth, almost polished-looking nakedness. They were painted with red and black, very delicately; there were neat square shapes and diamond shapes and on their right arms were little tufts of multicolored feathers. The whole effect was surprisingly beautiful. Two of them had their ears pierced with bamboo shoots. All of them wore a thin braided cord around the waist, which held the penis upright by a knot under the foreskin. Their hair was combed up into a crown, surrounding a shaved spot like that of a monk.

But the essential thing, at that moment, was the large bent arcs that were all pointed at Reb Klimrod. His total immobility must have had some effect on them. They came closer, circling him slowly, and grazing him lightly with the curare-dipped war arrows. Then one of them picked up the machete, tested its edge on his finger, and he checked the strength of the metal by trying to break it. He threw it suddenly, and a palm trunk was neatly severed. The man burst out laughing, and this laugh was like a signal. A whole group of men, women, and children came out of the forest, like silent shadows. As their timidity lessened, they formed a circle around the still-unmoving giant. The man holding the machete touched Klimrod, and laughed again when a thin line of blood appeared where the blade had just passed. Other men came forward, some of them scratching him with their nails to make sure that the color of his skin was not due to some sort of paint. (One of the stories told by the *seringueros* was the one about a black man who had been captured by them, and they, surprised by his strange color, had skinned him almost completely before realizing that he was naturally black.)

Finally, they were all around him, even the women, touching him and pulling his hairs. His eyes, especially, seemed to fascinate them. But the difference in size was such that, in order to look at his eyes, they had to take a few steps back and look up: Gulliver in Lilliput country. Not a word had been spoken yet, and the first one to speak was an older man, whose cheek was swollen up to his eye by something he had in his mouth, from which a greenish juice was running out. The utterance had the tone of a threat. At the same time, a few men seized the clothes, the boots, and the bag. One or two of them tried the shirt and pants on, on their heads, while others took the boots, balancing them on their heads, to the general merriment of the others.

"*Atchika*," said Reb. "Friend." He smiled.

For some reason, his offer of friendship went unanswered. Suddenly, the whole group packed up, and within a few seconds the clearing was empty, with the miraculous instantaneousness of dreams. Twice, Reb yelled, "*Atchika!*" But the only response he received was in the form of three arrows that landed right at his feet, one of them exactly between his legs. And he had not even seen the archers. . . .

The King said that he started following them, that he followed them "for eight to ten days," always keeping one hundred yards behind them, he still naked. They had taken everything from him except the two books, which he had hidden before going into the clearing. He said that on several occasions they tried to dissuade him from following them, either by coming back toward him and screaming menacingly, or by simply shooting some of their little hunting arrows at him, hurting him slightly twice, but obviously not wanting to kill him.

After this lapse of time of eight to ten days, which the King recognizes could have been longer, he reached the extreme limit of his physical strength. His entire body was covered by millions of insect bites, his feet were bloody, gnawed by the chigoe fleas and some of the horrible little beasts which, when one goes through water, incrust themselves under the skin by opening sores that look like oysters out of their shell, hideous and terribly painful. Besides that, in his obstinate craziness not to lose track of the Guaharibos, he did not take time to eat, even with the experience he had acquired during the last few months, while making his incredible journey that had begun at the foot of the Andes.

The King said simply: "There came a moment when I could not go any farther, and when I came to, they were all around me, smiling at me. I spent the following months with them, before going farther south, on the Rio Negro. . . ."

The trading post established by the Indian Protection Service, the evil SPI, north of Maura, on the Rio Camanaú, was operated by a man whose name was Ramos. In 1948, he was thirty-four years old; he had married one year before at Belém, and had decided to take his wife along with him when, seven months before, he had been selected for this trading post. Of all the civil servants of the SPI working in Amazonia, he was far from the worst. In seven months, he had not killed any Indians, and had even put an end to a practice that had been in use until then, which consisted of infecting the natives with certain germs— starting with one for a head cold, a benign ailment for white men but an almost always deadly one for the autochthonous race. The sale of guns to the gold and diamond prospectors was a normal activity; he did not have to know what these guns were used for. And he was not aware that these Winchester 73s were the very ones that had previously been used in the United States and in Mexico during wars with the Indians there.

The first signs of animosity among the Indian visitors to the post operated by Ramos began in October of 1948. Until then, the exchanges had always been pleasant: trinkets or metal kitchen implements were traded for nuggets, little diamonds, and bows and arrows, all these operations being financially rewarding since Indian arms were sold as far away as Rio. And it had a strategic advantage: the Winchesters were more effective when their owners had to defend themselves against savages who were unarmed. But as of October, the Indians began to show reluctance, about the bows specifically, refusing to trade them for anything else.

As for the white man, he appeared in November. None of Ramos's sixteen subordinates, nor Ramos himself, could have been mistaken: although entirely naked, he was a white man, very tall, with very light eyes, long hair held back by a green band, and a rather sparse beard. He came three or four times, but never really approached the post, standing back somewhat.

When addressed in Portuguese or Spanish, he did not react, appearing not to have heard. His Waimiri companions showed him great consideration, never completing any transaction without his approval. And he spoke their language, in a low, slow voice.

Ramos remembers a remark made to him by one of his employees, a man named Rocha, who noticed that there were three of four Guaharibos among the Waimiri, a surprising thing, because the hostility between the tribes of the Parima and those of the Negro was well known. Ramos is sure of one other fact: once at least, the mysterious white man came to the post accompanied by a very young Indian girl, extremely well-developed, twelve to fourteen years old.

In early December an incident occurred about nineteen miles to the northwest of the Rio Jauaperi that Ramos characterized as "regrettable." Some prospectors massacred an entire village, including the very young children. In his report to Belém, Ramos distributed the responsibility equally. "You have to understand that the *garimpeiros* lead an extremely harsh and difficult life, and that the Indians are often hostile toward them for no reason. . . ."

On December 29, a group of rather angry Indians arrived at the post with some unacceptable requests: ten bows for one Winchester. Or one Winchester for some diamonds. Ramos refused indignantly. Curiously, this refusal did not seem to affect the Indians too much. Ramos concluded that the "regrettable incident" must have been forgotten. But Rocha, a young man who was born in Moura, whose Christian name was Ubaldo, and who spoke many Indian dialects, pointed out that the Indians were now coming to the post without their women and children, which was contrary to their custom, and that the spectacular change in the Waimiris' attitude, from aggressiveness to easy-going, was due to a few words spoken by the white man, who always stood back.

Ramos shrugged his shoulders, laughing. "It just goes to show that however much he tries to make himself look like a monkey, he remains a white man, one of us. . . .

Two days later, on December 31, Claudia Ramos, who was seven months pregnant and suffering greatly from the heat, was splashing herself with water from a pan when, through the paneless window, covered simply by a mosquito net, she saw a dozen

132

Waimiri standing motionless at the edge of the forest, fifteen or twenty yards away. Afraid of being seen naked, she quickly put on a blouse and was stepping into her skirt when the mosquito net burst open, slashed by a machete. She shrieked and, encumbered by both her pregnancy and the skirt, which she could not quite get on, rushed to her husband's office. The first war arrow, which measured almost four feet, went through her right thigh; the second one went straight into her back, between shoulder blade and collarbone. She managed to drag herself onto the veranda, where she discovered her brother-in-law, who had been literally nailed to the wood side of the building by fifteen or twenty arows, six of which had slashed his throat and another, shot point-blank, had gone through his open mouth and come out almost eight inches beyond the back of his neck.

Claudia Ramos finally collapsed, and as she fell to the ground, an Indian appeared, right in front of her face. She saw him brandishing a club, but the man did not complete his gesture. A shout stopped him; the white man appeared, giving a command. The Wiamiri hesitated, grumbled, and ran off.

"Oh, my God!" cried the young woman.

The white man with the light eyes and the green headband leaned over her. He put out his hand, and with the tips of his fingers caressed her cheek and her lips, then left, without having said a word.

Ubaldo Rocha was coming back from the river when he saw, thirty feet from where he was, one of the trading post employees fall, his throat shot through by an arrow. He understood immediately what was happening and ran into a little nearby storeroom, which, luckily, had shutters. He closed them, as he did the door. The attackers saw him, but too late, so they satisfied themselves by furiously hitting the planks of the building. Then they seemed to give up and walked away. Through openings between the planks, Rocha witnessed most of the massacre and his testimony is in total contradiction to that of Ramos (whose young brother was killed, probably because of his resemblance to the trading post's chief). To Rocha, not only did the white man not lead the attack, but, to the contrary, he did everything to appease the murderous fury of the Indians, running from one to the other and speaking to them in their language.

It was he, in particular, who interfered when the attackers came back to the building where Rocha had taken refuge. They set it on fire, and if not for the white man, who appeared again, Rocha would have died, either burned to death or killed while trying a desperate escape. But the white man pushed away the Indians and yelled in Spanish: "Get out of there and go to the river!"

With his hands burned and his hair scorched, Rocha threw himself out of the building just before it collapsed (it contained gasoline and alcohol), and ran to jump into the river.

There were, in all, among the employees of the trading post, nine dead, counting Ramos's brother, and four wounded, among them Claudia Ramos, who survived and still lives in Santarém.

In April of 1949, Ubaldo Rocha, who was in Manaus, was asked if he would take part in an attempt to go up the Jauaperi to try to renew friendly contact with the Waimiri. Since the December incident, the Indians had practically disappeared, having gone to the north, perhaps even up to the territory of the Yanomami. The man who asked this of Rocha was named Barbosa. He was what is called in Brazil a *sertaniste*, a specialist in the *sertao*, the Amazonian forest, and one of the more serious ones. To Rocha's surprise, he turned out to be a sincere friend of the Indians, in spite of his belonging to the SPI. Since 1943, he had worked in the Mato Grosso with authentic "native specialists," the brothers Villas Boas, Orlando and Claudio. He told Rocha he had had no experience with the Indians of northern Amazonia, although he knew those from the south rather well, and that he was looking for dependable men to help him. He was accompanied by two anthropologists but no soldiers. Rocha had left the SPI; he had then worked for the Booth Line, which, since the beginning of the century, ran a service between Liverpool and Iquitos, which necessitated a twenty-four-hundred-mile trip up the Amazon.

He accepted Barbosa's offer, out of love for the jungle.

The small group left Manaus on May 9, went up the Negro, past its numerous islands, reached Moura, and there, instead of taking the Jauaperi, they chose, on Rocha's advice, to go by way of the Rio Branco, which actually flows north.

Rocha had spoken to Barbosa about the tall white man with the headband and told him his idea: if they could find this man, who apparently had enough prestige, even enough of a hold on the Indians, to circulate among them without danger, and even to arrange for the cohabitation of tribes as different as the Waimiri and the Yanomami, then perhaps he would agree to help them in their mission of peace.

They went up the Branco, which sometimes was several miles wide, and after three weeks began to see in the distance massive elevations, crowned by endless forests, the unknown and awesome Serra Pacaraïma. Rocha and an interpreter, an evangelized Waïmiri by the name of Sebastião, disembarked at a place called Caracaraí, on the right bank of the Branco. If the information they had received was true, the white man might be in this area.

During the entire month of June, Rocha searched those parts in vain, encouraged, though, by the attitude of the Indians. At the approach to each village, he found, planted in the middle of the path, an arrow decorated by two crossed white feathers, the sign of peace. He asked numerous questions but was never answered: the faces remained impassive, either because of ignorance or because they refused to answer.

At the end of June, he crossed back over the Branco, and this time, accompanied by Barbosa, an ethnologist named Nelson de Andrade, and Sebastião they traveled up the Rio Ajarani for about thirty miles, heading straight toward the Serra do Mucajaí. On July 6, the four men came in sight of a village, where, strangely, they seemed to be expected. They were offered fruit and roasted peccary, prepared without salt or pepper, in the style of the Yanomami, who like only bland-tasting food, reminiscent of the forest under the rain, and who instinctively eat earth to compensate for a deficiency of iron and other minerals. Rocha thought he recognized certain faces.

"I could swear that these were the ones who came to Ramos's post," he said to Barbosa. "They are Yanomami, no doubt about that. Look at the drawings. They are not quite on their own territory."

Through Sebastião (his own Yanomami was no longer sufficient), he obtained permission to visit the village. Barbosa and he were allowed to enter all the huts—except one. As soon as the two Brazilians came near it, three men jumped up and blocked the entrance, without giving any explanation, and refusing to answer Sebastião's questions.

"That does not mean very much," admitted Rocha. "They often forbid strangers to enter a *maloca*, and sometimes even women, for religious or other reasons. Perhaps they are keeping something in there . . ."

Or someone.

Rocha immediately thought of the white man. He tried something. Raising his voice, as if he were speaking to someone at a distance, he said, in Portuguese: "My name is Ubaldo Rocha. You saved my life six months ago, at Ramos's post. I was locked in the storeroom, and, if not for you, I would have been killed. We simply want to talk to you. . . ."

No reaction. But a minute later, a young Indian woman appeared, and Rocha recognized her immediately: she was the one who had accompanied the white man one day. In her arms she was holding a child about two months old, whose skin was astonishingly light. Completely naked except for a minuscule red-colored fringe that decorated her pubis, she had a beautiful body and wore no paint on her face. Most especially, she was not wearing one of those bamboo rods Yanomami women put through their nostrils, lips, or ear lobes. She was not at all intimidated by the sight of the white men; in fact, she gave them an amused look and went into the forbidden hut.

It occurred to Rocha that perhaps the white man did not understand Portuguese: during the December massacre, he had yelled in Spanish. Andrade translated Rocha's sentence into Spanish, but once again there was no response.

It was becoming difficult to insist. Sebastião issued a brief warning. The Yanomami (he called then Guaharibos) were becoming restless and began menacingly fingering their war bows, which were larger than they were, and none of the white men was armed, except for machetes. But Barbosa, sharing Rocha's conviction, decided to remain close to the village for a few days.

"Silencio . . ."

There was a slight pressure on Rocha's shoulder. He opened his eyes. If he could not make out the face, he could at least identify the silhouette, very tall and very thin, outlined in the moonlight.

"Silencio, por favor."

The words had been whispered. Momentarily worried, Rocha

slipped out of his hammock. Following the man, he walked along the river, feeling at once apprehensive, yet enormously curious and even exalted. After about one hundred yards, the white man with the headband turned around and faced him. Two things particularly struck Rocha: the height and the eyes.

"Do you speak Spanish?"

"A little," answered Rocha. "But I understand it well."

"I was watching you, when you were working for Ramos. You were one of the few employees who behaved correctly with the Indians. . . . Do you understand me?"

"Yes."

"And now you are in the forest, unarmed. Why?"

Rocha told him of Barbosa's mission, and of the confidence he felt in the ethnologist.

He risked adding: "You should talk to him. He is a man"— he was looking for the right Spanish words—"*muy sincero, de buena fe* . . ."

"No. Tell him to leave, him and his companions. This is not a zoo. They should leave tomorrow."

The voice was slow, as if indifferent. There emanated from this man, entirely naked except for the headband, extraordinary natural authority, and, had Rocha known the word, exceptional charisma. This justified to a certain extent the naïveté of his next question.

"Are you the chief of the Indians?"

What happened then on the thin face, accentuated by the light of the moon, was almost a smile.

"No. And I will never be. They have simply accepted me. Ubaldo Rocha—that is your name, is it not? How old are you?"

"Twenty-three."

"Do you know Manaus?"

Rocha said he had been born in Moura, but that of course he knew Manaus, where he now lived. The white man went on.

"Tomorrow, you will leave with the others. But I would like you to come back. Either alone, or, if you wish, with that Waimiri you call Sebastião. You will not be in any danger; no one will hurt you as long as it's only you and the Waimiri. I would like you to bring some medicine that you can buy in Manaus, or elsewhere. Some sulfanilamide, some penicillin, and some streptomycin. Do you know what they are?"

137

"The penicillin, yes."

"Will you remember the names?"

"Yes. But I do not have any money."

The bony hand came forward, opened to reveal the palm: diamonds. Rocha was speechless. There were enough diamonds to buy half of Manaus.

He said in a whisper: "I could take these diamonds and never return."

This time, a genuine smile slowly came over the thin face.

"But you won't," said the man with the headband, calmly. "I trust you. Come back as soon as you can. Go up the Negro to the waterfalls that are beyond Caracaraí. There you will see a large island in the middle of the river. Wait there. Two men will come, one after the other. The first one is named Jaua; he is a Yanomami, actually a Shamatari. The second one, Maduaraga, is a Waimiri, and you know him; he led the attack on Ramos's place. As much medicine as you can, please. You will give it to them."

"And you? Where will you be?"

"That is of no importance. *Adios.*"

There was something magical in the way that, within a few seconds, he disappeared into the bushes.

Ubaldo Rocha made eleven trips in all between Manaus and Caracaraí during the following twenty months, almost always, especially at the beginning, accompanied by Sebastião, whose presence reassured him. But as time went by, and as his knowledge of Yanomami and other dialects of the territory of Ronaima grew, he began to travel alone.

From the proceeds of the sale of the diamonds, which he sold off one by one so as not to arouse greed, he permitted himself a salary exactly equal to the one he had been paid by the Booth Line. Except for this deduction, a modest one, he assigned all the collected money to the purchase of medicine, to the acquisition of a boat, and to strictly necessary expenses.

This was all the more meritorious because never, during those twenty months, did he see the white man with the headband.

And there was something even more extraordinary.

On his first trip to the island north of Caracaraí, he met Jaua, the Shamatari, whose name he had been given. The Indian, who seemed intelligent, was about twenty years old, had a sculptured athlete's body, and was remarkably tall, at least six feet six.

Jaua's eyes, like shiny black diamonds, did not blink when Sebastião, relaying Rocha's question, asked him about the man with the headband. It was as if he had never heard of him. And it was the same on other trips, when Rocha met with Maduaraga, the Waimiri chief, who was less reassuring than Jaua, since he was the one who, alone, during the attack on the post the year before, had killed at least four men, and almost smashed Claudia Ramos's head.

It took Rocha almost eleven months, and eight meetings, before Jaua came out of his impenetrable impassivity. By that time, Rocha was almost fluent in Yanomami, and Sebastião's intervention was no longer necessary. He therefore asked his question directly, and said that his curiosity was based only on the friendship he felt toward the white man, and, more than friendship, there was respect. "I have obeyed him in all things, Jaua." And he thought that it was either his arguments or the absence of an interpreter between them that suddenly freed the Shamatari. But what he told him then showed that that was not the case, and that the Indian, so silent until that moment, had simply been under the strain of a violent emotion.

Jaua revealed to him that his own sister had been the wife of Caraïbe—that was apparently the name he gave to the white man with the headband—that she had just been massacred, she and her child, along with twenty other members of his tribe, by a powerfully armed group of Pará nut seekers and prospectors, who had banded together a few weeks earlier.

"And Caraibe?" asked Rocha, sincerely affected by this new phase of Indian genocide.

"Gone," answered Jaua.

"Gone where?"

Out of the jungle. The Shamatari pointed toward the southeast. "Very far away."

"And is he coming back?"

"He is a Shamatari," answered Jaua simply, with definite conviction. "And the Shamatari's place is in the jungle. He will be back."

Reb Klimrod left the upper Branco area around the end of May 1950.

Or thirty-two months after he first entered the Green World after leaving Bogotá. This long immersion, marked by so much suffering, but also by a peace that he probably never found again anywhere, had profoundly changed him.

He arrived in Manaus. He did not bother to get in touch with Ubaldo Rocha, but went down the Amazon to Belém.

There, he embarked on a cargo ship—as either a bunker hand or a cook's helper. He didn't have one cent in his pockets and had not bothered to take any diamonds, believing, probably, that he had no right to.

He arrived in New Orleans on July 12.

And left the same day.

The Black Dogs

1

"There is a man here who wishes to speak with you, sir," the butler said to David Settiniaz.

There was a detectable diffidence in the tone of the servant as he pronounced the word "man." It was July 16, 1950, and Settiniaz was preparing to celebrate two great events in his life: his twenty-seventh birthday and, more important, his marriage, both to be held this very day. It was nine o'clock in the morning, and he had just finished dressing. The night before, he had arrived at his in-laws' home on Park Avenue in New York, after brilliantly finishing his course and receiving his degree from Harvard Business School two weeks earlier.

"His name?"

"This man has refused to give his name," said the butler.

"Please ask him to wait a few minutes."

The telephone rang for the hundredth time. It was Christopher Page, his future brother-in-law, who was sixteen and wildly excited by this marriage of one of his sisters, the first in the family, and by the fact that the following morning he was leaving for France, for Provence, with Suzanne Settiniaz, David's grandmother, who would be returning home after the ceremony. "Yes," said David, "there really is a swimming pool at my grandmother's. And yes, you can go horseback riding. No, you are not disturbing me at all. See you later, Chris." There were other calls, and a few visits; the home of his in-laws was as active as a beehive. Finally, having put on his ridiculous fancy coat, Settiniaz went down to the main floor, which had been transformed into a flower show. Another of the servants managed to remember that "the-man-who-would-not-give-his-name" was probably in the library, at least he was still there fifteen minutes ago. Settiniaz was again assaulted, this time by bridesmaids and ushers. Walking at last into the designated room, he thought it empty at first. Then he felt a presence, a stare, and the next instant he recognized the boy from Mauthausen.

"Obviously, I have come at the worst possible time, and I apologize," said Reb Klimrod in his soft voice.

Suzanne Settiniaz liked to say of her only grandson that he was satisfactorily intelligent, irreproachably obliging, boundlessly courteous, and affectionate and kind and true to his friends as to his family, that he was, all things considered, the ideal grandson, except for two characteristics: he was almost completely devoid of humor and of the aggression, the ferocity, that leads to great success. She did not really mind. From his father, from his mother, from his grandparents, David possessed, or would possess a small fortune; and Diana Page would bring to the marriage a dowry of ten million dollars or more. As for the lack of a sense of humor, she remained inconsolable.

"I called Boston," said Reb, "the number your grandmother gave me. I was told that I could find you here, but without any other explanation. I was going to leave, but a young woman insisted that I wait for you. I am truly sorry."

Settiniaz was surprised; in fact, he was stupefied. Five years had passed since Mauthausen, and Linz, and the war. And now a young man he had barely known had suddenly appeared.

"I did not know you were in New York," he managed to say. "Or even in the United States."

"I have only recently arrived. I simply came by to thank you, for what you did for me. I am going to leave now. May I extend my very best wishes for happiness to you?"

He was wearing a blue cotton shirt, washed-out sailor's denim pants, and sandals. His hair was very short, and he had a strange line of lighter skin across his forehead. But the figure was the same, even though he appeared to be taller: gaunt, lean, lanky. But from him there emanated a rather intimidating feeling.

144

"However," he said, "you might be able to give me some information. I know only his name: Georges Tarras. Would you know where I could find him?"

"This is summer vacation for the university, so he is not at Harvard, but he probably went to his house in Maine. I'll write down the address and telephone number for you. . . ."

Four years later, to the same offer, he gave the same smiling answer: "That will not be necessary. I will remember, thank you."

He took three steps and was at the door.

"Listen," Settiniaz said quickly. "Don't leave like this. When my grandmother told me about your visit to her, I was sorry she didn't think of asking for your address."

"I did not have one then," said Reb.

"And in New York?"

"I do not have one yet."

"Is there anything I can do for you?"

"No, really. But thank you again."

"I could perhaps lend you . . ." began Settiniaz, embarrassed.

Reb shook his head. His eyes were laughing.

"I will be leaving on a honeymoon," said Settiniaz, "and I'll be gone for about two weeks. After that, I'll probably spend some time at my mother's in Boston. But as of September 1, I will be working at the offices of Wittaker & Cobb, on Madison Avenue. If you're still in New York then, I would be very happy to see you. I mean it sincerely. Will you come?"

Reb nodded, the same amused look still dancing in his eyes. His hand was on the brass door handle, but just then the door opened. Settiniaz saw his future sister-in-law; she was standing face to face with Reb, almost within touch.

"Reb Michael Klimrod, an Austrian friend. My future sister-in-law, Charmian Page."

"We have already met," said Charmian, her eyes on Reb's.

"This young lady literally locked me in here so that I would not escape," said Reb, looking at her with the same intensity.

Their hands touched. Even Settiniaz felt that something had just happened.

2

Zbi looked up and said to the tall guy: "So you're Polish?"

"I never said that," answered the tall guy, in Polish, casually.

"But you speak Polish."

"That's true," said the tall guy.

Zbi spit on the ground and shook his head.

"No one speaks Polish if they are not Polish. No one in the world would take the trouble to learn Polish unless they absolutely had to."

Silence.

"And sit down, for God's sake! There, on a step. How could someone be so tall. What's your name again?"

"Reb."

"Reb what?"

"Reb."

One after the other, three men and one woman stopped at the stand and bought a newspaper or a magazine. One of the men asked Zbi what had happened to him. He answered that he had fallen under a subway train, but he was all right, and he should see what happened to the subway, that it was in worse shape. Zbi was having a great deal of trouble just standing, in fact; he was suffering greatly and at times had to take deep breaths, his light-blue eyes widening.

"O.K., Reb then," he said. "Gozchiniak told me you are O.K., and usually he doesn't say that about just anybody. Have you ever sold newspapers?"

"Never."

"Have you ever sold anything?"

"Cigarettes."

There were more customers, and also more pain coming over Zbi. It wasn't so much the bruises on his face—they looked terrible but he could stand them. But his chest was killing him; he could scream from the pain; and his back, and his left hand, on which the three jolly fellows had jumped repeatedly with both feet. He couldn't use his left hand at all, not even to give back change. He went on.

"All right. You'll have to do. I will be gone one or two days, no more. Do you know how to read?"

"Rather well." And he guessed the next question and answered it before it was asked. "Yes, in English also."

"How'd you meet Gozchiniak?"

"His brother is a truck driver, and we traveled together from Memphis, Tennessee, to New York. Can I call you Zbi? I don't know your surname."

Zbi pronounced his name, his official surname, the one that had driven the immigration agents crazy many years before.

The tall guy's eyebrows went up, and he smiled.

"And how do you spell it?"

"Just the way it sounds," said Zbi. "Listen to me, kid . . ." He had to stop for a few minutes; his chest was pounding from the pain. Then he opened his eyes again. "I hope for your sake that Gozchiniak hasn't made a mistake about you. I would like to find my stand still here when I come out of the hospital. . . ."

He looked hard into the light-gray eyes for a few seconds, then turned away as a young woman asked for *The New Yorker*.

"O.K.," he said. "O.K., Reb."

In spite of his bruised lips, his swollen cheek, his loose teeth, he smiled, not at the young woman, who was walking away, or at the tall guy, but, rather, at himself, in a way. In fact, he suddenly gave in, gave in to his exhaustion—he had not slept the night before—to the accumulation of pain and nervous tension following the terrible beating he had taken.

Fingers brushed against his left hand, then his chest. The tall guy said, in his slow and calm voice: "Your hand is broken. They will have to put it in a cast. Your ribs are also broken, and pressing inward in the back, probably. And your cheekbone has collapsed. Not to mention your teeth. You should have gone straight to the hospital."

"So that someone can take my spot?"

But Zbi's protest was only a last gesture. He was cracking, he was about to collapse.

"I am going to take you to the hospital," said the distant voice of the tall guy.

"And leave the stand empty?"

"Gozchiniak's son will take over for the time it takes me to go there and return. Come on, let's go."

"Those sons of bitches who beat me up are going to come back, tomorrow or the day after. They told me so."

"I will also take care of that," answered the tall guy in very pure, academic English. "I will give it my full attention."

Exactly thirty-two years later, at the beginning of spring 1982, David Settiniaz asked his computer for a complete list of all the companies, in all areas and in any form, that belonged to the King, both those he owned exclusively and those in which he had a share of between fifty-one and one hundred percent. The computer began functioning and, hours later, produced a bewildering enumeration. The list must have been more than fifteen yards long. There were exactly one thousand six hundred and eighty-seven companies.

Among the hundreds of men and women whose services the King had used at one time or another as trustees—beneficiaries or figureheads—one name appeared ten or fifteen times, mentioned by the computer for the years 1950–1960, and it attracted Settiniaz's attention. First, because the name was completely unknown to him, and then because the name itself was so extraordinary.

The name in question was Zbynv Szblzuszk. Absolutely unpronounceable; it looked like a joke. After consulting an interpreter at the United Nations, he was told that the first name was pronounced *Zbyniev* and the second was pronounced *Cybulski*, a rather common Polish surname.

"That leaves one dollar and eighty-three cents."

The tall guy dropped the change on Zbi's bed. "And I kept one dollar for myself, as agreed."

"Thank you," said Zbi, suddenly choked up. A former miner from Silesia, he had walked the streets of New York without expecting anyone to help him. His accession of a newspaper stand—simply the right of usage—actually no more than a shed protecting him from inclement weather, had marked the pinnacle of his social ascension.

"Tell me about these men who hit you," said Reb.

"Don't worry about it, kid. If they come back, just tell them you're replacing me, that you don't know anything. I'll take care of them when I get out of this damn hospital."

A smile. "Please, tell me about them."

"There were three of them," said Zbi. "Wops from Mulberry or Elizabeth Street. Young—twenty, twenty-two. With knives, and metal things with points that you pull over your hands. Their first visit was two or three weeks back. And I'm not the only Polack newspaper vendor they've visited. Gozchiniak also. And Kowalski, who's on Fifth. And the Altman brothers in Union Square." Zbi mentioned many names.

"They want one dollar a day, from each of us. Two dollars from the big guys like Gozchiniak. Shit, there are almost two hundred of us! In downtown Manhattan alone. That makes at least three hundred dollars a day, for those rats!"

Some vendors agreed to pay. "Sure, there are some who make eight or ten dollars a day! When you're in Times Square or in front of Grand Central, it's easy. But for us to spit out one more dollar, we'll sink; we may as well croak. What with the dollar fifty we give the Irishmen . . ."

"What Irishmen?"

"The guys who deliver the papers to us."

Three of the largest daily New York papers had consolidated their distribution systems, and the Irish ran that deal.

"And we don't have a choice, Reb. Either we pay or we don't get any deliveries. Everyone pays. And that's why we can't pay any more. That would come to two fifty a day. . . ."

It was July 17, 1950. Young Ernie Gozchiniak, and old Zbi himself, as soon as he came out of the hospital, were the privileged witnesses to what happened next.

"Don't be a smart-ass. You a Polack?"

"Not really," answered Reb. "Actually, I am from Patagonia, from the north."

The two thugs looked at him, their eyes narrowing.

Then one of them, the smaller one, said: "What are you trying to do? Be a smart-ass? If you try, we're gonna change your mind. You're gonna have an accident. You a Polack or not?"

"At this moment, I am a Polack," Reb conceded. He turned to smile at young Ernie, who was fourteen then and was sitting on the same step. He turned back to the two young men and smiled at them also, aimiably: "I am completely Polack, for the moment," he added.

"We don't like guys who kid around with us," said the smaller one. "The last guy who did had an accident. And we don't like Polacks either. You sell papers, right?"

149

"I am a completely Polack newspaper seller," answered Reb with admirable suavity.

"Then you pay one dollar for protection. So that other guys don't come looking for you. You pay one dollar a day, every day. And a dollar twenty on Sunday, because the Sunday editions are more expensive and you guys make more. You pay and you're protected. No one will come looking for you. If you don't pay, you have an accident. Get it? You pay just one dollar every day and a dollar twenty on Sunday, easy, right? Even a Polack can understand that."

"I think I am beginning to understand,," said Reb. "Polish as I am. I have to pay you six dollars and one dollar twenty." He took time to think. "That's seven dollars and twenty cents in all. Well, I think."

The two young men snickered. That was right, they said. For a Polack, he wasn't so dumb, after all. That was exactly seven dollars and twenty cents. He paid it and he was protected; no one would come to bother him; he would be protected and would be a good happy Polack.

"That would make me very happy," said Reb. "I have always dreamed of being a good happy Polack. There is only one problem. . . ."

"What problem?" they asked.

"I am not afraid of you," he said. "Not at all. You are two, and even if I try very hard, I cannot make myself afraid. It's not my fault. Maybe it's because you are only two. If you were three, then maybe. Yes, then, I might be frightened. But two, no."

A knife appeared in the hand of one of the two men.

Reb shook his head, looking rueful.

"Sorry, no!" he said. "Even with that, I am not afraid. I am trying, though. Really, I am trying."

His long bony hand moved, quickly. His fingers caught the armed wrist, pulled, and brought close to him the sharp point of the blade. He pulled again, and the blade went almost an inch into his flesh, between the deltoid and the large pectoral muscles. His face showed no reaction, and his eyes had a dreamy look.

He said, with the knife still planted in his chest: "Even now, I am not afraid. But, of course, if you were three, that would change everything."

He pushed the wrist back. The blade came out. Blood ran down and made a round spot on the faded blue shirt.

"If you were three, yes. I would surely be frightened then. Come back when you want."

They came back. One hour and a half later, just after the truck that picked up the unsold newspapers and magazines had come, when Reb and young Ernie were closing up around eight o'clock in the evening. And there were three of them.

Reb nodded. He said: "Well, then, that's it! You see? I told you. Three of you, that changes everything. Now, I am afraid."

The three men exchanged glances.

One of them said, in Italian: "He's crazy. This guy is completely nuts."

"And I think I will pay this dollar," added Reb. "Now that I am frightened, I will pay. But it's a shame. One miserable dollar a day. You really don't ask for very much, you can't make a fortune that way. But, still, if that's enough for you, it's your problem. It's a shame though to be content to take just one dollar from these Polack jerks, who really fooled you, when there is so much to take from them. But I am not going to meddle in your business. Here, here is your dollar."

And naturally they asked him, in arrogant tones, what he meant by that, that it was a shame and all that, that meant what, exactly, that they were assholes? He took them for assholes, was that it? What was he looking for? Did he want to get beaten up like the little old Polack who had the stand before him?

"If that's what you want, just say it. And anyway, what is your trick to get more from the Polacks?"

Reb and young Ernie had finished piling the magazines into the truck, which pulled away. Reb started walking, taking long steps. Followed by the kid and, obviously, the three others.

"What is it, eh? You really want us to work you over? Is that what you want?"

They reached a warehouse. Reb went in first and walked all the way to the back. The place was practically empty, except for some broken crates and some bags that still had some grain, perhaps wheat, spilling out of them. Rats could be heard running around, and some even came forward, not in the least bit frightened, defying the men, and showing their sharp teeth.

"Look," said Reb. "Look, and you will understand everything."

151

His left hand seemed to be touching the wound he had given himself an hour and a half earlier, when he had forced the knife to go into his flesh; it slipped under his shirt and came out holding what appeared to be a very long stick, almost twenty inches long.

He brought one end of it up to his lips and announced: "The third rat from the left."

Immediately after, there was a slight noise, like a silent whistle. Hit right in the middle of the body by the tiny dart, the rat took two quick steps, then two slow ones, then fell, curling into itself, its scared little eyes already glazed by death.

Reb said: "O.K. That's called 'curare' and it is deadly. In Amazonia, we Indians, we kill anything with it. And we are very skillful. And quick. You three, for example: if you were to take one step, any one of you, you would be dead within the next two seconds. . . ."

He held up the blowgun and directed it toward the three men.

"I do not know which one of you I will kill first," he said, with a terrifying softness. "I have not decided. You will laugh, but I have not decided whether I will kill all three of you, or only two. Of course, if you were to move, if one of you were to start running, that would simplify things for me. I would no longer have to choose."

He smiled.

"Isn't one of you going to run?"

Silence.

Then the smallest one swallowed and managed to say: "You're really crazy. You're really a crazy Polack."

"Now, I am no longer a Polack," answered Reb. "I was a Polack earlier, but now that's finished. Now I am an Indian, a Guaharibo, a Shamatari, and I am very ferocious."

He walked around the three men slowly, cutting off any possible escape.

"Do not turn around, please. You saw? I've put three little darts in position. Three. And I can shoot the three of them in less than four seconds."

The tip of the stick brushed the nape of the smallest of the three men, who uttered a strangled little cry.

"But maybe I will not kill you after all. Only, in exchange, you will lie down on the floor. There . . . NO! . . . Please do not touch that knife. . . ."

He leaned over and with his large hand grabbed the weapon, crushing the wrist at the same time.

"On your stomachs, please. Arms and legs apart, if you do not mind . . . I am not going to kill you, after all. Next time I see you, I will. Definitely. I am a Shamatari, you understand? If I did not kill you the next time, my brother Jaua and my whole family would be ashamed of me. We would all be dishonored, and they would have to come and kill you in my place. . . ."

He put the point of the knife against the back of the hand of the smallest of the three men.

"The next time you appear before me, even if only to buy a newspaper from me, I will see you first and you will be dead before you even see my face."

He pressed on the handle. The blade entered the hand, between the bones of the index and middle fingers. He stood up, put his foot on the handle, and pressed down. The blade went completely through the hand into the floor, where it remained stuck. The shriek rang out in the echoing air of the warehouse.

Using a plank, he finished barricading the door of the warehouse, where the three men remained, flat on their stomachs, not daring to move. He smiled at Ernie.

"Are you hungry, Ernie? But you should have been home already. Your mother is going to be worried."

The boy's blue eyes were staring at him.

He asked: "Can you really put in three little darts at the same time?"

Reb started to laugh.

"No, Ernie, of course you can't. You are intelligent, Ernie. I like you. Perhaps one day we will do business together, you and I, if you want to. . . ." He tousled the young boy's blond hair.

A little farther on, he threw away the bamboo stick he had picked up the night before in a park. As for the wooden toothpick he had stuck in the blowgun the second time, he put it between his teeth and began chewing on it.

But he was careful to replace the matchbox that contained the curare, wrapped in a leaf, in the bottom of his cloth bag, which otherwise contained two books, eaten away by humidity and practically illegible.

3

For Zbi, there was something miraculous in the way Reb approached, accosted, and conquered the young woman.

Her name was Hester Crawley. She was about thirty years old, was not extraordinarily beautiful, but had a pleasant face, a voluptuous body. She was one of those New York women Zbi would see go by and would no more dare dream of than he would have imagined buying the Empire State Building. The first evening, twenty feet in front of him, he saw Reb go toward her, and very deliberately bump into her, so hard that the paper bag she was carrying tore open, spilling most of what it contained onto the sidewalk. The young woman was furious, but then, quickly, calmed down while Reb busied himself picking everything up, with an amazing clumsiness. She began to smile, and finally burst out laughing. They left together, he carrying what was left of the bag, and while she was waiting for her train, Zbi, from a distance, could see them still laughing.

The second evening, he took the train with her.

The third, he did not return home the whole night and only appeared after ten o'clock in the morning, smelling faintly of a charming perfume.

And it was that same day, the afternoon of July 22, 1950, that they went, he and Reb, to the East Forty-second Street offices of a major newspaper Zbi had been selling for years. They took an elevator to the executive floor.

"Wait for me here," Reb said to Zbi.

"I can't leave my stand in the hands of little Ernie. I don't like this at all. What if those three pigs come back . . .?"

"They will not come back."

Zbi sat down, ill at ease among all the elegant secretaries. He watched Reb walk by them. Most of them looked up, attracted by the tall figure, the slow, almost imperial walk—and by those eyes. Reb went back to the office where Hester Crawley was sitting, near a large padded door, behind which was the Holy of Holies. He began talking to her, and at first she shook her head resolutely. She continued to refuse for interminable minutes,

154

all the while interrupted by comings and goings, which she controlled, and by telephone calls. After each interruption, she resumed her discussion with Reb, who was still smiling, charming as the devil, and probably repeating his arguments over and over. Finally, as she had done before, she gave in. She and Reb smiled at each other, while she shook her head, incredulous, as if to say: What you can make me do . . .

Reb came back and sat down next to Zbi, and said to him, in Polish: "That's it. She is going to squeeze us in, between two appointments. Even if it takes a little while."

"Squeeze us in where?"

"To see the big boss."

"For what, in God's name?" asked Zbi, panic-struck.

"I already explained it to you."

"You explained it but I didn't understand."

Reb started to laugh. "You let me speak. Don't you trust me, Zbi?"

"Sure I do," said Zbi, with complete sincerity. "I sure do."

They had to wait almost two hours, while many men and women passed back and forth in front of them, some of them glancing at them with surprise, seeing these two men in blue work shirts sitting in the waiting room of one of the most powerful newspapermen in the world. Finally, Hester Crawley motioned to them. They got up, went toward the padded door, on the threshold of which the young woman whispered one last time to Reb: "I am crazy. How did you get me to do this, you bastard?" But she was smiling lovingly, and even managed to caress his hand.

July 22, 1950, around five-thirty in the afternoon, according to Zbyniev Cybulski, as he now spelled his name, were the date and time when Reb Klimrod began his most amazing and fantastic rise.

"I know," said Reb to the man sitting across from him and Zbi, "that you have very little time. My purpose: I have an idea. It will permit you to save five percent on the distribution cost of your newspapers, to improve by fifteen percent the speed of the delivery of these newspapers, and will guarantee you an eighteen to twenty percent increase in sales at all the selling points in downtown Manhattan, that is, three hundred and twelve spots.

155

That is for the moment. My idea can be used for all your other areas as well. That's it. You can throw me out now, if you want."

But his eyes had that special sharpness that day.

The man asked him what his idea was, and Reb told him.

The man then asked, "And who the hell are you?"

"My name is Anton Beck," said Reb.

"German?"

"Swiss."

"And would I be dealing with you, if I wanted to go ahead with this?"

"Not with me personally. With the company that Mr. Cybulski here represents, as its founding president."

And Reb immediately said in Polish: "Zbi, please don't say a word. Except 'yes' when I move my right hand, and 'no' when I move the left one."

The man was looking at Zbi.

"And your company has consolidated the three hundred and twelve vendors of downtown Manhattan?"

"Yes," said Zbi, who was desperately repeating to himself: Yes when it's the right one, no when it's the left. Right yes, left no, right yes, left no . . .

"Are the vendors really behind you?"

"Yes," said Zbi.

"Right now the distribution of our newspapers is in the hands of a service we ourselves created, which is run by a man named Finnegan. Do you know Finnegan?"

"Yes," said Zbi.

"Do you really believe that your company could be more efficient, less costly, and more reliable than Finnegan's?"

"Yes," said Zbi, now completely frantic and hardly understanding the questions.

"I'm sure there are enough escape clauses to get out of our arrangement with Finnegan, but he is not the kind of man who will take kindly to having his job taken away from him. Nor are his Irishmen. Do you think you can handle the eventual problems Finnegan might cause without my having to interfere?"

"Yes," said Zbi.

"And when do you think your company could start operating?"

"In nine days," said Reb. "The first of August. Before dawn."

Coming out of the large lobby with the enormous globe, Zbi finally dared to open his mouth.

He asked, in a low voice, and in Polish: "Who is this Finnegan he was asking me about?"

"The guy who takes a dollar fifty from you every day to deliver the newspapers he is supposed to deliver, since he is paid for that. And three hundred and twelve vendors times one dollar fifty per day makes four hundred and sixty-eight dollars, over one hundred seventy thousand per year. Next to that, your three knife wielders were just children."

Reb smiled.

"And Finnegan is also the man who is going to try to break our ribs, yours and mine. With metal rods, probably. That's his style."

"And will he be able to?"

"I don't think so," said Reb. "It would truly surprise me."

As it turned out, only two hundred and seventy-eight of the three hundred and twelve answered the invitation given by Zbi, Simon Gozchiniak, and others. The first general meeting of the future shareholders of the first company ever created by Reb Klimrod took place the evening of the next day, the twenty-third, in a building not far from what is today the World Trade Center.

To Zbi's knowledge, and Settiniaz's, this venture was also the first appearance, in their capacity as lawyers, of two men of Rumanian origin, Jews, Lerner and Bercovici, who were, undeniably, the first of the famous Black Dogs of the King.

And it is certain that there was something frightening, fascinating, truly mind-boggling, in the way that Reb Klimrod, in a few days—he was two months away from his twenty-second birthday—established the first step of his fabulous pyramid.

Reb, using the name Anton Beck, began to speak, and explained to all the advantages of the operation he was proposing. They would form a company, of which they and he would be the main shareholders. The main ones, but not the only ones—he made that clear. This company would buy trucks and motorcycles that would assure the delivery of all the newspapers and other publications they were in charge of selling. It would do so on the basis of a contract signed by three of the major New

York daily papers, who would agree to entrust them with the distribution of their respective publications in downtown Manhattan. Zbyniev Cybulski, whom he recommended for the post of president, had that very day made a deal with the big boss of the newspaper on Forty-second Street.

The necessary capital would come from a bank.

He said that Zbi and he would take care of convincing the bank, and would also take care of finding the trucks and their drivers.

And that everything would be ready the night of July 31.

To the questions immediately raised concerning Finnegan's Irishmen, who were certainly not going to have their racket taken away from them, not without a fight at least, Reb answered that Zbi and he would personally take care of the Irishmen, and of Finnegan himself, and that all they, the vendors, had to do was to refer the Irishmen to him, Anton Beck.

He explained to them how the company would function, in which they would be holding thirty percent of the shares. In order to become shareholders, they would, as of August 1, have to give the daily dollar fifty, not to Finnegan's men, but to Zbi. No, this was not another racket like Finnegan's, because this dollar fifty would no longer be given away by them; instead, since it would make shareholders out of them, it would rapidly earn them money.

He told them how he and Zbi would develop this company in such a way that soon, perhaps within two months, this dollar fifty that they would be regularly investing would come back to them little by little in the form of profits. He even thought that within three months, their profits could possibly be greater than the dollar fifty they would be spending.

He gave all these explanations in English, but, knowing that a great number of them were recent immigrants, he repeated his explanations in Polish, in German, in Spanish, in Italian, in French. And in Yiddish.

He walked among them slowly as he was talking in his slow, soft, calm, and reassuring voice, with an extraordinary power of persuasion, slowly wrapping them around his little finger, figuratively speaking, of course.

To the point where Zbi began feeling an incommensurate sense of pride, he who was the friend and confidant of this man, and who even, at this period of the King's life in New York, was housing him.

And what did they risk by accepting, he asked, since he was not asking them to give more than this dollar fifty they were already giving, and had for years now, to the Irishmen? And, should the Finnegan thunder threaten to fall on them, they could simply use him, Anton Beck, as a lightning rod.

Cybulski never knew the name Dov Lazarus. Yet that was the name Reb Klimrod, in July of 1950, must have used to open certain doors. Perhaps even those of people as well known as Meyer Lansky, Lepke Buchalter, Mendy Weiss, Ab Landau, Bo Weinberg, Abner Zwillman, Bugsy Siegel, and "Dutch" Schultz, the Crazy Dutchman, whose real name was Arthur Flegenheimer.

Many of these men were dead or in prison in July 1950, but there were enough of them left for Klimrod to find some who had known Lazarus and were prepared to listen to someone who had been referred by him.

This is the only explanation for what took place on July 23, the day following the meeting of the shareholders.

"Tell me your name again?"

"Hubrecht. Or Beck. Or Klimrod. Whichever you like."

Across from him was Abie Levin. He had, after Lepke Buchalter was executed in 1944 for an ordinary murder, taken over the running of the clothing syndicates and the trucking concerns that dealt with the garment business in general. His gaze went from Reb to Zbi.

"And what's he got to do with this?"

"He will officially be running the company."

"But, in reality, you'll be behind?"

Reb nodded, his eyes twinkling.

"With what kind of share?"

"Sixty."

"By a trust agreement, and this one"—he pointed to Zbi— "will be your trustee?"

"Yes."

"And I would have to put in how much, to get in?"

"Nothing," said Reb. "I will take care of the drivers, and the

159

expenses, if there are any, if the Irish make a move. You won't have to put out one cent."

"Ten percent just so that it will be known officially that I'm involved, is that it? And you think Finnegan will back down as soon as he hears what kind of partners you have?"

"Exactly," said Reb.

Levin smiled back at him.

"Where do you come from, kid?"

"Tangiers," said Reb. "I was there with Sol Mancusa and others—who can answer for me."

Silence again.

Then Levin said: "Forty for you, thirty for me, thirty for your men."

"Twelve for you," said Reb. "You don't put up a cent, and within two months between fifteen hundred and two thousand dollars a month, regularly. I have told you only part of my plan. I have other ideas. I will come tell you about them one of these days."

"Finnegan might be harder to convince. You can never tell with the Irish. Twenty-five."

"Fifteen," said Reb.

They smiled at each other. Abie Levin had started out in the twenties as a cab driver; he became a bodyguard, ending up in the immediate circles of Louis "Lepke" Buchalter and Jacob "Jake" Shapiro. In 1942 he was imprisoned for one year in the Tombs for extortion, but his stay in prison had been most comfortable; he was even allowed to return home whenever he wanted to.

"Let's say twenty and we won't talk about it any more."

"Nineteen. Bottom line."

"That leaves you fifty-one. You'll have to get some insurance for all those vehicles."

"It's already taken care of. Alcor."

Levin nodded his approval. Alcor was the name of an insurance company directed by two men, named Lewis and Pizzo. Pizzo was a close political pal of the Mayor of New York, Vincent Impelliteri, and also controlled the Yonkers race track. Actually, Alcor was part of a whole group of syndicate insurance companies run by none other than James R. Hoffa, the vice-president of the International Brotherhood of Teamsters.

"Double protection, eh?" remarked Levin. "On one side, my friends and myself; on the other, Jimmy and the Teamsters. If he's smart, Finnegan will emigrate to Alaska."

"You can never be too careful," said Reb.

He made a sign to Lerner to take out the prepared contracts—with the figures they had just agreed on!—and present them to Levin.

After they were signed, Reb said to Levin: "One more thing, please. Suppose my friend Zbi and I, or another friend and I, wanted to repeat the operation in other cities besides New York?"

"What other cities?"

"Philadelphia, Baltimore, Washington, Boston, Pittsburgh, Cincinnati, Detroit, Chicago, Cleveland, Montreal. To start, of course." He smiled. "There might be others, but not right away."

Levin's black eyes narrowed. Zbi was frightened, just a little.

Levin explained softly: "With the same company each time? Aren't you rushing things a little?"

"Different companies. Totally. One in each city. Would you want to help me?"

"Fifteen for my friends there, ten for me."

"Eleven and seven," said Reb. "Take the time to think it over. I will not be back for a few days. I have quite a few things to do."

Then there was their approach to the bank in Newark, New Jersey, in the company of the other Black Dog, Benny Bercovici. This took place on the afternoon of the same day they met with Abie Levin. Zbi signed again, this time a loan agreement for thirty thousand dollars, negotiated by Bercovici. The lawyer must have made the most of the agreement with the head of the Forty-second Street newspaper, and perhaps, also, of the participation, through an intermediary figurehead, of Levin.

As soon as they left the bank, Bercovici went back to New York, where, with Simon Gozchiniak and others, he called on the newspaper vendors, so that as many as possible would become shareholders in the company. Only nine out of the three hundred and twelve refused.

As for Zbi, he went with Reb and Lerner to Baltimore on the train.

There, the next day—only six days after Reb had arrived in

New York!—Zbi signed a contract with the U.S. Army to buy thirty-four GMC trucks that had just been brought back from Europe, war surplus, as well as seventy motorcycles, of similar origin.

Zbi had been bewildered for some time—rarely worried, and then only for short periods—as he was faced with this mind-boggling series of operations, which he was not always able to connect. "But I would have signed the Declaration of Independence had Reb asked me to. I trusted him. And I was fucking right. Wasn't I right? Look at me: a millionaire in the Florida sun! And I started working in the mines of Nowa Huta when I was ten years old!"

He asked only one question: "And all these trucks, are we going to leave them like that, in khaki?"

"We are going to repaint them; that's been decided. Tonight. I hope you don't have any objection to green, Zbi?"

Naturally, things began to move a little faster after that.

As soon as they returned to New York, after a meeting with the Bercovici team, Reb and Zbi went to visit three plants, two in the Bronx, one in Brooklyn, which produced, respectively, hot dogs, rolls, and candy. Contracts were signed that same day. They provided that the first deliveries would be made on August 1; they provided also that these purchases could be stopped at any moment, with two weeks' notice.

That day, July 25, Zbi discovered that he was, besides president of the Union of Newspaper Vendors of Downtown Manhattan, and chairman of the board of Oneself News Distribution, Incorporated, also the chairman of the board of something called Jaua Food Organization.

"What's Jaua?"

"A reminder," said Reb.

"And what the fuck are we going to do with these millions of hot dogs?"

"Sell them, Zbi. At the same time as your newspapers and magazines. The Mayor's office has agreed. You and your three hundred associates already own the trucks. These trucks make deliveries in the morning and in the early afternoon. Plus the special editions. But what about the rest of the time, Zbi? Do you think it would be right for your trucks and your drivers to sit around the rest of the time. You see? Besides, it's just a question of organization. The trucks can carry newspapers and hot dogs at the same time. As for the soda and the fruit juices . . ."

"What soda?"

"Think, Zbi: you would give all these people something to eat and you wouldn't offer them something to drink?"

For the beverages, they went to New Jersey again. In one day, the 26th, they were in touch with six manufacturers, of which three accepted the curious conditions imposed by the Jaua Food Organization: there would be no deliveries; these deliveries would be taken care of by the Jaua Food Organization itself, which had its own trucks and would come make pickups between midnight and four o'clock in the morning.

"Think, Zbi: that is the only time of the day when we can be sure there will not be any special edition to be delivered. We will just have to double the number of drivers. The trucks can run twenty hours a day. That's a simple question of upkeep."

This problem was solved during the evening of the twenty-sixth, by the purchase, on credit (funds provided by a Brooklyn bank), of a huge garage, which doubled as a warehouse, whose function was to assure the maintenance of the trucks and motorcycles.

Zbi remembers that in the transactions with the beverage suppliers, Reb, or rather, Lerner, required that all contracts be valid for one month only, and that they would be renewed after that for two weeks at a time, with the possibility of termination on two weeks' notice.

Klimrod's intention had been, from the very start, to be his own supplier, in all things.

The business of the newspaper, or, to be exact, the newspapers, started at the same time.

The printing plant was in the Flatbush section of Brooklyn. There had been a time when it had flourished, a dozen years earlier, when it belonged to the Monaghan brothers. It printed, among others, the Italian newspaper *Il Martello*, which was edited by a man named Tresca, an anarchist, antifascist, and anti-Communist who had been assassinated in 1943. One of the Monoghan brothers had died, the other had retired. Roger Dunn bought the business at the beginning of 1946, a short time after his service in the Pacific with the Marines. Dunn says his first meeting with Reb Klimrod took place the night of July 26. Reb was alone. He explained the reason for his visit. Dunn was surprised.

"Several newspapers? You want to start several papers at the same time? What did you say your name was?"

"Beck. And it would not really be several entirely different newspapers. I was thinking that the classified pages could all be the same. And other pages, also. But we would change languages: one edition would be in German, one in Italian, one in Polish, one in Yiddish, and so on."

"Even if it's the same copy," countered Dunn, "I would still have to reset. And therefore charge for new typesetting for each language."

The large shop was deserted. It was about seven-thirty in the evening, and the last two men had left a half hour earlier. At this time, Dunn's business was surviving, with difficulty, thanks to the printing of circulars and commercial catalogues.

"I have never seen a printing plant before," said Beck in his curiously slow, soft voice, which was marked by an undefinable accent. "Perhaps you could explain to me how it functions . . . if you have time. I know it is late."

Dunn looked into the gray eyes, almost on a level with his own. He heard himself answer that he was in no particular hurry that evening. During the next hour, he gave the owner's tour, explaining even the function of the trimmer. He lingered, with a regret he must not have concealed, by the big rotary press, which had not functioned in four years. He asked his visitor how he had found him.

"Someone told me about you, a foreman at the Brooklyn *Eagle*. A young printer, ready to take risks, in financial difficulty . . . No, wait: my proposition is legal, in every respect. Is that what you meant?"

"Yes."

"You have my answer. Fifty thousand copies to start. I supply the idea, the editors for four languages, the distribution, the advertising, the advertising department, the short- and long-term financing. Our newspapers . . ."

" 'Our' newspapers?"

"Yours and mine, if you agree to an association. Our newspapers will be delivered free of charge for ten days. I have at my disposal a few dozen trucks and as many motorcycles, which will come to load at the exit by your rotary press. There will be drop-offs at three hundred and three selling points in downtown Manhattan, under the same conditions as the *Times*, the *Herald Tribune*, the *Mirror*, the *World-Telegram*, the *Post*, and the *Journal-American*, and two thousand one hundred and six other selling points throughout the metropolitan area. The downtown Manhattan vendors will be our associates, and they agree to sell without taking their percentage for the first month. What's more, they will promote the papers with their customers; they are well placed to know which ones might be interested in a newspaper in German, Yiddish, Polish, or Italian. The principle of an association, of a limited partnership, will then be applied to all the vendors in New York who will accept its principle, within the framework of a company that has just been formed, New York Migrant News, Incorporated.

"You spoke of . . ."

". . . free distribution. I know. One of my lawyers is working with his team to establish a list of merchants who are at the same time potential advertisers, recent immigrants who speak one of the four languages I mentioned, and who have among their clientele a large proportion of potential readers of our newspapers. All these merchants will be given free subscriptions. They will serve as a basis for canvassing for the advertising agency that will soon be created. All establishments, public or private, where, for whatever reason, there are recent immigrants or those still speaking their own language will also get free subscriptions. That way our future advertisers will be guaranteed distribution, within three weeks, of forty-five thousand copies, or two hundred thousand readers at least, selected readers, for the first issue. What advertisers refer to as targeting."

Roger Dunn opened his mouth . . .

"A few more words, please," said Beck. "I can set up this business with a larger plant than yours, with the help of a bank, even with the collaboration of an already existing newspaper. I would rather not. I want to maintain control of the business. Our newspapers will have a format half the size of standard daily papers . . ."

"Tabloid," Dunn managed to say.

"Tabloid. Because it's easier to read in the subway, because a full-page ad in that format is worth more than a half-page in a larger size, because you can pretend to offer twelve pages when it's really six. These newspapers will have twelve pages, six of which will hold classified ads, which will not change from edition to edition but will be printed in each of the four languages. A common trunk, if you will. These small advertisements will be obtained by our associates the vendors. As shareholders in New York Migrant News, Incorporated, it is in their interest that the newspapers of this company earn a rapid profit. Four motorcycles will make continuous rounds to pick up the copy from these men. This until we have our own offices. I have two places under consideration, one in Manhattan, the other here in Brooklyn. I will take care of the Bronx and Staten Island tomorrow. When they have finished their rounds, they will be back at your place at 9:30 P.M. at the latest, deadline time, all ads submitted before that time definitely being published the following morning, unless the client demands otherwise.

"How much time will you need to set up six pages of small ads? Eight columns per page. At the *Mirror*, the foreman told me last night that it would take him one hour. You don't have the typesetting facilities of the *Mirror*. So let's say three hours. Let's say four, figuring you will have to hold two linotypes for the other pages, in case of a last-minute article. That means the page setting will be completed by one-thirty in the morning. You said half an hour for the mold and blocking. You can roll, then, around two o'clock, and deliver as of four o'clock. Our delivery service will be in place by four-forty-five. The vendors will be supplied by six o'clock at the latest, in all of New York.

"In reality, I don't think that the profit from sales will play a large part in the financial equilibrium of the operation. The advertising and the classifieds, yes. We should begin to show a profit by the fifth edition. Our purpose is to be a means of communication for all Americans of German, Italian, Polish, or Jewish origin.

"Along with the advertising agency, I am also trying to set up a legal information and social center, which would be open to all subscribers free of charge. And, while I think of it, don't worry about the copy to be printed in Yiddish, Polish, or German, even with their special typography. I have found you three linotypes, on credit, and the letters and characters you probably don't have. You have them? No, you see. As for the linotypists and the proofreaders, I have also taken care of them. They are professionals—don't worry—who work at the consolidated presses of the *Sun* and the *Times*. I have spoken with them, and they are willing to do some moonlighting. Any questions?"

"God Almighty!" exclaimed Roger Dunn falling back into a chair.

Anton Beck (Roger Dunn knew his real name only much later, when he himself became one of the King's men) smiled and shook his head slowly.

"Your only investment will be the paper and the ink."

"And my men's salaries. And mine. And the electricity. And I'm not sure what else. . . ."

"For one week only."

"Without mentioning the other work that I won't be able to do. I don't have the means, technical or human, to do everything at the same time. I will lose my customers."

"You hardly have any left anyway. Within three months you would have had to close up."

"That's my business."

Beck was carrying a bag over his shoulder. He laid it down on the ink-stained marble, taking care to slip an old proof under it so that it would not get stained. He opened it and took out wads of bills, some of them still wrapped in the Newark bank's bands.

"Three thousand one hundred and forty-three dollars," he said. "That is all I have at the moment. I can pay you for the first editions. In full."

"Two at most," said Dunn. "And I'm not sure."

"I can pay for them. You will make my newspapers and I will pay you for them, as I would an ordinary printer, with each printing. But as soon as the papers start earning a profit, I will go elsewhere, or I'll buy my own printing press. And you, you can close up shop and go back to the Marines."

He remained absolutely still, his eyes glued to those of Dunn, and, what's more, he looked as if he was really enjoying himself.

"I don't see what's so funny," said Dunn bitterly.

"You are going to accept, of course. We are both playing a game. So, I am amused."

Dunn walked away, along the marble, in front of the linotypes, into the room where the rotary press had not been in use for four years. And, furious with himself, but at the same time feeling an inexplicable exaltation and the beginnings of a giggle, he was thinking: I must be nuts.

He asked: "And if I go along with you?"

"As soon as the money starts coming in, you will collect for your expenses, plus twenty-five percent of the profits, plus five percent of the shares of New York Migrant News, Incorporated."

"Ten," said Dunn.

"All right," said Beck, in a soft voice, still amused.

Without making the slightest noise, his bag over his shoulder, he came up behind Dunn. For a moment, both men looked at the enormous machine. Then Dunn kicked the concrete base of the rotary.

"Do you understand: for four years I've dreamed of seeing this machine work again, of being a real printer again."

A warm and friendly smile.

"Well, then, that's that."

There was, in Reb Klimrod's strategy at that time, a deliberate desire to call upon men and women of fairly recent immigration. That was the case with Lerner and Bercovici, although they had arrived during the thirties, when they were both fifteen.

They had other points in common: their Rumanian origin, the fact that they were Jewish, the ferocious obstinacy with which they had pursued a legal degree by taking evening courses, the same tardy success in obtaining this diploma after a bumpy road filled with transitory occupations, taken just so they could eat—in the garment business for Lerner and in dental supply for Bercovici. And, diplomas finally in hand, on the verge of at last reaping the benefits, the same ironic fate, which sent them away—one to sail the Coral Sea with the U.S. Navy amid unfriendly Japanese, the other to Tunisia, Sicily, Italy, and France, in the pursuit of Hitler's armies. Liberated in 1945 and safe—except for Lerner, who still limped a little—not knowing each other, they returned to New York to take up their climb where they had left it three years earlier.

With identical somber fury, they sought fortune, tracking it day after day, whatever form it took. David Settiniaz, who never cared for them, baptized them one day "the King's Black Dogs."

Lerner and Bercovici were not the only Black Dogs; there were others, in time, several others, a real pack of them, in all countries. But the two Rumanian immigrants in New York were the first, and certainly the best.

There is an old and well-known nursery rhyme, in which Robert Penn Warren found the title of one of his best books, that goes: "All the King's horses and all the King's men . . ." That is exactly what they were, the King's men, his horsemen and his jesters, or his rooks and his pawns, which he moved about as he pleased on his personal chess board.

Lerner was tall and slim, with deep-set eyes. He spoke little, and when he did, he did so in a hollow voice, rushed between two abrupt silences, as if pushed by a hatred he could not express. From his former occupation as a fabric and clothing salesman, he had kept a bizarre tic: he would run his fingers over tables or papers, over and over again, to the point where he would almost hypnotize those he was speaking with. (It is not so certain that he did not do this on purpose.) He showed up at Reb Klimrod's side for the first time at the shareholders' meeting of the down-town Manhattan vendors. It was he who accompanied Reb and Zbi when they went to see Abie Levin to sign the contracts he had drawn up. As far as Settiniaz can tell, he also handled the newspaper operations and those connected with them.

And, of course, the ferry operation.

"Three ferries," said Ferguson. "Plus two slips, the docks, and the offices."

He looked at the three men triumphantly after this enumeration of his worldly goods.

"All in all, I make about one thousand dollars a month. And I'm fifty-four years old. Since I expect to work eleven more years, you can figure it out for yourselves. I'll settle for one hundred and twenty, if you handle it right."

"Ha-ha," said Reb, calmly.

Ferguson looked at him. Of the three men he was talking with, he was the one who drew the most attention: he was the youngest, the tallest, and he had a look that could go through a door.

"And what exactly does that mean, ha-ha?"

Reb smiled at him.

"You are not fifty-four years old, but sixty-two. The building in which what you call your 'offices' are situated has been expropriated, you have already been compensated, and in four or five months it will no longer exist. It isn't worth a hamburger without onions. One of your ferries floats only thanks to divine intervention, which is renewed daily. You have at most three thousand two hundred and fifty dollars in the bank, an amount that is security for a current loan, of three hundred and twenty dollars a month, for this house you purchased last October 14, in Albuquerque, and on which you still have to pay six thousand seven hundred and seventy-five dollars. Your only car is a 1938 Ford, which has seventy thousand miles on it. You have only one son, who is an engineer in a food plant, in Albuquerque, of course, and your wife tells you six times a day that she has had it with New York, the cold weather, and only seeing her son and granchildren once every two years. As for your actual income, we estimate it to be between eight hundred and fifty and nine hundred dollars a month."

"Who are you, the FBI?"

"I am making you," said Reb, "the following offer, take it or leave it: ten percent of the Jaua Food Organization, of which you become joint general director. In that capacity . . ."

"What is it?"

"A newly created company that handles the production, the distribution, and, in many cases, the sale of food products. As joint general director, you would be entitled to two hundred dollars per week, with the guarantee of a salary adjustment of ten percent a year. For life. With one special condition: you will have no function, of any kind, in the company. The ideal proposition for you, since you will have the title and the related salary without having to work. You can actually be paid monthly in Albuquerque, at the bank of your choice. If you make any noise about any illegality in the running of the company, or if the payment terms are not as I have just set forth, the transaction will be immediately terminated. Your real estate and your personal estate would then be returned to you. You will tell me that

170

in such a case you might find your affairs rather disorganized. I will answer you that, after an evaluation, up to that day, of this estate, and with a yearly ten percent cost-of-living increase, we will arrive at a figure of compensation that we will give you in the improbable event that we do not respect the terms of the agreement."

One of Ferguson's three ferries, which ran between Manhattan and Hoboken, New Jersey, was just pulling in. It began discharging its passengers.

"Ferguson," said Reb, "you answer yes or no. All the financial information concerning the Jaua Food Organization will be made available to you by my bank in Newark. If you accept, I see no reason why you and your wife should not, within the next three days, take the train for Albuquerque.

Push-pull. Each created company was pushed by the preceding one and pulled a new one behind it. This was always Reb Klimrod's strategy. And he always connected his operations at lightning speed, without the slightest material infrastructure, without offices or secretariat, for years.

David Settiniaz points out the extraordinary rhythm of the finalization of the contracts between July 21, 1950—the date of the papers setting up the Oneself News Distribution Incorporated, for New York—and August 24, of the same year.

During this period, Klimrod set up no fewer than fifty-nine different companies.

As for Oneself, that is to say, the companies in charge of newspaper deliveries and made up of shareholders as varied as vendors, clothing syndicates (Reb was the first to make an official association with a syndicate), the Teamsters Union, and Klimrod himself, *twelve* companies were created in this period. Twelve companies legally independent of one another, all using the same system as the New York one: in Philadelphia, Baltimore, Washington, Boston, Pittsburgh, Cincinnati, Detroit, Cleveland, Indianapolis, Chicago, and in Canada, Toronto and Montreal. All respected the principle of the participation of the syndicates, as in New York, but not necessarily the same ones. And in Chicago, Settiniaz discovered that the United Packinghouse Workers had a seven and one-half percent share in the business.

But there was one constant in the twelve companies: Reb

171

Klimrod each time held at least fifty-one percent of the shares, whoever the associates were.

And he never owned them officially, but always through an intermediary, by means of a trust agreement.

The twelve Oneself companies were set up in nineteen days, with the help of Abie Levin and some of his friends. Each time, one of the Black Dogs was there, either Lerner or Bercovici, and sometimes a third one of their kind, who appeared around this time, Abramowicz. But, though they did not know each other, their work methods were so similar, or, rather, Klimrod's instructions were so precise and rigid, that it is impossible to determine who did what.

Second round: the Jaua companies.

The first one was born in New York, July 25, 1950. The second one, the Chicago one, on August 6. There followed a veritable salvo (Bercovici at work here): in four days, from the eighth to the twelfth, no fewer than seven other Jaua companies appeared in other cities.

The case of the New York Jaua was unique. Klimrod did not buy the ferry business from Ferguson; he exchanged it for shares in the company he had just formed. There was, therefore, no money involved—not strange, since he did not have any. The only capital that passed into his hands from July 21 to August 24 was that thirty thousand dollars lent by the Newark bank, which he used to buy the trucks and motorcycles from army surplus, and the three thousand and some dollars he showed to Roger Dunn on July 26.

During these thirty-three days of the summer of 1950, Reb Klimrod operated without a single cent of his own. He arrived in New York on July 16, empty-handed, having hitched a ride on a truck driven by Simon Gozchiniak's brother, and during his first few weeks in New York, he lived at Cybulski's and survived by helping Cybulski, or Gozchiniak, sell newspapers. He was an immigrant with no other baggage than a little cloth bag containing two books and a little curare, who was in the United States for the first time in his life.

Third series of operations during this period: the *Migrant* companies, and the printing business.

The first two newspapers, in Yiddish and in German, appeared on August 2. The Italian edition on the fifth, and the Polish one a little later, in New York anyway, because in Chicago and Detroit the Polish edition was the first to appear, even before the New York one. Later, there was a Spanish edition. The advertising agency he had created had almost immediate and fantastic results. Klimrod had Dunn prepare an unnumbered edition, which the runners used to canvass the advertisers. At that time, this was a new idea. As of the fifth edition, the returns from the advertising covered more than seventy percent of the costs. Then the little classified ads started coming in, in unbelievable number. He had wanted four pages of ads to start with: as of August 16, the papers had six, and ten by the end of the month, which forced them to add an extra sheet; and another by the end of September.

These publications had an unprecedented success in non-English-speaking communities. Most of these people spoke little English, were looking for work, for relatives, for old friends who had previously emigrated, and, moreover, they felt the need to maintain contact with their original culture. Reb then created the Information Center, where all subscribers to the newspapers could come for any kind of information. He began renting buses that normally were in use only during the week. He organized weekend pleasure trips, for a reasonable price, and transported hundreds of families to the Jersey Shore, Long Island, and elsewhere.

It was from this activity that he eventually created his vacation centers and his hotel chains, not to mention his transportation ventures.

The one-hundred-thousand mark of copies sold was reached and passed by the twenty-fourth edition. The same newspaper appeared at the same time in ten, twenty, thirty cities. Dunn sent the common type molds by truck or by plane, and the corresponding printer in Chicago, say, would set only those pages pertaining to his region. Of the *Migrant News* then, there were up to eighty-six editions that were different, in principle; in reality, they were sixty to eighty percent identical. Total circulation passed the million mark.

The fourth salvo occurred during this same period, July–August 1950. Though many of the businesses engendered then blossomed only during the following weeks or months.

The Ferguson ferry deal was typical. The contracts with Ferguson were dated August 16. The very next day, snack bars were set up on the ferries, the result being that an employee who lived in Hoboken, Jersey City, or Newark, could have his breakfast while he was crossing the Hudson to his work in Manhattan. A team run by the Black Dogs, especially by Lillian Morris, began, the same day, canvassing other ferry companies around New York, proposing the installation of similar snack bars. Supplying the food and beverages was, naturally, the monopoly of the Jaua Food Organization, which was soon, and for twenty-four years thereafter, managed by Lillian Morris.

This was only the first step. Eventually, the Jaua Food Organization extended its activity to everything that sailed on the Great Lakes, as well as all the major rivers in North America, and then shipping companies and airlines.

The second expansion step took the form of putting to use warehouses and other buildings that were formerly Ferguson property. The ice-cream factory was officially started on August 20, although production did not begin until four weeks later, with a staff of fifty. A subsidiary company of Jaua Food Organization headed it legally, with Jaua handling distribution.

Contracts for renting premises in the Bronx, Brooklyn, and New Jersey are dated August 22. The manufacture of hot dogs, rolls, mustard, and all the necessary ingredients for sandwiches, as well as candy, began between October 10 and 30. And here is the explanation of the curious clauses that had appeared in Reb's early deals with suppliers: he already had in mind, on the first day, to do everything himself.

Settiniaz even discovered rental agreements, made through another subsidiary of the Jaua Food Organization, for three locations in Manhattan. These were in areas that contained the first Jewish and German delicatessen chains and the fast-food restaurants that were to have such a spectacular development.

Reb Klimrod arrived in New York on July 16. Forty days later, he had created fifty-nine companies, without having at any time invested any of his own money, which he did not have.

But this is not the most essential matter.

4

On the evening of August 5, Zbi and Reb went to the movies. Zbi remembers the title of the main feature: *Casablanca*, with Humphrey Bogart and Ingrid Bergman. "I had already seen it, and Reb had, too, but he was crazy about movies, and about this Swedish girl, so, as usual, I gave in." They came out of the theater around eleven-thirty, and began walking back to Zbi's studio apartment, which he was still sharing with Reb.

A car came to a stop along the curb and two men got out, one of them visibly armed. They ignored Zbi and spoke to his companion.

"You Beck? The Boss wants to talk to you."

"Finnegan?"

"Get in. And the Polack, too."

Reb said slowly: "Beat it, Zbi. They won't shoot."

A group of five or six people, men and women, Puerto Ricans, had just appeared. Reb called out to them in Spanish. They smiled and came over.

"Come on, get in," said the man with the gun.

Reb kept talking in Spanish. The Puerto Ricans burst out laughing, and Reb himself was smiling.

He said, in English: "It's O.K., Zbi. Everything will be all right."

He leaned over into the car.

"What do you think, Finnegan? Are you coming out or am I going to pull you out?"

There was some commotion inside the car. Zbi saw a man about forty, not very tall, but massive, with the reddest hair imaginable.

"It's very simple, Finnegan," said Reb in his quiet voice. "If your friend behind me shoots me, he will also have to shoot the Pole and all my Puerto Rican friends. I believe that would be called a hecatomb, a slaughter in English. You cannot let that happen. And you cannot do anything to restore . . . Do you know the word 'restore,' Finnegan? I don't think so, given the look on your face. . . . To re-establish the old order of things. To get once more your one hundred seventy-plus thousand dollars a year. It's over, Finnegan. So, it's one of two things: either you retire or you insist on getting your dollar fifty from the downtown Manhattan vendors. You choose. My name is Reb. You make your choice, and if you want to, you can get out of this car and try to hit me. And I'll kill you. Just you and me. You decide, Finnegan."

Reb stepped back and spoke again in Spanish to the Puerto Ricans, who laughed. Then he said, in Polish: "Zbi, he is going to jump me. Don't get involved, please. Everything will be all right."

In the next seconds, many things happened, in rapid succession. Reb's large bony hand flew out, hitting the man with the gun right in the Adam's apple. The man with the gun doubled over and from that point on lost interest in the situation. Finnegan burst forth, there where Reb had just been standing. As he passed, he received a blow in the back of the neck from Reb's other hand, and a kick in the lower stomach. He headed straight for the wall, bounced off it, and turned around just in time to catch a left-right in the face, two blows in the neck, which he had the misfortunate to expose, a kick between the legs, and five or six hooks to the face.

He collapsed.

Reb smiled at the third man and asked him what he intended to do.

"Nothing," said the man. "That was enough."

"I prefer it that way," said Reb. "In any case, someone has to pick them up. I hope you know how to drive."

He was standing, very straight, with a faraway look on his face. But the third man was not mistaken, and Zbi did not mistake it either, nor did the Puerto Ricans, who had suddenly stopped laughing: from him came an aura of ruthless ferocity.

The elder Gozchiniak was from a little town called Wagrowiec, in northwest Poland, north of Poznan. He had arrived in the United States in 1924 and had anglicized his given name, Zygmunt, to Simon. He began selling newspapers less than two weeks after he had gone through Immigration. In 1950, he was forty-four years old and was the undisputed owner of three newspaper stands, one of which was in the prime location in New York's Grand Central Station. In the little world of Manhattan newspaper vendors, he had arrived. As of 1927, he had the means to finance the emigration of two of his brothers, and it was one of these who had picked up Reb in Memphis and brought him to New York.

It was Simon Gozchiniak who had sent Reb to see Cybulski; he, also, who played a decisive part in convincing the majority of newspaper vendors to go along with Reb in July.

On August 6, 1950, around five o'clock in the afternoon, Gozchiniak left his stand near Park Avenue and Thirty-sixty Street and began walking toward Grand Central. A witness saw him, near the Church of Our Saviour, talking to two men who had just stepped out of a blue Chevrolet. Gozchiniak finally got into the car, which went uptown.

They found him the next morning, in a construction site where they were building the future United Nations headquarters. A great deal of care had been taken to break every single bone in his body, with lead pipes and extreme savagery. Only his face had been left intact, as if to permit easy identification, and a newspaper printed in Polish, German, Italian, and Yiddish had been stuffed in his mouth, all the way down his throat.

Finnegan died two days later, on August 8. The investigation revealed that he had been absent for one week from his job as head of the newspaper delivery system and that he had spent the preceding nights in Atlantic City, under an assumed name, accompanied by two other men, who apparently were his bodyguards. These two had been shot in the back of the neck. As for Finnegan, he was discovered hanging, but not by a rope. One of those hooks that longshoremen use to pull crates had been used. The steel point had been pushed into his mouth, had pierced the palate and gone through the brain.

The weather had changed around August 20. First, rain had come, surreptitiously and hypocritically, over New England. The ocean had started turning shades of purple, the air had become cooler, and even Adolf and Benito, those two crazy cormorants, who were always perched on the edge of the dock, had come out of their habitual coma. In other words, summer was over.

This was not going to send the Tarrases into great depression.

They both despised the heat. Had it been up to them, they would have their country home in Greenland. But they needed a decent mail system to receive books and to mail out, each week, Shirley's chronicle for *The New Yorker*. They settled for Maine, with the rarely disappointed hope of cold and humid weather.

In 1950, at fifty-one, Georges Tarras was completing his third book, in which he demonstrated in a peremptory fashion, that the Constitution of the United States had been copied almost word for word from the one previously established by Pascal Paoli for the Corsicans. He was hoping, by the publication of this book, to provoke the anger of the specialists. By September 8, he had only about fifty more pages to write. As was his habit, he woke up early, had his breakfast, and set to work. Shirley appeared around seven, with the rain, the two events being completely unrelated. She had to work on her literary piece. Married for twenty-three years and childless, they shared, with great tenderness, an extremely cynical view of mankind in general.

Around eleven o'clock, Shirley looked up and, pointing to one of the bay windows, said: "We have company."

Georges looked out, and it was as if five years of his life had just disappeared. The memory returned, incredibly precise in its details, the gestures and the absence of gestures, the particular speaking voice of Reb Michael Klimrod.

Tarras's house in Maine was wooden on a stone foundation. You could see the ocean from all sides, or almost, and sometimes the spray from the Atlantic reached right into the house if the windows were open. It stood on a low promontory between Penobscot and Blue Hill bays. The closest house was almost two miles away.

"I have come to return your books," said Reb Klimrod.

He took the Whitman and the Montaigne from his cloth bag and handed them to Tarras.

"There was no rush," Tarras answered. "If you haven't finished reading them, you can keep them. Would you like some tea or coffee?"

"Nothing, thank you. I like your house. And I really have finished reading them."

178

The rain had stopped, but with the promise of starting again shortly. Nevertheless, the two men walked outside. They took a little path that led to the ocean.

"How did you find me?"

"David Settiniaz."

"Have you been in the States long?"

"Almost two months."

"Did you speak English before?"

"A little."

Tarras sat down on his personal rock, which he had been using for the past twenty years. The bay where they were sitting opened to the southeast and was whipped by the wind coming off the ocean. He was examining Klimrod—or Kimrod? No, it's Klim—and found him almost unchanged. The absurdity of the scene suddenly hit him. Lord, he thought, I must have seen twenty thousand men and women in Europe who also had come out of concentration camps, all telling hideous stories, many of them exceptional in more ways than one. And yet I don't remember ten names, and were they to appear before me, I would not recognize them. So, why him?

"I hope you did not come all the way to America to return my books?"

"No, not just for that," answered Reb, smiling.

He was wearing sandals made of rope, cotton pants and shirt, and carried his bag over his shoulder. Curiosity was devouring Tarras, but again he had that feeling of shyness he had experienced at Mauthausen, which he remembered clearly.

"No, this is not the only reason for which I have come to Maine," added Reb.

He began to speak, of himelf, telling how after he had left Austria he had gone to Israel, then all over the world, all this without being very precise.

"Your English is remarkable," Tarras said.

"Thank you."

His gray eyes were staring at the ocean. Then he lowered his head and looked at Tarras.

"I have read one of your books," he said. "The one that deals with the legal aspects of high-seas piracy. Do you still teach at Harvard?"

"They haven't thrown me out yet. Although I've tried my best."

"I need some help in a very specific area," Reb said. "Could you spare me an hour?"

"Stay and have lunch with us. That's my condition."

They smiled at each other. "All right." Reb, sitting on a neighboring rock, stretched out his long legs.

"Recently," he said in his slow voice, and in an indifferent tone, "I formed a few companies. A few dozen, actually."

"I teach international law," Tarras interrupted, in a reflex. "I don't know that much about corporate law."

"I know. I understand the difference. I have lawyers who work for me, drawing up contracts and that sort of thing. My problem is something else."

At that moment only, the words sank into Tarras's mind; he was usually swifter.

"You said that you've created a few *dozen* companies?"

"About eighty now."

"All in the States?"

"In the United States and Canada."

"How old are you?"

"I will be twenty-two in ten days."

He began to laugh.

"Yes, I have been in this country not quite two months. But things happened rather quickly. A little too quickly, actually. I did not have time to organize myself as I should have."

Tarras was staring at him, mouth open, in complete astonishment.

"And that is precisely the reason for my visit. All these companies were formed on the same principle: that of a trustee who replaces me in all things and who appears to be the official owner. I suppose that, however specialized you may be, you know what a trust agreement is."

Tarras could only nod.

Reb went on, tranquilly.

"These companies are in very different fields: publishing, transportation, delivery, real estate, advertising, food, restaurants. I believe they all have a good chance of being successful. Some of them are already showing a profit. Do you want to know how much, in case you are concerned about your fee?"

Tarras was rubbing his eyes.

"Wait one minute," he said. "Perhaps I am dreaming, but I am having a little difficulty keeping up with you. Was I hallucinating or did you just tell me that you have created eighty companies in less than two months, when you have just landed in this country?"

"Eighty-one," Reb corrected, with a mocking look in his eyes.

"And you have never been in the U.S. before?"

"Not in this life."

"And you are alone?"

"The way you mean it, yes."

"You don't look like a multimillionaire. No offense meant. What happened after Linz? Did you get your hands on some Nazi war treasures?"

"I arrived without any money," said Reb quietly. "That complicated things a little, of course."

Tarras leaned closer.

"You're pulling my leg, right? I suppose this is an example of Austrian humor, or *halbjude* humor?"

A shadow came over the gray eyes, just for a second.

"I am no longer Austrian, or Jewish."

Then, immediately, he said: "And as for my actual income, I guess it could be estimated, for the month of September, at thirty-five thousand dollars. But it should increase rapidly. So you do not need to worry about your fee. That being said . . ."

"Would you leave me alone with this fee business?"

"That being said, then, the problem that brings me here is the following: all these trust agreements have been signed with my real name, Klimrod. Reb Michael Klimrod. K-l-i. I noticed you were hesitating over the *l* in my name."

"So where is the problem?" asked Tarras, ready to give up.

"I do not exist," said Reb. "I came into your country illegally. I have no papers of any kind. No passport. Not even a driver's license."

He scooped up some dirt in his hand.

"That could present a problem, one of these days."

They ate steamed lobsters for lunch, which was not then a

special event in Maine. During the meal, Shirley and their young visitor spoke of painting—something Tarras was not particularly interested in—to the point of arguing, very politely, over a certain Pollock.

When they were alone, Shirley having gone to mail her piece in Bar Harbor, Reb formulated his wish. . . .

"You want to become *what?*" asked Tarras.

"A stateless person. I do not want to be a citizen of any country."

"You are Austrian. Why is it so annoying to be Austrian?"

"Do you mind answering my question?"

"I can, but it won't get you anywhere. Such a thing does not exist, or almost not. Do you really want me to give you all the details? I don't have my books, which are in Boston, where I will be in one week, to prepare for the fall term."

"I would like an initial answer, Mr. Tarras. That can be expanded later on."

"Well, the first modern stateless people were born from denationalization decrees passed by the Soviet Union in the early twenties, in response to nationals who were against the Communist regime, then by Hitler's Germany and Mussolini's Italy. These do not affect you. The different peace treaties that were signed three years ago, in 1947, contain, if I remember correctly, certain clauses relating to stateless matters. I don't remember them exactly. I am sorry. But one thing is certain: the stateless status is undesirable: no state protection . . ."

Stopping himself, Tarras stared at the tall, skinny young man with the false nonchalance.

"But you probably feel you can do without state protection. Am I right?"

A smile.

"No."

"Nevertheless, things could be made extremely difficult for you when, for example, you wanted to cross a border. International laws apply, in principle, only to those who possess a nationality. Giving it up would deprive you of advantages such as reciprocity. . . . Do you follow me?"

"Yes."

"Stupid question, Tarras. O.K., then. As an Austrian arriving in the United States, you can benefit from the advantages offered to an American who goes to Austria. As a stateless person, you are nothing and have nothing to offer in exchange for the advantages you are asking for. . . ."

"Such as the right to form companies."

"Exactly."

"Can that lead to the cancellation, the invalidation of all the transactions I have made?"

"Yes. Among other things. If someone really wanted to, someone who really had it in for you . . ."

Klimrod got up. Tarras's house was over a hundred years old, and the ceilings, painted from room to room in different shades of red, were low. His head almost touched them. He went to the window, seemed to be absorbed in contemplation of the dark islands, the jagged shorelines.

"Do you think a day will come when one will no longer need a passport, a stamp?"

"I would be surprised if it did," answered Tarras. "I do not have a very high opinion of men and women, but as far as idiocy goes, nations surpass them by far. You should read Proudhon. He is a very interesting Frenchman."

"And the solution?"

"Remain Austrian or become American."

"Neither."

"Or obtain an accommodating passport."

"Which means?"

"You buy them, I am told. In your place, since you are decidedly vexed with Austria, the United States, France, and a few other countries, I would become Cuban, or Argentine. Flip a coin."

"But not Papuan."

"No Papuan state at the moment," said Tarras. "But you never know."

He burst out laughing. "Papuan!" He was looking at Reb, straight into his gray eyes, trimmed with long lashes, those eyes that were so impressive, so grave, burning so fantastically with intelligence.

And the miracle happened: Reb Klimrod also began to laugh. In fact, he was overcome with uncontrollable laughter.

That, Georges Tarras shared, with a keen feeling of happiness he would never forget.

5

Diego Haas was happily splashing about in the pool when the butler came to announce that he was wanted on the telephone; the call was coming from the United States.

Mamita remarked: "I did not know you had friends in the United States."

"It must be Harry," answered Diego.

"And who is this Harry?"

"Truman. Who else?"

Diego caressed the hand of a certain Concepción Something (or was it Incarnación?), whose father owned seventy-five thousand acres. She nevertheless was quite pretty. He went to take the receiver the butler was holding, and smiled at Concepción-Incarnación Something, whom he had no intention of marrying, whatever thoughts his mother might have on the subject, "but whom I would love to get in a dark corner so I can look under her skirt."

"Hello! Hello!" he said happily. "Diego Haas-here-in-person-in-all-his-splendor."

During the next seconds, he felt a chill run down his back.

"Villavicencio," said the distant calm voice. "A truck and a Madonna. And a river beneath the trees that was impossible to cross. Do you remember me?"

"Yes," said Diego in a choked voice.

"Do you remember a conversation we had?"

"Word for word."

"I need you."

"I am interested," answered Diego. "I am very interested."

Wild excitement swept over him. Through the wide-open door, he could clearly see his Argentine future, from which there was no escape but for a miracle of God: Concepción Something, with her seventy-five thousand acres, the paternal canning factories, her heavy breasts and her indolence, to whom he would wake up married one day without even realizing how it had happened, thanks to one of Mamita's more underhanded maneuvers. And you'll be big and fat, Dieguito, he thought, surveying Daddy-in-law's factories or his forestry developments, smoking a cigar, and stuffing yourself with overcooked red meat, under the ferociously tender gaze of soft women dripping with diamonds, with octopus mouths . . .

He said, into the telephone: "Whatever you want, whenever you want, wherever you want."

Then he listened for a long time to the calm voice, his yellow eyes shining in the damp shade.

"I won't need more than three days," he said.

He hung up, shaking. His mother left the group of matrons and came over to find out the news, with unrelenting sweetness.

"You know Harry Truman, *querido mío?* The President of America?"

"I know him," answered Diego. "He calls me whenever he has a problem. I must have forgotten to tell you about him, Mamita."

That day, for want of the money Mamita was measuring out to him in the hope of obtaining his surrender, he sold his platinum watch and his diamond-studded cigarette case, his twenty-ninth-birthday present. With the money, he had a passport made in the name of Michael Klimrod, born in Buenos Aires on September 18, 1925 (three years earlier than his actual birthday). Two days later, on September 11, 1950, using a visit to his uncle, a banker in Bahía Blanca, as a pretext, he took a plane for New York.

Not realizing, certainly, that he was beginning an adventure that, in his case, would last thirty-two years.

One of the things that the strange Diego Haas is most proud of is the fact that he was one of the very first to have been called by the King and to have immediately answered.

The man's name was Sussman and he was a tailor. As such, he worked with his two sons, his daughter, his wife, his brother, and the six people who made up his sister's family. Seventeen people in all, crowded into two rooms, which, together, did not measure thirty square feet. The two rooms served also as bedrooms, kitchen, bathroom, living room, library, boudoir, and even closet, after working hours, between midnight and five o'clock in the morning. He looked at Reb over his glasses and his Singer sewing machine.

"What did you say your name was?"

"Saperstein," said Reb. "And what I am proposing is very simple."

"I understand exactly what you are proposing. What I understand less well is what your interest is in all this. And, by the way, you speak Yiddish with a very peculiar accent."

"It's because I learned it by correspondence course. And there was a great deal of static on the line."

"The day I'll believe somebody does something for nothing, it will be much hotter than today," said Sussman. "What do you gain in this exchange?"

"Let's start over," said Reb patiently. "You work and live in Brooklyn. You work out of your home. You don't have very much space. You could say that when someone in your workshop wants to stretch his arm out to measure a piece of material, he has to open the window."

"So they get a breeze," answered Sussman, mockingly.

"And you sell the dresses you make to the outlets on Orchard Street, in Manhattan. Hours taken up going and coming back . . . You would have more space, you would be close to your selling point, you could increase your production, have better housing, better . . . "

"Et cetera," said Sussman.

"I don't have to tell you. Now I know a man near there who has a warehouse above which there is a four-room apartment. He has no use for the warehouse, and the apartment is too big for him. And he works in Brooklyn, in the Bushwick section. He takes your apartment, you take his. He pays your rent. You pay his. You set up your factory in half of the warehouse, and I pay you rent on the other half. Of course, you will be spending more for your rent, but that will be largely compensated by your increased income."

"And what do you intend to make in the other half of the warehouse?"

"A kosher restaurant," said Reb. "You won't even have to cook."

Ten minutes later, Diego Haas asked: "And what do you call this kind of thing?"

"A swap. Or a relocation operation. In a way."

"You should have just sublet half the warehouse to the guy who already had it, no?"

"And where is the pleasure in that?"

They took the subway back into Manhattan.

"And also," said Reb. "I am practicing. I have a rather amusing idea . . . "

The "rather amusing idea" was the "fabulous and fantastic Wall Street operation," which would earn Reb Klimrod three and a half million dollars in two days, and one hundred million in ten months.

Diego Haas had arrived in New York on the evening of September 11. This was not his first trip to the United States. He had almost married there, after one of Mamita's Machiavellian tricks. "In her paranoiac obsession to have me marry someone who had at least as much money as she," he said later, "she had set a horrible trap for me: nothing less than the daughter of the Yankee Ambassador to Argentina. I got out of it by claiming I had become a homosexual. But I felt the weight of the ball and chain." He had spent two months in a suite in the Waldorf-Astoria, then had gone to Florida and California with two or three dancers. "But Mamita cut me off."

In September 1950 he did not check into the Waldorf. He stayed in a tiny room in Greenwich Village, where Reb was living. At a cost of ten dollars a week, it was not much better than a night shelter.

He traveled around, already following Reb's orders, always thoroughly carrying out the most surprising missions. He thus moved in and out of Klimrod's life at the time when Klimrod, having laid the groundwork for his first expansion, was preparing to extend his operations to other states.

Diego gives October 14 as the date on which Reb had the fun of exchanging the Jewish tailor's two rooms in Brooklyn for the insurance salesman's loft in Manhattan, gaining at the same time a place to set up the fourteenth of his restaurants.

And he gives the seventeenth, three days later, as the date of the real beginning of the Wall Street operation.

"Look," said Reb.

Diego looked up and saw the well-known facade of the New York Stock Exchange.

187

"Very nice," he said. "Do you want to buy it or simply rent it?"

"Lower. Below the cornice."

Diego lowered his gaze, and saw only a little outdoor stand selling hot dogs, sandwiches, and sodas. A crowd of men, wearing dark suits and ties, was standing around it, eating and drinking.

He asked: "Yours?"

"In a way." Reb smiled. "But I have not put the shares on the market yet. I ran this stand for a few days. You hear the most interesting things there. Now, let's go."

They walked to Pine Street and stopped in front of a building.

"And here, what do you see?"

Diego looked up.

"May the devil strike me dead!" he cried. "Am I surprised, Sweet Jesus, if it isn't a bank! And in an area of Manhattan where there are at least fifty or sixty thousand of them! I am dumbfounded!"

He pretended to be near-sighted and almost glued his nose to the enormous brass plaque: HUNT MANHATTAN

"Just about the biggest bank in the world. Only the best, eh?"

"Turn around," said Reb.

Almost directly across the street was an empty lot, surrounded by a fence.

"Do you understand, Diego?"

"Not a thing."

"Come."

They went to another street in the same area. A man in his thirties was waiting for them on the sidewalk, in front of an office building. Reb made the introductions. The man was Daniel Hasendorf; he was a broker, a high-ranking one, in the firm of Webster, Ryan & Kalb, which specialized in real-estate transactions. The three men entered the building and took the elevator to the fifteenth floor. It was October 17, 1950, and it was 9:15 A.M.

A man named Norman gave a friendly smile to Hasendorf, whom he knew, but he slowly looked over the other two men, Diego Haas and, especially, Reb Klimrod, who was still wearing his cotton pants and shirt.

He asked: "And it is you who wish to purchase this lot?"

Reb nodded.

"The price has been set at four million five hundred and fifty thousand dollars," he said, in a tone that was not without irony. He had the look of a Buckingham Palace butler preparing to show the door to American tourists looking for a night's lodgings.

"I am offering four million seven," said Reb in his quiet voice. "I would like an option."

"We already have a buyer."

"Now you have two. And I am prepared to negotiate today. In two and a half hours. Certified check."

"You would be paying how much?"

"The usual deposit: five percent, or two hundred and thirty-five thousand."

Norman looked at Hasendorf—who nodded.

"Yes?" said Reb.

Outside, Hasendorf shook his head. "When I think that in Missouri, where I come from, we talk for a week before selling a cow!"

"I would take my time, too, for a cow," said Reb. "And this meeting?"

"I spoke with him over the telephone and I have to call him back. He should see you at one o'clock. I really had to insist. A lot."

"Don't bother. You won't get more than ten percent. See you later."

Reb pushed Diego into a taxi.

"A taxi! We're squandering! Next thing you know, it will be a Cadillac!"

Diego had never seen Reb, in New York or anywhere else, ever use any means of transportation but the subway, the bus, or his feet. They went through the Holland Tunnel and down to Newark.

"And what are we going to do in this far-off land?"

"Get the two hundred and thirty-five thousand dollars. Where else am I going to get it?"

He got it in the next hour, after the Newark banker examined, one last time, the series of stock certificates Klimrod laid in front of him, having taken them out of his eternal cloth bag.

And Diego knew enough to understand that Reb had negotiated

the two-hundred-thirty-five-thousand-dollar loan by giving as security almost all the companies he had formed.

Agreement was reached.

"Let's go," said Reb.

Once again, Wall Street. This time it was not Hasendorf who was waiting on the sidewalk, but Benny Bercovici, with whom Diego had already worked, in Chicago and in Baltimore. "But we never really got along," he commented later, "and for a good reason: Benny was slightly more talkative than a clam, but hardly."

They met with Norman, who announced that his clients, having been consulted, agreed to a three-month option. There was some discussion, with Norman trying to obtain a payment of ten percent instead of five. But he obviously did not expect to get it.

They walked out half an hour later, and went back to Pine Street, to the Hunt Manhattan building.

"I have an appointment to see David Fellows, at one o'clock sharp," Reb said.

He and Diego walked through solemn dark offices. We look like two plumbers who have come to fix the toilets, thought Diego as they crossed one barrier after another. If he would at least get rid of that fucking cloth bag! Another series of secretaries filtered them, one last time, and let them through. They were finally standing before David Fellows.

"Ten minutes," said Fellows. "And that is only because that animal Hasendorf really insisted."

The "animal" was standing there, looking a little tense.

"It is extremely simple," said Reb. "We are living in, and we will be living in, a period of increased expansion. Everything points to this, and it looks as if it is going to continue on an upward scale. No one will profit from it more than the banks. You are the director of . . . excuse me: you are part of a board of directors of one of the largest banks in the world. As such, you are highly prosperous. And you have a problem: your departments are at present spread out in eight different buildings, some of which are far away. You are considering a consolidation. . . ."

"Where did you get such an idea?"

"Selling sandwiches and sodas to your lowly employees," muttered Diego under his breath, on the verge of a monumental laughing fit. He was feeling euphoric. This maneuver of Reb's, which he was just beginning to understand, enchanted and delighted him.

"You are considering a consolidation. Within your board of directors, you are the most ardent supporter of this move," said Reb in his soft voice. "And you are planning to consolidate in midtown Manhattan. Other banks are considering this, too, but less important ones than yours. No one wants to make the first move, and be alone miles away from here. That's the dilemma. Because leaving Wall Street for Fifth Avenue or Madison Avenue will cause midtown congestion and a slump for all downtown real-estate investments. Yours among them. And you have seven important buildings in this area, worth about thirty million dollars."

"Forty," said Fellows with a mocking smile.

"Thirty-five," said Reb automatically. And he also smiled.

"You are enormously amusing," said Fellows.

"Wait until you get to know me better. You have only one choice: to group all your departments into a single building."

"Which is where?"

"Nowhere. It doesn't exist yet. But you are going to build it. It will involve about one million dollars."

"Why only one for that price?" Fellows asked, laughing. "Why not twelve? And where am I building them?"

"Second window to your left. On the other side of the street. All the way down."

Fellows almost go up. But he didn't. His eyes narrowed. "I know that lot, of course. One of my partners is supposed to look into it."

"Tell him not to bother."

"Sold?"

"Yes."

"To you?"

"Yes. Sold to me," said Reb. "And I will sell it to you for eight million dollars. Today. Today is the day."

This time, Fellows got up. He went around his desk—without, however, going to the window through which he could have seen the lot. Although it looked as if he wanted to.

"I know," said Reb. "You are going to tell me that you are afraid that all the other banks will eventually leave Wall Street, which would leave you here alone. Which would be pretty ridiculous. But they will not leave."

"Why?"

"Because you are staying. And for another reason, almost as important. Most of them have the same problem as you: lack of space."

"And you have bought lots for all of them as well?"

"That was not necessary. Your bank is the most important one on the East Coast. The others need much less space. Suppose I were to sell this very building to another bank . . . "

"Which other bank?"

"A large bank, rich enough to buy what you are selling. One already in the Wall Street area. And which, by the purchase of this building, will also remain in the area."

Fellows went to sit down.

"After that, what will you sell to whom?"

"What do you want to sell?"

"Everything."

"Your seven buildings?"

"If we buy your lot and build, let's say, a sixty-story building, I don't see why we should hang on to the old buildings. And even a bank doesn't mind having some ready money, from time to time."

Silence.

Reb's eyes were veiled, as if gray smoke had come over them.

"Agreed, then," he said. "I will sell your buildings, all seven of them. To banks, of course. Or financial establishments of some kind."

Silence again.

Then Fellows said: "I will have to consult with the other board members. I could not make this decision on my own."

"Yes, you could," said Reb. "Each member of the board of Hunt Manhattan can pledge up to fifty million dollars. My price for the lot today is eight million. Tomorrow it will go to nine, Monday ten. A sixty-story building will cost you about one hundred and twenty million. . . . I have a proposition: in exactly two hours and thirty-four minutes, I will be back here. I will give you a letter from a banker you know personally. In this letter, he will agree to buy your building, probably on the condition that you buy my lot and build on it. In that case, will you buy my lot?"

"I understood everything," said Diego. "You are selling this guy, for eight million dollars, a lot that you bought two hours earlier for four million seven. Or, that you didn't buy for four million seven, but only for two hundred and thirty-five thousand—which was loaned to you by a bank. A profit of three million three. Minus the bank loan and expenses: three million. Roughly speaking. And besides that, you get a commission on the sale of the Pine Street building. Without laying out one cent. May I express my delight and amazement!"
"You didn't understand anything."

The next appointment was on Broadway, ten minutes away by foot. This was the fourth appointment of the day, and had been set up, like the others (except for the one at the bank in Newark), by Hasendorf, and it was for two-thirty.

Harvey Barr, the Chairman of the Board of the Commercial and Industrial Bank of New York, was massive, reddish, and patient. He let Reb Klimrod speak without interrupting him once, and as if to make sure he understood correctly, he said, once Reb stopped talking: "One, you assure me that Hunt Manhattan will not leave Wall Street; two, you claim that it will move across from its current location, to a building that it will put up; three, it will, for this purpose, buy a lot from you; four, it is in our interest to buy or to pledge to buy the Hunt building on Pine Street and to move into it as soon as Hunt leaves the premises; five, this will take place in about six years, when the new building will be completed; six, we should give up the idea of a move to midtown Manhattan, which we have considered, for the double reason that we might end up alone up there, like idiots, and that our departure would lower the value of real-estate investments, specifically ours, in the Wall Street area; seven, the announcement of our decision to stay would, on the contrary, bring about an increase in the value of this very real estate; eight, you have seven buildings to sell, exchange, and re-exchange, in such a fashion that six or seven other banks or financial establishments will certainly follow the move that Hunt and we will have started; nine, finally, I must give you a letter by which I pledge, in the name of my bank, to purchase the Hunt building as soon as it is vacant, in six or seven years, on the condition, however, that we have the assurance that Hunt Manhattan will not skip to midtown Manhattan, that it will purchase your lot, and that it will build on it a building costing at least one hundred million dollars, where it will consolidate its departments and have its headquarters."

"In a word, yes," said Reb.

Diego was ferociously struggling against his second attack of giggles that day.

"Cigar?" offered Barr.

"I do not smoke, thank you."

"A whisky, perhaps?"

"Thank you, no."

Barr nodded.

"What I am trying to tell you is that I have some bad news for you. This location of ours on Broadway is not the property of our bank. We have almost three more years on our lease. It will end June 30, 1953. We have tried everything to obtain an extension. Without success. The landlord has absolutely refused. In other words, we cannot wait six years, or seven or eight, for Hunt Manhattan to move. We have to move before June 30, 1953. Do you think the new Hunt building will be completed by then?"

"No."

"Do you think we would be foolish enough to move once in June of 1953 and then again three or four years later?"

"That would not make very much sense."

"I don't have to tell you that. Your operation can't work, Kimrod."

"K-l-i-m. *Klim*rod. Can I show you something, Mr. Barr?"

He motioned to Bercovici, who spread documents out on the desk.

"Your landlord's name is Churchill, Mr. Barr. James Andrew Churchill. I met him yesterday. He has agreed to sell me this building. You see before you the signed agreement of sale. Now do you agree to purchase the building on Pine Street, on the added and imperative condition that within one year, at most, I furnish you with proof that I am your landlord and, as such, I agree to extend your lease until the time when you can move into the former offices of Hunt Manhattan?"

The following day, October 18, Hunt Manhattan, represented by the man who would become its major shareholder and most influential administrator, David Fellows, took an option on the lot situated across from its headquarters on Pine Street, with a deposit of ten percent of the price of the lot, or eight hundred thousand dollars.

The very same day, Reb Klimrod deposited that sum in the Newark bank—the same one that had agreed to lend him thirty thousand dollars for the purchase of trucks and motorcycles, and had given him a second loan, of two hundred and thirty-five thousand dollars.

Thanks to this deposit and on the strength of the option taken by Hunt Manhattan, he was able to take title to the lot, and therefore actually purchase it, through means of a short-term loan of four million five hundred thousand dollars from the same Newark bank.

He was then able to sell the lot to David Fellows—a transaction that took place October 26—and thus repay, in full, the loan from the Newark bank.

Klimrod's net profit on this first deal was two million nine hundred and twenty thousand dollars, and he earned it, not in forty-eight hours, as the Argentine claims, carried away by his veneration for the King, but in nine days.

It was only later, only later, that the real craziness began.

6

Four things must be kept in mind to understand the Wall Street deal.

One: the entire maneuver took place over ten months.

Two: Reb Klimrod headed it while he was, at the same time, heading, ten, twenty, thirty other businesses, all different, not only outside of New York but also outside of the United States.

For him, it was only one of the dozens of chess games he was playing simultaneously.

Three: Reb Klimrod, as was his habit, operated alone. Trusting only his memory. He formed companies (twenty-nine in all), many of which were dissolved as soon as they had served their purpose. And he used many men, of whom Daniel Hasendorf was the most visible; but none of them ever had a sense of the whole picture.

Four: the Wall Street relocation—which actually changed the future of the financial district—affected sixty-seven banks and several financial institutions and insurance companies. The total sums that were set in movement reached and probably surpassed the billion-dollar mark.

David Fellows said: "I have finally obtained the agreement of the other directors. First, on the lot I have purchased from you, we are in fact going to build a sixty-story building in which we will group all our departments. Then, for the seven other buildings . . ."

"I have already taken care of the first problem, this building."

"That my friend Harvey Barr has pledged to buy. His letter is a masterpiece. I think I will have it framed. Anyway, that leaves six other buildings."

"I have declared myself ready to sell them in your name."

"Barr told me that you made the same sort of pledge to him, for two buildings belonging to his bank, one on William Street, the other in Brooklyn. Is this true?"

"In a way."

"Six for us, two for Barr. Eight in all. What the devil do you want to do? Buy and sell all of Wall Street?"

"I don't see who could imagine such a crazy scheme," Reb said quietly. "Will you give me the authorization to sell these six other buildings in your name?"

"Yes."

"I would like you to give me an official proxy, which would permit me to negotiate these sales. What my lawyers call an 'exclusive sale agreement,' along with a power of attorney. Is that possible?"

Fellows looked at one of his lawyers present, who nodded.

"You have it," said Fellows. "Your lawyers and mine can work out the details."

"Now, the price. What is your estimate for the group of buildings?"

"Including this one or not? In his letter, Barr doesn't mention any figures. He pledges to purchase this building in six years, but the louse never mentions a figure. . . ."

An amused look came over Fellows's face. "Your idea, I presume?"

"Yes."

"You are thinking of a package deal for all seven buildings, including this one, is that it?"

"Yes."

"I remember having mentioned an amount for all of them."

"Forty million. And I answered thirty-five. What do you think of thirty-seven?"

"It's a reasonable figure, which the other board members would probably accept. Klimrod?"

"Yes?"

"Am I mistaken or do you already have a buyer in mind?"

Reb looked down, then up, and smiled.

"Me," he said. "I would like to buy these buildings from you."

Fellows burst out laughing.

"And I almost didn't see you. I would have regretted it for the rest of my life! What's your proposition?"

"I would like a one-year option, starting tomorrow. The price of each building won't appear on it, but an essential clause will specify that, in any case, the proceeds from the sale of the six buildings, added to those from the sale of this one, will total thirty-seven million dollars."

"Klimrod?"

"Yes?"

"Are you sure you don't want to come work for us?"

"I don't feel like buying a bank, at the moment, but thank you anyway."

This was October 26, the day when the deeds for the Pine Street lot were officially signed over—by a company of which Diego Haas, without much surprise, discovered himself to be president—to Hunt Manhattan.

The following day, in possession of two million six hundred thousand dollars (Daniel Hasendorf's commission having been deducted), and through another company, also represented by Diego Haas, Reb Klimrod took an option on the seven buildings belonging to Hunt Manhattan, on payment of a deposit of one million eight hundred and fifty thousand dollars, or five percent of the total price of thirty-seven million.

The day after that, still using the same principle of "leverage" which enables one to sell to B that which he has not yet bought from A, other than in the way of a deposit of five or ten percent of the buying price, and only when having been paid by B does he pay A, Reb Klimrod acquired two other buildings, belonging to Harvey Barr's Commercial and Industrial Bank.

For this, he used a third company, represented this time by Daniel Hasendorf. He took an eight-month option in exchange for the payment of five percent of the price asked by Barr (six and one-half million), or three hundred and twenty-five thousand dollars.

In other words, eleven days after he began his Wall Street offensive, having reimbursed the Newark bank for the loans it had extended to him, he found himself—after starting without one cent but not owing a cent to anyone—the legal owner (or, at any rate, able to resell them at any price) of nine buildings.

And he had four hundred and twenty-five thousand dollars left.

And not just any buildings . . .

"Musical chairs," said Hasendorf, in a constant good mood thanks to all the commissions he was receiving.

The expression puzzled Diego. The broker explained to him that it was used, especially in the real-estate business, to refer to choice properties as though they were seats used in a children's game.

And it was with these first musical chairs that the symphony began.

The decision taken by Hunt Manhattan, followed by that of Barr's Commercial and Industrial, started an irresistible movement. All at once, everyone felt freed: it was to be Wall Street then that would have to be "restabilized," as the expression went. . . .

Number 15 Broadway was sold to the J. P. Flint bank for twenty-one and one-half million dollars. The transaction took place in three days, after an initial refusal by Alexander Haines, who claimed he did not need additional space. But Haines gave in suddenly when he learned that the Mutual Guaranty Corporation was considering a merger with the Flint bank. An argument used by Hasendorf, most probably rigged by Klimrod, though he was clever enough to find it on his own, was: "When Mutual comes to offer to merge with you, your position will be stronger and, in addition, you will need more space."

On his personal scorecard, Diego wrote, "Twenty-one and one-half million dollars." Out of all this high finance, he had retained one figure: thirty-seven million. That was the amount Reb had agreed to pay Hunt Manhattan for the seven buildings.

"And thirty-seven minus twenty-one and one-half leaves . . . fifteen and a half. And there are still six buildings to sell. *Madre de Dios*, Reb, let your pal Barr make a little effort and the last five buildings will all be profit!"

His eyes met the amused gray ones.

He asked: "I still don't understand anything, right?"

"In a way."

Harvey Barr agreed to pay seventeen and one-half million for the old Hunt building. With a doubled commission because of the quality of his services, Hasendorf received an extra four hundred thousand dollars for the sale of the first two buildings of the Hunt Manhattan lot.

Lot number three was a building on Beaver Street. Klimrod did not sell it. He traded it. For two smaller buildings that the New York Civic Bank offered him. The bank agreed to the exchange provided they were given the possibility of constructing another building next to the one on Beaver Street.

The building next door was occupied by a division of the Washington Trust Company.

To the Washington Trust Company, Klimrod proposed a consolidation—similar to the one Hunt Manhattan was going to undertake—on three plots of land on William Street that he was undertaking the purchase of, since the occupants, the Island Commercial Trust and the New York City Financial Corporation, had accepted the offer he had made them to move to two buildings on Broadway.

These buildings were supposed to be vacated because Life Atlantic Security had agreed to relocate on Wall Street, at a location vacated by the Continental New Yorker Bank, which was moving to Nassau Street—to one of the two buildings for which Klimrod (what a happy coincidence) had taken an option to purchase within the framework of his transaction with the New York Civic Bank, and the second building . . .

"Is there something you did not understand?" Reb asked Diego.

"Only one thing," said Diego with his mouth full. "I am the president of how many companies?"

"Nine."

They were standing in front of the New York Stock Exchange, wolfing down hot dogs supplied by the Jaua Food Organization.

"Nine? Last week it was ten. I'm sinking, or what? Are we in a depression?"

"You dissolved three yesterday."

"So, that should be seven."

"But you formed two others this morning."

"Boy, am I busy!" exclaimed Diego.

7

In reconstituting the bewildering skein of options, exchanges, transfers, and other types of transactions carried out by Klimrod at that time, no fewer than thirty-eight options could be found, some lifted very quickly, in a few days, others left in suspense for months. Settiniaz was never able to determine the exact amount of capital that was used; the entanglement of banks, financial establishments, and companies was such that "it would take an army of experts a year to make any sense out of it. Maybe. Eighty percent of the companies he formed to serve as relays were dissolved, their assets going to offshore banks and disappearing in the meanders of Panamanian numbered accounts." One thing is certain: Reb Klimrod started out with only the two hundred and thirty-five thousand dollars loaned to him by the

New Jersey bank, which opened its doors to him on Abie Levin's intervention. The rest of the time, he operated by reinvesting his own profits. He never brought in fresh money from his other businesses that were starting to show a real profit. It was perhaps coyness on his part, or a deliberate decision to maintain airtight separation between this incredible speculation and the rest of his businesses.

He made great use of bank credit. He was in a good position to do so: his operations put him in contact with the key leaders of the largest banks on the East Coast. He often had personal friendship with these bankers, as with David Fellows, who remained his discreet friend until the end.

On several occasions, in order to buy something through a bank, he would borrow the money from the same bank, through one of his many companies.

All of the operations were perfectly legal. In 1952, the Internal Revenue Service submitted Diego Haas to a thorough examination: they could come up with nothing. Reb Klimrod was never the object of any investigation. And for a good reason: his name and signature never appeared anywhere.

The next operation was a little more complicated, at least in its final phase. Klimrod began it by obtaining, rather easily, an option of that part of a Wall Street property owned by Hunt Manhattan.

He got hold of a second part, which was divided among the distant and bad-tempered nephews of the Icabott family, through the good offices of Nick Petridis, a future King's Man.

This left the third part.

It belonged to the company that had built the building in 1920.

"An over-the-counter company, with interdealer price quotations," explained Hasendorf. "The building itself and their share of the land are today the only assets. And they refuse to sell. Not without a good reason: according to New York State law, such a sale can take place only with the agreement of two-thirds of the shareholders."

Hasendorf was anything but a fool. He saw the idea in Klimrod's eyes at the very minute it was born.

"Oh, no!" he exclaimed. "Not that!"

"Not what?" asked Diego

Hasendorf was watching Reb's dreamy expression. He explained: "If I am not mistaken, he wants to bring about an auction, thanks to which he could buy at least sixty-seven percent of the Brubaker shares. Then, owning two-thirds of the company, he could liquidate its assets as he pleases. He is completely mad."

Diego's yellow eyes shone savagely. "Watch your mouth, Daniel." He was shaking with rage.

Hasendorf threw up his hands,

"O.K."

"Diego?"

"Yes, Reb."

"It's O.K."

This scene took place in the little room that Klimrod was still living in—he lived there for ten years—in the shabby and decrepit building in Greenwich Village. Diego had taken the room next door.

After a moment, Diego asked: "Is this really what you want to do, Reb?"

"Yes."

Klimrod turned to Hasendorf,

"How many shares?"

"Two hundred thousand."

"Held by?"

"The Brubaker and Nash heirs, about fifteen percent each. The rest are all small shareholders."

"Quoted at?"

"Fifty-three and three-quarters yesterday."

"With what trend?"

"It moved a little during the last few weeks. Up. It went up two points, down one-half, up a little more. It will probably keep climbing."

"Sixty?"

What surprised and shocked Hasendorf most (aside from the fear he felt of him) was this total indifference of Klimrod's which he didn't have the decency to feign, even, just as he did nothing to maintain an image as to his appearance, his clothes, his eating habits, his living conditions, all the things that to Hasendorf and hundreds of people were the basics of life. For his part, Hasendorf had just purchased a magnificient apartment with a terrace on Park Avenue. But Klimrod was lying on his bed, his hands behind his head, in this hovel that contained nothing but one or two hundred books, piled right on the floor.

"I would be surprised if it hit sixty," said Hasendorf. "Good God, that would be twelve million dollars! And . . . "

He stopped suddenly. He was about to say: And you certainly don't have twelve million dollars. But Klimrod's eyes were on his and he felt a strong malaise.

"Daniel," Reb said softly, "how much have you earned in commissions since you have been working with me?"

"Quite a lot," Hasendorf conceded.

"I don't have the exact figure in my mind," said Klimrod with that same disquieting calm. "I could probably find it, if I wanted to. I would guess it to be around three million seven hundred and fifty thousand nine hundred and twelve dollars, give or take a dollar. Am I wrong, Daniel?"

"No. That must be right."

A tremendous pride came over Diego Haas. He did not care for Hasendorf. That son of a bitch, he thought, goes all over Wall Street and up to Fifth Avenue claiming that he is saving Wall Street and the whole New York economy with his infernal trickery. But in front of Reb, he is only a slave—as I am, but I am happy about it—in front of Reb, he wets his pants. . . .

"Daniel," said Reb, "what do you think would happen if I decided to make trouble for you?"

"I did not say a word."

"Do you want to stop working with me?"

"No."

"Do you think you would have the slightest chance of working on your own—I won't even mention against me—without my knowing about it?"

"No."

"You are absolutely sure?"

"Yes. Absolutely."

Reb nodded.

"Which brokerage firm would you recommend for this operation?"

"Aquaviva. They are the best in this field. And they are related to the Brubaker family. Harry Brubaker is married to one of the Aquaviva daughters."

Reb smiled,

"By a happy coincidence, I called them this very morning, as your secretary. You have a four o'clock appointment with Tony Aquaviva. You are going to offer him seventy-five dollars for each of thirty thousand Brubaker shares. I am sure that you will convince him to accept. You will have him start auctioning off all the other shares of Brubaker, Incorporated. At the same price, up to the amount of one hundred and thirty-five thousand, or two-thirds of the total shares. Did you know that George Nash, who also holds thirty thousand shares, has started negotiating with First National about a global sale of the building we want?"

"No."

"You should go sell hot dogs, from time to time. You learn more doing that than by reading the *Wall Street Journal*. Daniel, tell Aquaviva to keep quiet, and don't go see Nash; I'll take care of that myself. Daniel?"

"Yes?"

"Of course, you will officially be buying these shares, in the usual way. You are associated with Diego Haas, here present, in a company that was formed yesterday. See Lerner for the details. And, while I think of it, you got a little carried away with your passion for fishing, it seems. That boat you bought in Key West last Sunday wasn't worth the price; you could have gotten it for five hundred dollars less. But I saw the pictures of it. It's very nice. I hope you'll catch many fish. Any questions?"

"Everything is perfectly clear."

"That's what I thought," said Reb, yawning.

"It's extremely simple," said Klimrod to the people of Hunt Manhattan. "You wish to sell your part of the ground for ten million dollars. You have given me an option, and I will exercise it as soon as I have the money to do so. We are therefore allies in a way. I have already bought the Icabott share. This leaves the Brubaker share. I am trying to buy one hundred and thirty-five thousand shares from them. At seventy-five dollars a share. It will cost me between twelve and thirteen million dollars, with expenses and commissions. I could find this money at another bank, but I would not like to deprive you of my business. Your services have always been most satisfactory."

They thought he had more nerve than was possible. They didn't say so, though. They asked him how much he needed, and he answered that he could get three million together, no more. He smiled.

"That leaves ten. That you will lend me, not at once, but little by little, as I buy the shares."

And how would he guarantee this loan?

He explained: "I am prepared to discharge in your favor each Brubaker share that I am able to buy. And, of course, I will deposit in your bank the three million dollars' worth of shares that I have brought or that I will buy in the next few days. As security."

He raised one of his large hands to prevent the objection.

"I know: you will tell me that if I do not succeed in obtaining control of Brubaker, Incorporated—in other words, if I don't reach the two-thirds quota—these shares for which I will have paid seventy-five dollars will immediately drop to around fifty. But the risk for you is nil. Let's take an example. Suppose I obtain only one hundred and ten thousand of the one hundred and thirty-five that I need. My operation will have been a failure. The shares will drop down to around fifty dollars. But what will you have in your vaults? You will have financed the purchase of only eighty thousand of these shares. Or six million. They will be worth—let's say, and it could happen, that they drop to fifty-five—four million four hundred thousand. But you will have my three million, right? That will certainly cover the difference. So you see, you risk nothing. What's more . . . "

From inside his cloth bag, he took a copy of a letter.

"What's more, I already have a buyer for the building. Urban Insurance Life. Here is the letter by which they state their intention to buy the building from me as soon as I have purchased it. I would like an answer soon, please. The company owned by Messrs. Hasendorf and Haas has already acquired over two million dollars' worth of shares. Thirty thousand of them, actually. And the auction will take place shortly. Time is of the essence."

Diego Haas had two absolute certainties: the first was that the King was an infallible genius; the second, that he himself did not have a natural gift for arithmetic.

However, after having added up, twenty consecutive times, eight million (paid by Hunt Manhattan for the piece of land), four and one-half (for the Icabott share), and twelve and one-half (repurchase of seventy-one percent of the Brubaker, Incorporated shares), he felt himself authorized to conclude that that was twenty-five million.

"Plus expenses. There were expenses, right, Reb?"

"Yes."

"Many expenses? And commissions?"

"Diego, leave Hasendorf alone."

"Shit, that guy runs around telling everyone he is the inventor of *your* consolidation scheme in Wall Street! He was even interviewed by the *Daily News* and *Fortune*!"

"It doesn't matter. I don't want to be interviewed."

Time passed.

Reb smiled. "O.K. Diego?"

"O.K. Can I ask you a question?"

"Yes."

"What do you want? To be the richest and most unknown man in the world?"

"In a way. It's my turn to buy the hamburgers tonight. Then we could go to the movies. But you buy the tickets."

Naturally, Hasendorf won out during the Brubaker and Nash share auction.

David Settiniaz gives one hundred and twenty-four million dollars as the figure for the total profits earned by the Klimrod companies during the Wall Street operation. Daniel Hasendorf had received thirteen million dollars in commissions.

Settiniaz figures that the Wall Street deal alone—just one building at the start—along with, of course, its related transactions, must have earned twenty-seven million for the King. Even though this operation made the front pages of the newspapers (only Hasendorf was mentioned, never Klimrod), it was not the most important one, although it remains the most spectacular. His profits were not made as much on large buildings as they were on smaller, more modest locations, which, because of the restabilization of the Wall Street area, had seen their value skyrocket. A simple restaurant, a bar, a shop, or an apartment tripled and quadrupled in price only for the reason that the neighborhood had been resurrected by the now definitive proximity of all those banks.

Klimrod divided his Wall Street activities, those conducted with Hasendorf, Haas, and other figureheads, from another entire fabulous series of operations, conducted with two other teams, of which maybe only Diego knew the existence.

Putting Hasendorf in the limelight (who was less happy, eventually, when he was separated from Reb) and keeping Klimrod in the shadows was a plan both men had agreed to at the start. Klimrod already had the greatest aversion to personal publicity.

The Wall Street operation began in October 1950 and ended in June 1951.

But before that, there was the trip to London and to the Continent.

And mostly—before, during, and after—there was Charmian Page.

The Caracaraí Falls

1

"David Settiniaz."

The voice that pronounced his name was calm and slow, standing out clearly, without shouting, in the diffuse noise of the crowd that was rushing by. Walking out of the elevator, Settiniaz turned and saw him, wearing a blue shirt, a cloth bag at his feet, casually leaning against the marble wall. It was September 18.

Settiniaz said to the two men who were with him: "Excuse me. I will call you tomorrow."

He walked over to Reb Klimrod, and looked at him without knowing exactly what to say.

Klimrod finally smiled and said: "How was your honeymoon?"

"Marvelous. Where have you been? Georges Tarras called me last week and told me you had been to see him and had returned his books."

Settiniaz felt somewhat nervous, for no evident reason, the way one feels when one meets on old army buddy whom one had almost completely forgotten. Almost involuntarily, he walked across the lobby, too consciously aware of the presence next to him of the thin young man, strangely dressed, carrying that ridiculous cloth bag. They walked out onto Madison Avenue. It was very sunny and very hot. A group of secretaries walked by, smiling at Settiniaz, but looking curiously, and interestedly, at his companion.

"You were waiting for me?"

"Yes."

"Why didn't you come up to my office?"

"What did Georges Tarras tell you?"

That was answering a question with a question.

"Simply that you had come to see him in Maine, to bring back his books. And that you had charmed his wife."

Settiniaz made an effort to sound casual, although he was still feeling somewhat uncomfortable.

"It seems you have an extraordinary knowledge of painting."

"Nothing else?"

Settiniaz thought, searching his memory.

"No," he answered, sincerely. "Is it important?"

"Not really," said Klimrod. "I would like to talk to you. Are you free, or would you rather meet some other time?"

Settiniaz remembers that he had no other plan but to go home that evening to the beautiful apartment near Park Avenue that his mother and his in-laws had furnished. He and Diana, since their return home from their honeymoon, had had only a few miserably short hours together, caught up as they were in the whirlwind of society life, in New York as well as in Boston, and with the Page property near the ocean and the large horse farm in Kentucky that belonged to his mother. And since September 1, the day he joined the firm of Wittaker & Cobb, there had not been one evening when the newly married couple did not have to accept or reciprocate an invitation. "But, in all honesty," he said later, "that was not the only, or even the real, reason for my reticence: the idea of bringing Klimrod to my home, to introduce him to what I considered to be my social circle, seemed absurd. It was 1950, and at that time we were infinitely more preoccupied with conventions than we are today. Of course, in the light of what happened eventually . . . "

He said, very hesitantly: "Listen, I . . . "

Klimrod's large hand came down on his forearm, a gesture that made Settiniaz even more uncomfortable.

"May I call you David?"

"Of course."

Klimrod began to laugh. "I could not have accepted your dinner invitation anyway. Unfortunately, I am busy this evening. Another time, perhaps."

He had an amused look in his eyes.

I am a real fool, thought Settiniaz with his usual honesty.

Klimrod continued.

212

"In about five or six months, I will need a lawyer such as you. No, no, I do not want to deal with Wittaker or Cobb, or any of their associates. I have looked into your background. . . . "

He smiled that curious smile.

"Don't be angry, please. By the way, I did not come up with anything that was not—how shall I put it?—favorable. I will need your services in the spring. Whether you accept or not will be your decision. But before that, for the months to come, I would like to make you an offer. I would like us to meet for three or four hours every week. Of course, if it will make things easier, I am prepared to rent your services from Cobb or Wittaker. But yours only. I will pay whatever I have to. I would like us to meet for three or four hours, every week, but not necessarily the same day of the week, depending on your schedule and mine, and I will ask you questions, usually theoretical ones. . . . "

Settiniaz was looking at him, dumbfounded.

"You want me to teach you law? Three hours a week?"

"In a way. But not really. I want to learn the essentials, what I need to know. And I know exactly what I need to know and what I don't."

"Any evening course would accomplish the same."

Klimrod shook his head.

"No. I've tried."

He laughed, and his youth (Settiniaz discovered later that he had turned twenty-two that very day) was obvious.

"It doesn't go fast enough, and they waste time on unimportant matters, and besides, the schedule does not always suit me. I've thought it over, David. Is it a question of money?"

He dug into his bag and pulled out some rolls of thousand-dollar bills.

"Forgive me, I would never want to offend you in any way. Just tell me how to go about it and I will take care of all the financial problems. Vis-à-vis Wittaker & Cobb, or you."

"In God's name!" exclaimed Settiniaz, with the feeling of being carried away by a huge breaking wave. "My services are not worth very much; I've only been working for eighteen days!"

"Please accept. After all, you saved my life, so you must owe me something."

His gray eyes shone with humor. But there came from him

also an almost oppressive power of persuasion and the feeling of an offered and warm friendship, unveiled suddenly, like a lighted door opened in the night.

"David?"

"All right," answered Settiniaz, giving way to the wave that was going to change his entire existence.

And as of the first minutes of their next meeting, which took place four days later in the lounge of a hotel, one thing was evident to Settiniaz: Klimrod's intelligence was assuredly the most astounding he had ever come across. "It was almost frightening," he remembers. "He had an ability to go right to the essential point that could disconcert and, worse, stupefy you. You could feel it, of course, this intelligence, just by looking in his eyes, but it was something else to see it function, without hindrances, naked, free from all the obviously deliberate camouflage of the ordinary impassivity of his face, the dreamy expression of his eyes, the slowness and calm delivery of his voice, and his gestures. Then, it would reveal itself in its enormity, in its monstrosity— the word is not too strong—fascinating, of course, but often exasperating. At Harvard, I had been, I think, what one might call a brilliant student. At that time, Wittaker & Cobb was the best in New York, and even in the whole country, when it came to law firms. The tops. To be recruited by them, for a young lawyer starting out, was like—I don't know how to put it—being hired over Gary Cooper for a film part. They had recruited me—for once, on my merits only and not through some family intervention—and I was bursting with pride. And I had studied law and business for six years. Yet after those first hours spent across from Klimrod, I came away crushed, feeling exactly like a four-year-old forced to teach nuclear physics. I was almost ready to refuse to go to the second meeting.

"Which I went to, of course. You could not understand the King, and the extraordinary influence he had over us, without taking into account his power of seduction. The masks that Reb Klimrod wore—face, voice, courtesy, softness—were only concessions he made to us, to make us forgive him for being so superior. Once we had understood it, we could live with it, more or less.

"We saw each other about fifteen times before November 20,

that year. And by then I was not sure who was teaching the law to whom!

"Just as I admit that it never occurred to me that he could have premeditatedly used our meetings, not only to gain introductions that he needed, and not only to judge me, to size me up before trusting me entirely, but also to see Charmian again. . . . "

"That will take us too far," said Settiniaz, a little annoyed. "As always with you, we jump from one idea to the next, so that . . ."

He switched to English to avoid the possible use of the familiar *tu* form.

"But could I find it anywhere?" Reb asked softly.

"In Goldenweiser's charts. Unless Chandler deals with it in his *Economics of Money and Banking*. I have his book, but not here. It's at home. I could bring it to you next time."

"Or I could go home with you, and you could give it to me tonight. Would you do that?"

They left the hotel lounge together. A taxi dropped them off on Park Avenue. On the way, they pursued their discussion about the dollar and exchange rates and international finance. Settiniaz was getting caught up in the game, losing himself in it up to the point where he found himself in the entrance hall to his apartment, handing his briefcase to the Hawaiian butler . . .

. . . and discovering his wife and his sister-in-law in the living room, looking quizzically at Reb Klimrod.

On November 20, 1950, Charmian was just past her twenty-third birthday. Although very much in love with his own wife, David Settiniaz had always realized that, of the two sisters, the younger was by far the prettier. Yet, had a knife been held to his throat, he would not have married her: she had always had the knack of embarrassing him, almost scaring him. Laughingly, Diana explained it as "Charmian's special sense of humor." For the past fifteen years, starting with his own French grandmother, Settiniaz had been told over and over again that he had as much sense of humor as a washcloth or words to that effect. By now, he had started to believe it.

So that, accepting the consensus, he began to consider his sister-in-law's eccentricities as normal.

She was totally independent financially. The Page money dated back four generations. At the age of twenty-one, she had received ten million dollars. She had disdainfully turned down the services of the usual family lawyers. She was going to manage the inheritance herself. Causing general amazement, she had proved that she was not lacking in the instinct of great financial wizards.

One day, she had burst into the offices of Wittaker & Cobb—before Settiniaz joined the firm—to fume over a speculation that, in her eyes, had been badly handled, or at any rate, not according to the very specific instructions she had given. It had taken Jonas Wittaker, who was slowly and carefully, as he did all things, approaching his seventieth birthday, several days to get over the incident. He was offended by the reproaches, which he considered to be unjustified, and upset all the more by the fact that these reproaches were made to him by a woman—a breed he knew in the form of one woman only, his wife—whose role, he believed, was to bear children, make pudding, and do needlework, perhaps even petit point if she were mentally deficient.

Charmian had been engaged five times, each time with a steadfast consistency, leaving her fiancé waiting at the altar. She had traveled to India with the intention of becoming a Hindu. She had accepted the offer of a Hollywood producer to make her into the next Ava Gardner, whom she resembled, had even decided on a script, but had left on a cruise to the South Seas on the third day of shooting. On the occasion of her sister's marriage to David Settiniaz (whom she terrorized by sitting on the edge of the bathtub when he was in it soaping himself), she had had, as her gift, and using as a pretext the fact that he was of Savoyard origin, flown in from France, on a special plane, twelve wheels of Gruyère and six folkoric groups, who had, by all singing at the same time, made a terrible racket.

"Come on, David, it's funny, isn't it?" Diana had asked.

"Hilarious," he had answered, gloomy and dejected.

It was funny. But there was something else, which David felt he was the only one to notice and which he had not shared with anyone else: every so often, he would discern, in Charmian's admirable slightly slanted blue eyes, the color of amethyst, a strange, feverish look that worried him.

Charmian Page was now staring at Reb Klimrod with great intensity.

"She said: "We have already met, haven't we?"

She had been sitting on one of the large sofas. Now she got up, approached, slowly walked around him.

"German?"

"Austrian."

"Tyrolian, perhaps?"

"Viennese."

As tall as Charmian was, she did not reach his shoulders.

"But American citizenship?"

"I have an Argentine passport."

Reb's eyes went from Diana to David. The eyes had a dreamy expression, the sort of look that seems turned inside oneself.

She felt the fabric of this shirt, at the neck, under the leather jacket.

"In business?"

"In a way."

"Wall Street?"

"Among other things."

She faced him.

"I will get you that book," said David, in a nervous tone.

He took a few steps toward his study, stopped on hearing Reb's calm voice.

"In your place, I would not have bought those twenty thousand shares of Continental Electric."

Settiniaz turned around, surprised. During the fifteen meetings they had had, Reb had never said a word about his activities, or even about the way he lived and earned his livelihood. To judge from his appearance, Settiniaz had pictured him doing some kind of lowly work, on the docks or in a store. He had even thought that the Austrian (he knew nothing about this Argentine passport) had perhaps become mixed up in some shady business.

He said: "I didn't know you were interested in the stock market, Reb."

"David?" Charmian had her back turned to her brother-in-law. "Please butt out of this, David."

There was a pause.

"And I made a mistake with Continental Electric?"

"Yes," said Reb, smiling . "May I have the book, David?"

"Do you work at the Stock Exchange, Mr. Klimrod?"

"No."

"In a brokerage firm?"

"No."

"In a bank, then?"

"No."

He began to laugh.

"I sell hot dogs on the street. In front of the New York Stock Exchange. To the right when you arrive."

"And business is good?"

"I can't complain. About thirty-five to forty dollars a day, five days a week. Counting sodas, of course. And tips."

"And it's by selling hot dogs that you learned that I had just bought twenty thousand shares of Continental Electric?"

Reb was watching a hesitating David, who disappeared into his study, and came right out with the Chandler book in his hand.

"Oh, no," said Reb. "That sort of information doesn't turn up amid the hot dogs. One hears only important things, of a more general nature. No, I simply had you investigated, Miss Page. Your order of this morning was only half good. The principle of it wasn't wrong; you simply waited too long. Before yesterday would have been better. On the other hand, the Western stocks were a good idea, five weeks ago. Even if you were wrong to cancel your order for the Caledonian. You should have followed your impulse, and your flair. Thank you, David. As for the San Jacinto, let's not mince words: that was plain stupid. I will return the book next week, David."

He slowly placed the Chandler text in his cloth bag. Then he looked straight at the young woman.

"And if I were you, I would change my position on the krona. Maybe go back to it in three weeks. I would turn, instead to the Swiss franc."

He smiled, nodded to the two women, and left. There was a silence. Then Charmian Page burst out laughing.

"Had me investigated!"

In her eyes, David Settiniaz recognized that bizarre and feverish gleam that worried him so much.

Usually, there were two to run the wagon in front of the New York Stock Exchange, two Italian-Americans, very jovial and quite dexterous. Reb Klimrod and Diego Haas arrived around ten o'clock. Reb told the two men to go have a drink or something, and wait for a sign from him before coming back.

"I don't know how to make hot dogs" said Diego. "We proud hidalgos of the pampas disapprove of manual work. Don't count on me."

"At least you can uncap bottles?"

He could. And he did, wearing, as was Reb, a ridiculous white-and-green cap, and thinking: If Mamita sees me, she will drop dead, right before my eyes. I should have worn a false beard. But he was happily screaming: "Two sodas! Two!"

She arrived around eleven. The most beautiful young woman Diego had ever seen, and the crowd of secretaries and other workers naturally opened a passage for her.

"May I please have a hot dog?" she asked.

"With mustard?" asked Reb.

"Is it strong?"

"You can take it," said Reb. "You can take anything."

"Including you, don't worry."

"I'm not in the least worried."

He raised his arm. The two Italian-Americans came over and resumed their posts. Reb wiped his hands, removed the apron and hat.

He said to the young woman: "Can I buy you a cup of coffee?"

"My name is Diego," said Diego. "I am very nice and very friendly."

"I haven't even had breakfast. I wouldn't mind a cup of coffee."

She and Reb were face to face, looking at each other. "Coming, Diego?" said Reb, not asking him, but giving him an order.

The Argentine fell into step with the couple. They walked to Nassau Street. There was a restaurant with a French name.

"It's closed," she said.

He snapped his fingers; the door opened. Inside, one table, only one, but a large one, was lavishly set, in the middle of the room, with all the waiters and waitresses lined up.

"Would you like some toast with your coffee?" asked Reb.

"Please."

Her eyes didn't leave Reb. The three of them sat down.

"As I was just saying," said Diego, "my name is Diego and I am very interesting. My conversation, to begin with, is fascinating. I can't help it; it's a gift."

"An investigation of me?"

"Yes."

"Of all aspects of me?"

"Only those pertaining to banking and finance."

"No other areas?"

"Private property," he said. "For other areas, I prefer to do it myself."

"Am I rich enough for you?"

"I suppose it will do."

They were served coffee, tea, hot chocolate, toast, butter, thirty or forty different jams and jellies, eggs prepared in various ways, potatoes, bacon, sausages. . . . The silver platters accumulated with extravagant profusion.

"And physically do I suit you?"

"Yes, very well," he said quietly. "Very very well. No complaints."

"Shall I pour some coffee?"

"Yes, please. Thank you."

"I will have some also," said Diego. "Just a little, since you are insisting. And perhaps an egg or two. But no sausages. Lately, I can't stand sausages."

"This is Diego," said Reb. "This guy on your right, and my left, is Diego."

"Delighted," said Charmian without turning her head. "Hello, Diego. What do I call you? Reb?"

"Reb."

She drank a little coffee, nibbled on a piece of toast. He also drank.

"The restaurant is yours, of course."

"Of course."

"What else?"

"A few other things here and there. I am just starting out."

"You have gone pretty far already."

"Yes, I think so."

"To reach one's goal is sometimes disappointing."

He smiled. "I'll find out for myself."

A silence.

Then she said: " Your friend Diego is very nice and very friendly. His conversation, to begin with, is fascinating."

"It's a gift," said Diego, with his mouth full.

Again there was a silence. Reb moved his index finger, and all the employees of the restaurant left, disappeared, swallowed up by the back rooms. She look straight at him, looked down, looked up, and looked at him again, with great seriousness.

"How very strange, isn't it?"

"Yes," said Reb. "Very strange. And completely unexpected."

He stood up, reached out his hand. Into which she put hers. They walked out onto Nassau Street.

"Shall I come?" asked Diego.

"Why not?" said Reb.

He was still holding Charmian's hand.

The three of them boarded the ferry, which was completely empty except for the crew in charge of it. It changed its usual course and headed for the bay.

Diego Haas went to the back, alone, smoking one of those long, thin black cigars that only he found pleasant-smelling, his yellow eyes looking at the banks of the river without really seeing. The other two were in the front somewhere, out of his sight. He was thinking: We are going down the Hudson as we would the Amazon, and perhaps we will sail over the Atlantic, Dieguito, for years to come, eating hot dogs and drinking sodas, selling here and there three or four dozen buildings, entire avenues, simply, without any craziness, living on Park Avenue or in some similar no less sinister place. They will have children, for whom I will be the godfather, and I will push them around in their strollers, specially constructed by Rolls-Royce or perhaps by General Motors, which Reb will probably have bought in the meantime. And the adventure, *Madre de Dios*, will no longer be one. I would do better to go back home to Mamita and to marry the first Concepción to come along. . . . "

And just as intensely, he felt a sadness, a real sorrow, the feeling that the crazy, new, and exciting race might now be cut short, suddenly. He also felt, in ways that he was much too clever not to recognize, pangs of jealousy.

This made no sense, of course.

When they had passed Governors Island and were heading out toward the open sea, the ferry turned around and went back to Manhattan, docking at a slip of the Staten Island ferries. The trip was over, just as it was beginning.

Diego sensed that between Charmian Page and Reb Klimrod, things would not be simple.

The couple separated without exchanging a word, or even a

look. She climbed into a taxi and left. Reb began walking straight toward the Brooklyn Bridge, swinging his leather jacket from his shoulder. And Diego, taken aback at first, had to run to catch up to him.

At that point, Diego just walked alongside him, cursing this habit of Reb's of walking all over New York, and every other city, with long strides, hitting the pavement with his heels as if to leave his trace there for eternity.

It was only when they reached the bridge that Diego asked: "Any problems?"

No answer.

"Are you going to see her again?" he dared to ask.

"I don't know. Diego? Don't talk to me about it, please."

The thing that registered in Diego's mind was that "the crazy, new, and exciting race" was not going to be interrupted, and that was enough to make him happy.

2

The Wall Street consolidation operation was in full swing. It would have been enough to occupy several ordinary men. But it was only one part of a dozen other ones run simultaneously by Klimrod.

The same applies to the London operation, which was the first one where Reb worked outside of North America.

But the London operation was logically preceded by the one dealing with the two hundred and forty-eight Roarke stores.

In the beginning, there was the fact that one of the locations chosen as a site for one of the delicatessens was directly next door to a shoe store, and had to be sublet from them. A man from Bercovici's team took the first steps to secure the lease. He was turned down.

He reported this to Reb, who asked Benny Bercovici: "And the reason?"

"The smell of cooking would chase away their customers."

"Have your men found any other sites?"

"That one is the best."

Bercovici's sad, yet sharp black eyes met Reb's. He nodded.

"O.K. You'll have all the information you need."

The following day, he reported: one, the store was part of a chain spread out over the whole state of New York; two, this chain belonged to a corporation called Roarke Shoes, Incorporated, which manufactured its own shoes in two factories, in New Rochelle and in Buffalo; three, Roarke was a privately held company, the value of its shares being given in its annual balance sheet; four, its shareholders were principally the Roarke family itself, and the rest were small shareholders, among whom were the leather suppliers; five, the business was faltering.

"Their shoes are out-of-date; they have been making the same styles ever since the twenties. They haven't kept up with the times. Month after month they are more and more overwhelmed by the competition. Their next balance sheet will bring about a general drop in the value of the shares."

Bercovici wasn't speaking; he was sputtering, in a high-pitched whining voice. His sad expression was a permanent one; he looked as if a fatal destiny weighed him down day and night. While he spoke, he kept glancing around, even behind him, watching for an invisible enemy. But he could work eighteen hours a day, for weeks at a time.

"Are you interested in the whole business, Reb, or just this one store?"

"The whole thing."

"That's what I thought. I have looked into the Roarke family. There are two brothers. They haven't spoken to each other in twenty years. They send each other memos. They each hold twenty percent. Everett and Harold. Everett is the older one. And the bigger jerk. Harold will be more difficult to handle: he believes his mission in life is to perpetuate the Roarke family tradition in the shoe business; he believes Roarke shoes are part of the American heritage. At least five times a day, he repeats that when you buy a pair of Roarke shoes, they will last you a lifetime. We've got two ways to get at him: his pride as a member of the Roarke shoe family and a mistress named. . . "

"No," said Reb.

"Up to you. Twenty for Everett, twenty for Harold. The sister, Honor, has fifteen percent. Some cousins and uncles, about twelve percent. Forty plus fifteen, plus twelve: sixty-seven, a majority. The leather suppliers have eighteen percent. They are worried, will jump at any offer. The remaining fifteen percent is spread around. The main supplier's name is London & Allister. Allister is the one to see; he is younger and more dynamic. London will go along with him."

"The sister?"

"Married to a Tullett. Five children; two are already in college, three more to go. They need money, and have already taken out a loan. I can take care of it. You want to buy everything?"

"At least two-thirds. Benny, you take the sister, Allister, and Everett. With a direct first contact, and don't let any of them know you've been to see the others."

"And Harold?"

Reb smiled, turned to Diego, looked at his feet, insistently.

Diego raised his hands and said: "I see. I have to go buy a pair of shoes that will last me a lifetime."

Diego had tiny feet. He wore a six and a quarter. The shoes that were sold to him in the Roarke store on upper Broadway were large enough for him to float down the East River in, while standing.

He approached Harold Roarke.

"I am overcome with emotion," he said. "Would you believe that this cow, this very cow, whose skin is around my little feet, was a close childhood friend of mine? I loved it the most. When I learned of its death, I cried like a baby."

Roarke was a big guy, with thick eyebrows and the look of a fanatical Quaker. He asked Diego who the devil he was.

"My name," said Diego, "is Esteban Gómez-Gómez y Gómez. You must have heard of it."

"Not at all," said Roarke coldly.

"I am surprised. But still. Just a few months ago, we sold four or five thousand of our cows to a leather company named London & Allister."

"I know them," said Roarke.

Diego said that it was through them that he had followed the trail of Concepción—that was the cow—from Texas to the upper Broadway store. And there, he had hit the jackpot.

"As for the shoes, the workmanship is admirable. To the point that using such works of art for walking seems criminal. As soon as I return to my hotel, I will place them in the vault."

An idea that caused Harold Roarke's already bushy eyebrows to rise even further as he proclaimed that Roarke shoes were made for life and to be walked in. He gave many examples to justify his claim: just recently, he had attended the funeral of a man named Horn, who had been wearing Roarkes since 1893—"the very same ones, Mr. Gómez-Gómez, the very same ones!"—and had been buried with them on his feet, although they were still usable.

Diego was properly impressed, and said they should have been considered true antiques.

"And that is precisely why I am amazed," he said," by the nobleness of your soul in light of the catastrophe that befalls you. What courage! *Muy hombre*, as we say in Chihuahua. And, by the way, I am not really Gómez-Gómez; I exaggerated a little. My real name is Gómez. In Gómez-Gómez y Gómez, the first Gómez is my father, the second one is my uncle Cristóbal, and I am only the 'y Gómez,' no more than that. You can call me Gómez."

"What catastrophe?" Roarke asked for the fifth time.

"It cannot be that I will be the one to tell you about it. Is it possible that you do not know? Your brother, your sister, your cousins and uncles, your suppliers, and I'm not mentioning everybody, are all selling their shares of Roarke, Incorporated. Tonight, tomorrow, a year from now at the latest, your factories in New Rochelle and Buffalo will no longer manufacture the legendary Roarke shoes, and your age-old customers will drag behind them shoeless children, will run from store to store throughout New York, will cry over their lost happiness, in a world forever more deprived of Roarke . . . "

"He fell for it. It's a go," he said to Reb Klimrod. "We have signed all the papers. He and I will form a company that will manufacture and develop Harold Roarkes until the year 2050 at noon precisely. I assured him that all the Gómezes will reserve a corner of all the stores they have bought from him, under the name Haas. Under these circumstances he has given me forty-nine percent of his shares, or about nine percent the Roarke shares. Is that enough, or do you want me to go back?"

Reb was laughing. He shook his head.

"Gómez-Gómez y Gómez! Diego, you are crazy!"

The yellow eyes lit up with savage humor.

"Completely. But no less than you."

In the following days, Klimrod began to take apart Roarke Shoes, Inc. And a loan from Hunt Manhattan financed the setting up of one hundred and sixty-three new restaurants, reaching north as far as Niagara Falls, all supplied by the Jaua Food Organization, whose turnover in the spring of 1951 had surpassed the thirty-million-dollar mark.

Of the two hundred and forty-eight initial stores, twenty-nine continued to sell Roarke shoes. The traditional ones, as promised Harold Roarke, and the promise was scrupulously kept. But not only the traditional Roarke shoes were sold. In February of 1951, Diego Haas, operating for Klimrod, signed an agreement with an Italian firm in Milan, which sent a group of technicians to the United States to renovate and diversify the factory production in New Rochelle and Buffalo. These factories were redesigned so that they could also manufacture bags, and then—but only two years later—became the nucleus of a line manufacturing sports equipment.

That left fifty-six other locations, most of them in the suburbs of New York. They were exchanged as of December 1950 for twenty-eight percent of a cleaning business, on whose board of directors was a certain Arnie Hintz, who was the straw man, brought in by Abie Levin, the syndicate man. For once, Klimrod was part of a company in which he did not hold at least fifty-one percent of the shares. The cleaning business had first been traded against shares in a transportation company, then traded again for a stationery store in Brooklyn, where Klimrod, through Roger Dunn, had a large role and took advantage of the fact that he held two-thirds of the shares for a while to set up a merger with other companies that were in Dunn's name. All of these operations took place with a magical rapidity, and resulted, in the spring of 1951, in the acquisition of the *Java Blue Rose*'s cargo.

This was also when David Settiniaz was confronted with the most important decision of his life.

"In September of last year, I told you that I would one day need you as a lawyer. The day has come, David."

Settiniaz did not understand.

"But I am a lawyer. What prevents you from being my client?"

"You are a lawyer practicing with Wittaker & Cobb. From this point on, I would like you to open your own office, where you will be the only one in charge."

"I am only twenty-seven years old, Reb."

"And I am not yet twenty-three. Wait, I want to show you something. . . . "

From his ever-present cloth bag (just the sight of it made Settiniaz cringe, and he was usually placid), he pulled out a letter.

"Read this."

The letter was signed by David Fellows personally, the head of the Hunt Manhattan Bank. It gave, as a credit line for Klimrod, the amount of fifty million dollars.

"My God!" exclaimed Settiniaz, incredulous.

"That is not all, David. I could probably obtain the same commitment from Harvey Barr. And two or three other banks, although it might be for smaller sums. David, I would like you to work alone—I mean, for you to be the only one responsible. You would be free to hire men of experience whom you feel you would need at your side. But it will be you and only you who will know my name, who will know of my existence within all the companies through which I operate. I am, of course, prepared to finance you."

"I don't have that sort of problem, and you know it."

Settiniaz sipped a little of his now cold tea.

"And you would be my only client? Exclusively?"

"Not necessarily. but I would have priority over all others. Without exception. Actually, I expect to give you enough business so that you wouldn't even dream of accepting any other clients."

"Lord, I don't even know what it is you do, or why a man

227

Fellows has such complete confidence in you. For all I know, you could be working for the Mafia!"

Klimrod smiled.

"This idea has occurred to you before, hasn't it?"

"Yes," admitted Settiniaz.

"Accept my proposition and I will fill you in on all my current and future activities."

"You have that much confidence in me?"

"As much as one can have in another human being. We have been seeing each other for months now, three hours at a time."

He smiled again.

"And I have had you investigated again."

"To that point?"

"To that point."

The gray eyes became especially piercing.

"David, financially, I never run any risk that I can avoid. But you are not a very big risk. Are you going to accept?"

"I have no idea," said Settiniaz, with total sincerity.

He raised a question.

"Why such total anonymity? And why do you dress like this? I hate that dreadful bag!"

"I like it," said Reb smiling. "And I have no desire to have my photograph in the newspapers. No more than I want to have a house, or anything, of any kind."

"You must be worth I don't know how many millions of dollars. At twenty-three!"

"Are you going to accept my proposition?"

Settiniaz stood up, took a few steps, came back to sit down again.

"You are amazing!"

"Have you seen Georges Tarras recently?"

"Not for ages. But I've spoken with him two or three times on the phone."

"And he still hasn't told you anything?"

"About what?" You've already asked me this question, and I don't know what you're talking about."

Reb took out his passport,

"It's fake. I had it made in Argentina, and it cost me one thousand dollars."

228

"Now I understand your fear of publicity," Settiniaz said, as sarcastically as he could.

"That is not the only reason—or the real reason. I could straighten that matter out within a few days. There is another reason, and you should understand that. David?"

"Go to hell."

"David, there is another subject you have been dying to discuss with me. For weeks and months now. Your sister-in-law."

There was a silence. Reb stared at the ceiling.

"I would imagine that your wife also is curious. Even more than you, probably. I will therefore answer this question you have not asked. I have seen Charmian many times; we have even traveled together, several times. We are not going to live together."

"She isn't even in the United States now."

"I know very well where she is. No other questions, David. I won't answer. No more than she did when your wife questioned her, along with the entire Page family. Now you should hurry home and pack your suitcase."

"My suitcase?"

Settiniaz felt lost.

"We are leaving for London, tonight, David. Because you are working with me from now on. Don't worry, I booked first-class seats."

And of course David Settiniaz has the clearest memory of those hours they spent side by side flying over the Atlantic, on the first of many trips they took together.

He remembers the endless and breath-taking enumeration Reb Klimrod proceeded to give him, in his slow, calm voice, which was slightly veiled with fatigue as the hours went by. Settiniaz discovered then that, although the two men that he called the Black Dogs, Lerner and Bercovici, had done a considerable amount of work—working without ever crossing paths— they were far from being the only lawyers involved.

He also remembers that feeling of unreality that took hold of him at some point, making him think he had dreamed up this incredible succession of names, of companies, of businesses, of firms, in the most diverse areas, in New York City, in New York

State, and beyond, in Chicago, Boston, and even Canada, an accumulation that under other circumstances would have seemed delirious.

And each time, Reb mentioned the names of the men he had used, those he had gone through, those in which he had in a way invested his trust. For each transaction, and at that time there must have been at least a hundred, he indicated the exact figures, to the dollar, of the moneys invested, the dates, the specific circumstances, the financial situation; he told how much he expected to earn, as a profit, from each of the nine Baltimore companies, the fourteen in Boston, the twenty-three in Chicago . . .

He presented all this without ever going back to correct an oversight. This for the good reason that he never forgot anything; that everything was fantastically clear in his brain, in his memory, filed and accessible at any moment and with extreme rapidity and precision.

During these hours in the dim cabin of the plane, where most other passengers were sleeping, the lawyer no longer knew what to be surprised about most: the amazing organization Klimrod had set up, the enormous amounts of money involved, or the mind-boggling intellectual structure. Whatever the signs might be, it had a name: genius.

A half-hour before the plane was to land in London, a hand touched Settiniaz's forearm. He opened his eyes and saw the stewardess, offering coffee.

"We are soon to land, David," said Reb. "Did you sleep well?"

"Almost two hours," muttered David.

He drank the coffee, which was appropriately hideous. then he turned around, and recognized, right behind Reb, the short blond Argentine with the strange yellow eyes, of whom he knew only two things: his name, Diego Haas, and what Reb had said about him—"We can speak freely in front of Diego."

Haas smiled at him.

"Ever been to London?"

"Yes," said Settiniaz.

He had that bitter taste in his mouth that comes from being awakened suddenly when one has not had enough sleep. He rubbed his eyes, then his whole face, finally waking up. Through the little window, he could see the coast of Cornwall. It was daylight.

"It's almost two in the afternoon here," said Reb, answering the question Settiniaz was about to ask.

What the devil am I doing here, thought Settiniaz, with a bitterness bordering pure and simple exhaustion. "Just yesterday I was a young lawyer with Wittaker & Cobb, my life was structured, straight, without surprises, thank God. And here I am in a plane flying to England in the company of these two men—one of whom worries me and looks like a hired assassin—having left everything behind me, starting with my wife, who last night, thought I had lost my mind. And besides, did I ever actually say yes?

He asked: "I was not dreaming last night, was I? You were telling me about your businesses?"

Reb began to laugh.

"You were not dreaming."

"That's what I was afraid of," David said somberly.

Suddenly, he almost felt frightened at the thought of this immensity, of this avalanche Reb Klimrod had been describing to him.

He remarked, bitterly: "I hope you don't expect me to remember precisely everything you told me?"

"As soon as we have a moment, I'll go over it all with you again. You can then set it up however you please."

"An accountant would be more useful to you."

"In French, we call that getting up on the wrong side of the bed," said Reb. "No. It's not an expert accountant I need. You will soon realize that. When the time comes."

"Surely there are documents somewhere? Records, contracts? You did not conclude all these transactions with these men and women with a simple handshake?"

"In the vaults of banks, and at different lawyers' offices. You are going to centralize everything. David, don't worry; everything will be fine."

Below, they could now see the sunny soft English countryside.

"And I also told you what we are going to be doing in London: buy a boat or two."

"Boats?"

"Oil tankers, David."

3

In London, a man named Petridis was waiting for them, Nick Petridis, who turned out to be American, from New York, but who, of course, was of Greek origin. Later on David Settiniaz discovered he was the same Petridis who had been instrumental in the Wall Street consolidation.

For the time being, he just listened to him make his report, in the car that had picked them all up, Klimrod, Haas, and himself, at the airport.

Petridis said to Klimrod: "Things are as I described. I won't go back . . . "

"Yes," said Klimrod, "go back to it. From the beginning. David? Listen, please. You don't know about this yet."

"Approximately sixty ships," said Petridis. "Sixteen among them are tankers. The auction for the whole lot will take place here in three days. Already it is known that all the important shipowners will be here: Onassis, Livanos, Niarchos, Goulandris, Ludwig, Getty. Plus some Norwegians, some Englishmen, some representatives of American oil companies, including Gulf. And more. The auction will take place according to the principle of 'by mutual agreement to the highest bidder,' in the offices of Maritime Affairs. Each party bids in writing, with the possibility of overbidding the highest bid by ten percent."

"Do you follow, David?"

"Yes," said Settiniaz, annoyed, but at the same time interested and beginning to feel curiosity.

"May I ask a question?"

"As many as you wish, David."

"Are you going to participate in this sale?"

"Yes."

The gray eyes were shining, amused.

"Yes and no, David. I won't take in part in it myself, but through someone else."

"Me," said Settiniaz in a moment of illumination.

"You. Unless you refuse. You are not in London for that purpose. Let's say that I am simply making the most of your presence."

"And if I had not been here?"

"Nick would have gone. Actually, there is no reason why you both cannot go. Nick, continue, please . . . "

"Now for the owners of the fleet to be sold," said Petridis. "These owners are a family, of British nationality but Rumanian origin, named Major—the English form of their real name, Maiorescu.

"You have to know their story, which is not a common one. One part of the clan left Rumania in 1907, during a peasants' revolt. They went to Great Britain, became English. The rest of the family stayed in Bucharest and Constantsa. And that's when the plot thickened.

"In August 1944, the Russians entered Rumania. In the ports, there were at least forty ships belonging to the Maiorescus, to the one who was the indisputable leader of the clan, Costache Maiorescu, and to his two brothers, Ion and Nichifor. They sensed what was coming and started sending their ships out. But the Russians soon got there, and Costache and his brothers were blocked. Yet they managed to get out, not only their last two boats, but all the Maiorescu family members still on Rumanian soil, by giving themselves as hostages, parading in front of the administrative offices in order to distract the attention of the Russians and the Rumanian Communists.

"It did not take long for the scheme to be discovered. Costache and his brothers were thrown in jail. They are still there. No one even knows where. Maybe in the Soviet Union."

The black Daimler was approaching Hyde Park. Reb seemed not to be listening to Petridis. He had opened a book on his lap and was reading, turning the pages at an incredible speed. Settiniaz had recognized the book: *Ten Days That Shook the World*, by John Reed.

"The Maiorescus—excuse me, the Majors—of London, have tried everything, during the past ten years, to have the leader of the clan liberated, as well as his two brothers. Bucharest hasn't taken the trouble to answer them. Except once, when they said: 'Bring all the ships back to the Black Sea, and then we will talk.' "

The Daimler turned down Park Lane.

"The news broadcast is over," said Petridis, smiling, his black mustache making him look like a merry pirate.

The Daimler stopped in front of the Dorchester.

"What were you expecting, David?" Reb asked. "For me to

233

rent one room for the four of us in Whitechapel? You are going to be in contact with a group of multimillionaires, for the purpose of acquiring a fleet of sixty ships. You need an address that fits your role."

Two suites had been reserved, in the names of David James Settiniaz and Nicholas H. Petridis, both of New York. Nothing in the name of Klimrod or Haas. The latter had left for an unknown destination. Some expressionless and slightly sickly-looking porters, who had come out of the walls like Oscar Wilde ghosts, almost religiously carried the suitcases. Settiniaz soon found himself in the sitting room of his suite, along with Reb, who was contemplating the greenery outside.

Reb said, slowly: "I came to London for the first time in 1937. I was nine years old. It's a city I like very much. Go ahead, David, start asking those questions. . . . "

"You don't really intend to buy all those ships, do you?"

"Of course not. Against those Greek shipowners, who are all connected in some way to each other, brothers-in-law or nephews or uncles, against Getty or Ludwig, I don't have enough clout. Yet."

"So what is the point of this maneuver?"

"I will answer you later; please forgive me for that. It's not that I don't trust you, David, but I'm not sure of anything at this point."

"And my role?"

"You will really try to purchase these ships. In the name of a company I have taken the liberty to name the Diana Marine Company. I hope you're not offended by it. Sometimes I have difficulty finding names for the companies I create. Nick will furnish you with all the documents. About Nick, now: I recommend that you be discreet. He knows that I have made some real-estate transactions in the Wall Street area, but he is unaware of most of them. He does not know what else I do. I even think he believes I represent someone, or a group, maybe even the Mafia, as you yourself thought. I would like to keep it that way. You already know a hundred times more than he ever will, and a day will come when it will be a million to one, in your favor always. You are above him, David, and you will be more so."

"Should I spy on him?" asked Settiniaz in a caustic tone.

The gray eyes remained unfathomable.

"Why not, David? I do not have, and will never have, in a Nick Petridis or in anyone the confidence that I can have and will have in you. That's the way it is."

"You live in a rather cold universe."

Silence. Then Reb nodded.

"Maybe I wasn't given the chance to see it otherwise, or maybe I was born this way."

Suddenly he smiled.

"How about getting back to what brought us to London?"

"So I am to make a sealed bid?"

"Exactly. Unless you let Nick operate alone. Once again, I did not ask you to come with me to be a strawman. I would never ask you to do that, anyway."

"Why then? To watch over Petridis?"

"That could be one reason. But not the real one. I made you an offer. If you accept, which I hope you will but which you have not yet done, you will be the only man in the world— except for what Georges Tarras and Diego Haas might ever know—to know everything, or almost everything, about my business. This is the real reason for your trip to London. In the future, in the event that you say yes, you will always be in the background, in the shadows. I know that this suits your nature, your tastes, your qualities, which are infinitely greater than you suspect. But I hope that once, at least, you will be on the front line. I think I have made myself clear, David."

He was smiling again, that same extraordinarily warm smile.

Settiniaz once again felt lost, miserable, carried away by a torrent, but at the same time, overwhelmed by a strange exhaltation, which almost brought tears to his eyes, and which, for that reason, made him very uncomfortable. He was not used to such excesses.

He finally said: "Must I give you my answer right away?"

"Absolutely not. There is no rush. I will wait however long it takes."

"And you, what will you be doing while I am pretending to want to buy these ships?"

"I will be traveling with Diego."

"For other business or for this?"

"For this." He began to laugh. "And for other business. I rather like doing several things at the same time."

"I'm sure my question is impossibly naïve, but I'll ask it anyway. What you are about to undertake, what you have probably already begun to undertake, is it or will it be illegal?"

"Absolutely not. And I am not sure it will succeed. It's a rather . . . special operation. But certainly not an illegal or immoral one."

"Again there was a silence. Settiniaz looked at him, uncertain of his own feelings.

"You are absolutely sure that I am going to accept. Am I right?"

"In a way," answered Reb, smiling even more.

"Boy," said Settiniaz, "you really exasperate me at certain times."

The light gray eyes, trimmed with dark lashes, had, David thought, a diabolical shine. But amused also.

4

It was night of the same day when Reb Klimrod and Diego Haas landed in Paris. As planned, the two men parted company, Reb not telling Diego where he was going, and Diego going where Reb had told him to.

Diego went to the Georges V Hotel. He was announced and quickly found himself in the presence of two creatures, very obviously of the feminine sex, probably French, unquestionably of easy virture.

"What are you up to now, you little rascal?" asked the man seated between the two creatures.

"Watch out for the blonde," answered Diego, also in Spanish. "She is really a transvestite."

A worried look came over the man's face.

"Are you sure?"

"I was only kidding," said Diego, kissing the blonde on the lips. "Hello, Uncle Oswaldo. How is Mamita?"

"Your mother—that is to say, my sister—is out of her mind with pain, rage, despair, and shame. For weeks she thought you were dead, until you finally decided to send her a postcard from Quebec."

"Montreal," corrected Diego in a muffled voice. He had his head under the blonde's skirt, just to make sure.

"What were you doing in Canada? It's full of bears and snow."

"Business," said Diego, reassured; the blonde was not a man. "And speaking of business, did you set up that appointment for me for tomorrow morning?"

"*Claro que sí*," said Uncle Oswaldo.

He was in his fifties, with the same aquiline nose, the same eyes, the same mouth as his older sister, but whereas these features gave Mamita an air of imperial and definitive will, in him they had softened with the years. Yet, although he was quite rich, with a fortune he had inherited, he actually was, according to Diego, almost intelligent. He looked intently at his nephew, trying to maintain a tone of authority.

"And what exactly are you up to?"

Diego's eyes shone brightly.

"Do I ask you what you are up to with these *señoritas*? When did you arrive in Paris?

"Before yesterday," said Uncle Oswaldo.

"Did you see her before leaving Buenos Aires?"

"Your mother?"

"No," said Diego patiently. "No, not Mamita. *Her.*"

He was referring to Eva Duarte—better known as Eva Perón—who, thanks to Uncle Oswaldo, had, some years ago, landed a job as a journalist at Radio Belgrano.

"Yes," said Uncle Oswaldo. "I saw her. I told her everything you told me to tell her and she agreed."

"With all you give her for her so-called fucking charities, she wouldn't have had the nerve to refuse. And the letter? Did that jerk sign it?"

"Diego, you are speaking of our beloved President and of the most admired woman of the century."

"My ass," said Diego, with his nose buried in the blonde's blouse.

"He signed it. But if your mother knew that I was helping you, or even just talking to you, she would tear my eyes out."

Diego's head, and the rest of him, were making their way through the layers of rustling lace. His voice was once again muffled.

"And if my Aunt Mercedes knew what you were doing with this brunette, there's something else she would tear out."

He met Reb Klimrod again the next day, around noon.

With Reb was a tall man, almost as tall as he was, with large dark, sad eyes, veiled, as it were, with the apparent purpose of covering up the frightening tension he radiated.

"Your friend looks like an anarchist bomb thrower," Diego said to Reb in Spanish. "It looks like his tailor is a secondhand man."

"I understand what you are saying," said the man. "I understand and I speak Spanish."

"How about English? asked Diego, completely unperturbed.

"English, too."

"What about Lapp? Do you speak Lapp?"

"Keep quiet, Diego, please. Diego Haas, Bunim Anielewitch," said Reb, making the introductions. "Is everything in order, Diego?"

"Yes. And I will be quiet."

Diego never knew exactly who Anielewitch was, or the exact nature of his position in the Polish Embassy in Paris—if he really was at the embassy—or how and when Reb and he had met. In fact, Tarras was the first to establish a connection between the Anielewitch in Paris in 1950 and the one in Nuremberg in April of 1946, with whom young Klimrod had worked in the Nakam group.

"Sit down, Diego. We won't be much longer."

The two men began speaking again in Polish, or maybe Yiddish. To Diego it made no difference, since he understood neither, except maybe for a few words of the latter because of its resemblance to German. Diego had met Reb at a little café near the Place de la Nation, in a neighborhood where, until then, he had never set foot. The sun and the clear sky that had welcomed them on their arrival from London had changed into damp, cold gray weather.

After twenty minutes, minutes that Diego spent deciphering a French newspaper, trying to read about a war in Korea and another one in Indochina, Reb said: "Let's go, Diego."

"I'm hungry. I am still keeping quiet, but I am hungry."

"We'll eat something at the airport."

Reb pulled him along, hailed a taxi. Just before climbing into it, Diego looked back. The man named Anielewitch had remained seated and was watching them leave with his disquieting black eyes. Suddenly, and for no good reason, Diego felt a shudder that had nothing to do with the cold weather.

The plane they boarded in the early afternoon of December 29, 1950, took them to Copenhagen, then, after a short stopover, to Helsinki. Their Argentine passports elicited smiles; there weren't that many Argentine tourists in that part of Europe.

Diego remembers mostly that he was shivering during the entire trip from the airport to the hotel, which was not too far from a sort of white cathedral with green domes. After that, his time was taken up by what Reb was doing or saying.

For in Helsinki, as the result of a carefully structured plan, three men were waiting for them. The first one was named Harlan; he was about seventy and was Irish, from the Irish Republic. The second one was a high-placed Russian with pale, icy eyes, his name was Fedorov. The third one—whom Diego was meeting for the first time—was Georges Tarras.

"You get completely undressed and you whip yourself," said Tarras to Diego.

He burst out laughing when he saw the startled expression on the face of the little Argentine.

"Have you never tried a sauna?"

"Where I come from in Argentina," said Diego, "even the cows have one. All they have to do is to stay out in the sun."

Taking all his clothes off, he went into the little room. The suffocating heat made him stagger. He sat down on the bench, thinking: A little oil, some salt, some pepper, some seasoning, and in three minutes I will be medium rare. I hope these guys like their meat on the rare side. He turned to his companion.

"American?"

"Yes." Tarras was smiling. "You don't understand anything about what Reb is doing, do you?"

"I never understand what Reb does anyway. . . . We slap ourselves with these things?"

"These are birch branches. Don't be afraid; really go at it. May I call you Diego? Reb has spoken to me about you."

Diego waited. The man capable of questioning him, of making him speak about Reb Klimrod had not been born yet, and would never be. He did not answer.

"Don't be alarmed. I am not going to ask you any questions. On the contrary, Reb has asked me to bring you up to date, while he is speaking with Harlan and the Russian. Do you know who Harlan is?"

"I don't know anything," said Diego. "Absolutely nothing. It's amazing."

"Harlan is a professional revolutionary. He was in the Irish Republican Army, by the way, along with a man named Lazarus . . . or O'Shea, depending on the day. Familiar names?"

"No," said Diego. "I don't know anyone."

"Harlan was a revolutionary in other places besides Ireland. For instance: he was very close to someone named Ulyanov, better known as 'Lenin.' Have you heard of Lenin?"

"Ha-ha," said Diego.

"Harlan is also one of my oldest friends. It's purely a coincidence. I put Harlan in touch with Reb, and Harlan is going to help Reb try an operation he had thought of himself but on which I would not bet . . ." Tarras stopped and began thrashing Diego on the chest and shoulders. "Don't be afraid to hit hard, my friend! . . . On which I would not bet ten cents. Diego, do you know what Reb wants?"

"No."

"You know very well. Reb wants to acquire these oil tankers, sixteen of them, belonging to the Major, or Maiorescu, fleet. If he goes through normal channels —that is to say, the auction in London—he won't succeed. Even with his millions of dollars available, any one of those Greeks, or Ludwig, or Getty, or a Norwegian or British group would overbid him by ten percent. He doesn't stand a chance."

"Ah?"said Diego, absolutely determined not to say anything about anything. In the state he was in, had someone asked him if he was a man or a woman, he would have had to think before answering.

"Reb has already tried to buy some oil tankers. These past few months I have travelled all over the world in his name. There was a time, right after the war, when you could buy an oil tanker for the price of a Rolls. It wasn't even worth its weight in scrap iron. The Greeks and Ludwig and others bought them by the hundreds. Those happy times are long past, young Diego. The only way to find any today is to have them built. Reb has tried that also. I went to Sweden, to Norway, and to Germany, to visit naval shipyards. Even that didn't work. They refused. You know why?"

"Go on," said Diego.

"Because these Greeks had been there before us; the shipyards of Kiel work for Onassis. Because having an oil tanker built is a long-term investment that Reb cannot afford at this time. Because no bank has agreed to advance that money to Reb. The bankers are prepared to lend him millions of dollars, but not for oil tankers. The risks are too great, according to the bankers. Diego, you should know one thing: a banker will lend you money only if you don't need it. If you really need money, it's because you are in a desperate situation. And if you are in a desperate situation, then you are of no interest to a banker. Or then, it's a nationalized bank. All right, Diego, I don't mind if you hit me, but hold the branch by the other end, please."

"Excuse me," said Diego, pleasantly.

"Reb thinks that the world is going to need oil tankers. Europe especially. Europe actually consumes seventy million tons of oil per year. Reb believes that consumption will increase, that the price of oil will increase, therefore that the cost of shipping oil will increase. You'll tell me . . . No, you don't say much, do you? You'll tell me that he is not the only one to think so, that the oil companies think the same thing. You will ask me—I can see the question in your yellow eyes, through the steam, yes, yes, you are visibly dying of curiosity—you will ask me why the oil companies don't put together these fleets they know they will need themselves, and why they prefer to help the development of private fleets. Are you asking me this, Diego?"

"Absolutely not."

"I will answer by telling you that the oil companies would rather leave this up to the Greeks, the Norwegians, and to anybody else, because to invest in a fleet is, after all, risky business. There is nothing more costly than a ship that remains docked. And because they themselves are involved in enormous investment programs in the fields of prospecting and refining. The price of an oil refinery, my dear Diego, is actually five times

241

the price of a T2 oil tanker. You know, of course, what a T2 is?"

"The ones with two oars on each side?"

"It's a ship of sixteen thousand tons, like the ones used by the U.S. Navy during the war. Stop hitting me, please. We are going out to roll ourselves in the snow."

"NOOOOOOO!" screamed Diego, terrified.

But he did not stand a chance, two enormous Finns appeared, lifted him, and efficiently threw him outside into the freezing snow.

"Tomorrow, when we get to Moscow," snickered Tarras, sitting bare-assed in the snow, "you'll be acclimated to the cold weather."

"On November 16, 1917," said Harlan, "I saw, on the *Zagorodny*, at around seven o'clock, two thousand Red Guards, singing the *Marseillaise*. Their blood-red flags blew in the black wind of the icy night."

"Very good," said Reb Klimrod.

Harlan stared at him fixedly, ferociously.

"Have you read Reed's book, *Ten Days That Shook the World*?"

"No," said Reb.

Harlan nodded savagely.

"If you had said yes, I swear I would have left you standing right here, you and your idiotic story."

"Lucky for me," said Reb, placidly.

"John Reed was just an amateur, a bluffer. And he was an American! What could he understand? When I think that they have buried him in the Kremlin wall! All that because the idiot caught typhus! Had it been mumps, he would have died in his bed in Fergus Falls, Minnesota, blessing his shares of General Motors. Next to what I have done!"

Walking a few feet back, Fedorov was smiling at no one or nothing in particular. His icy look never left Klimrod or Diego Haas, as if he were afraid they would suddenly fly away. Three other men were following a little farther back, looking falsely indifferent, like classic detectives shadowing someone. The group was walking down Gorky Street in Moscow. Two hours before, they had landed on Russian soil. The cold was sharp but not disagreeable; there were still traces of snow but the sky was clear.

The colored domes of St. Basil's were shining brightly, and an orderly line had formed to visit Lenin's tomb. Harlan was walking at his own speed, leading the group, and talking all the while.

"I met Iosif, Stalin, that is," he was saying, "when he was still commissar for nationalities, in Petrograd. Before that, he was the co-director of *Pravda*, with Leo Kamenev. Did you know Leo?"

"Not really," said Klimrod.

Two black Pobedas were slowly approaching. Harlan continued to pour out his recollections. The cars stopped by the curb; their drivers got out, opened the doors. At the same moment, the men from the ministry of state security closed up, all of a sudden. Oh, Mamita, Diego was thinking, if you could see your son here with the Reds! Harlan got into the first car with Fedorov; Diego and Reb climbed into the second one. The windows of the car had curtains covering them.

Diego whispered, in Spanish: "Are we going to get out of this country?" He was about to continue when his eyes met those of one of the policemen riding with them.

"Speak English," said Reb.

They drove along for about fifteen minutes, very slowly. There was a stop, a checkpoint, under an archway. They drove on, for no more than ten yards. Fedorov appeared and, in slow but correct English, invited them to get out. Looking up, Diego saw that they were in a vast courtyard, icy in all respects, with civilian guards everywhere. Again a checkpoint, this time inside a hall with a large staircase. There was a discussion between Harlan and Fedorov, which Diego could not follow: begun in Russian, it ended up in Polish, with Reb's participation.

"Diego," Reb said, "only one of us can go up to see the Minister. Stay here and wait."

"Don't be too long."

With stabs of fear in this stomach, he saw Reb leave with Harlan, Fedorov, and a fourth man. They went up the staircase and disappeared. He finally sat down on a chair that was offered to him. Once, when he wanted to stand up to stretch his legs, he was made to understand that he had better remain where he was.

After perhaps an hour a big commotion could be heard upstairs, with much agitation and evident irritability. At the top of the stairs, a stout man with glasses appeared. He came down, but before he reached Diego, three men came to stand between the

Argentine and the stranger. The latter glanced up briefly and walked out, in the middle of a frightened group. He got into a large car and drove away.

Two more hours went by, and Diego was picturing himself in Siberia, dragging a ball on each foot, or with his eyes burned by a red-hot poker. It was Reb's fake passport, especially, which he himself had had made, that worried him.

But Reb, Harlan, and Fedorov finally appeared. Reb's face was impassive.

He said to Diego: "Not now; be quiet."

Outside, night had fallen in the sparsely lit city. When, at last, Diego was alone with Reb, in the Metropole, he opened his mouth to speak.

"Not yet," said Reb. "Be quiet."

They spent the evening with Harlan and Fedorov, the first one drinking as much as the second, neither seeming affected by it in the least. They had dinner in a restaurant called Araqvi.

"Tell me about your uncle Oswaldo and of all this land he owns back in our home, Argentina," said Reb, when they got back to their hotel. It was his way of saying: "And don't talk about anything else."

The next day, it was the same routine: cars with curtains, escorts, endless waiting in lobbies, morning and afternoon, for Diego Haas, Reb and Harlan, along with Fedorov, seemed to be visiting, one by one, every ministry in Moscow.

The following day was December 31. In the evening, they took a plane to Helsinki. And it was only there, walking out of any indiscreet earshot on the vast esplanade loaded with trams, that Reb said, smiling: "You didn't understand anything, of course?"

"Why be surprised?" said Diego bitterly. "I am sulking. Reb? Did we really go to see the Russkies? Did I just have a nightmare?"

"We went there."

"Who was that guy with the glasses and the terrifying eyes?"

"Lavrenti Beria."

"*Madre de Dios*," said Diego. "*The* Beria?"

"Yes."

"And you spoke to him?"

"Yes. And not only to him, Diego. To Stalin. And I even got what I wanted."

He took his Argentine friend by the arm.

"And it's extremely simple, Diego. First, there is this wheat that your Uncle Oswaldo obtained the right to export from President Perón, with the help of your friend Evita. Nick Petridis, or, more precisely, his brother Tony, will have it loaded onto this cargo ship of mine, and on others. Are you with me?"

"I'm trying."

"The wheat will arrive in the Soviet Union, in a port on the Black Sea. In exchange for the wheat: paintings, by Lanonov, Malevich, Tatlin, Lissitzky, Rodchenko, two by Natalia Goncharova, three by Kandinsky, three by Chagall, two by Rabin, and a few by Sobolov. And others. What's more, I've even been promised a few Cézannes and some Matisses, not to mention two or three Picassos, which had been bought by Shchukin and Morozov, the two connoisseurs you've probably heard of, before the Big Night set up by Lenin, with Harlan's help. But he won't keep that last promise, Diego."

"No?"

"No. He may profess to have the deepest disgust for decadent-rotten-Western-capitalistic-imperialistic painting, but he is not a fool, and someone is bound to tell him—well, that's not certain; they are all terrified of that sick old man—that a Cézanne or a Picasso is worth as much as gold to us crazy Westerners. Yet, Diego, he has arranged to give me, to give me personally, a Niko Pirosmanschivili, a painter who was Georgian, like himself, and, by the way, like Georges Tarras."

Diego was looking at Reb. He didn't know any of the names Reb was mentioning in a sputtering enumeration. With perhaps the exception of Chagall and Kandinsky, and of course Cézanne, Matisse, and Picasso. Diego knew almost nothing about painting, and it meant nothing to him. But he knew his Reb Klimrod, and the man's silences, his almost total muteness, which could last weeks if not months, and then, suddenly, his excited eruptions of emotion—like the one at this moment—when something stirred him and made him then talk for hours on end. Diego never tried to interrupt him. After all, it was during these moments, by revealing the fire he had inside, beneath the tranquil surface,

245

that Reb became human. So Reb spoke and Diego was quiet, as they walked endlessly through the icy rectangular streets of Helsinki, the center of which was designed like a checkerboard, in the Russian manner.

Reb finally smiled and said: "Diego?"

"Yes, Reb."

"I am boring you, eh?"

"What a thought!" said Diego, uisng just the right pinch of sarcasm. He asked: "And what shall we do with all these paintings? Open a gallery? We could do that, set up stands on Fifth Avenue, on Regent Street, under the arcades of the Rue de Rivoli, or in Buenos Aires, on Junín Street, or even in Tamanrasset, or in Ulan Bator, and we could sell them to the passers-by. Thanks to which we could then pay Uncle Oswaldo for his wheat, provided he agrees to a payment over seventy-five years."

"No."

"We are not going to do that?"

"No. I already have a buyer, Diego. In the United States. In exchange for the paintings, themselves exchanged for the wheat, the buyer will provide a completely set up textile plant, including the technicians, which will be installed in Argentina. And, in exchange for this plant, the government of your country will make arrangements with the Soviet Union for regular wheat deliveries."

"Is that ever simple! It's all clear to me now!" said Diego somberly. "And I suppose that as a commission for all these transactions, of which you are the enigmatic instigator, you will receive sixteen cans of paint, red of course, with which you can repaint the stacks of those oil tankers you won't be able to buy at the auction anyway?"

Reb burst out laughing, which was still exceptional for him, and indicated to what point, for once, he was giving in to the exhilaration of his triumph.

"Diego, it's true. We will receive a commission from the Argentines, for this operation and for the others, even if these deliveries of Argentine wheat to the Soviet Union take place over the next thirty or forty years. But I asked for something else, and, as of this moment, I have obtained it. That was the reason for the messages I received at the hotel, when we arrived in Helsinki. Two hours ago, Costache, Ion, and Nichifor Maiorescu arrived in Zurich. Tomorrow they will be in London, with their families.

"And Costache has agreed, the family in London has agreed: I won't be pulverized in the auction by any Greek or by anyone else, for the simple reason that the sixteen oil tankers will be withdrawn from the lot proposed by the Majors in the mutual-agreement sale. Before the sale. The oil tankers will be sold to me separately. And I will pay for them with the money that will be lent to me by the man who is buying all these paintings, who is a fanatical collector but who is also one of the principal share-holders of Urban Life, that insurance company to whom I sold the Wall Street property. Let's go have dinner, Diego. Georges Tarras has invited us to celebrate the New Year. And we won't repaint the stacks of the tankers red: that's Niarchos's color. Or in green. Green decks, that's Onassis. I am very hungry, Diego, very hungry."

Georges Tarras had given up Harvard and his professorship for good. He would spend the best part of his time rummaging through books and writing, rather than dragging, year after year, through the same course, or almost the same. His wife, Shirley, had pushed him to accept, not only because the change brought about important financial advantages (Klimrod had offered him five times his salary as a professor, and had proposed a ten-year advance on that salary), but also because she had, she said, maternal feelings toward Reb.

Tarras was enjoying tremendously his peregrinations through Scandinavia and Germany, as well as his search along the Atlantic coast of the U.S. for available oil tankers. He was then fifty-one years old, had taught for almost a quarter of a century, and except for the time he spent in Austria and in Nuremberg right after the war, had not taken much time off, going from the books he was reading to those he was writing. And the lack of success of his books didn't bother him in the least.

Of all the men in the world who were to know Reb Klimrod, he was the most clear-sighted and the one who felt the most natural love for him; the love of a father. He had never really recovered from the emotional shock he had experienced in Mauthausen, in May of 1945, at the sight of the boy resurrected from the dead.

5

After spending only one night in Helsinki on their return from Moscow, Klimrod, Tarras, and Haas had gone straight to London. They arrived in time for lunch, "which really wasn't worth the hurried trip from Finland," according to Diego.

That same afternoon, January 1, they met Costache Maiorescu, a small man who at first, without saying a word, shook Reb Klimrod's hand for a long time, and then said, in broken English, how grateful he was and how he was certain that all the promises the clan had made would be kept. His captivity, which he declined to discuss, had physically marked him, but it was clear that, now that he was free, he had once again assumed full control. He shook his head when Klimrod explained to him that the twenty-nine million six hundred thousand dollars, the agreed price for the tankers, had not yet been cleared by the insurance company. On New Year's Day, the banks were closed.

"Details. These tankers are yours. God knows you earned them! A man capable of pulling us, my brothers and me, out from where we were is probably more than capable of finding thirty million dollars. Klimrod?"

"Yes?"

"It was no accident that you sent us, I mean that you sent to my family in London, this Lerner and later this Bercovici, to suggest this extraordinary arrangement, was it?"

"They work for me."

"But they are of Rumanian origin, as we are. It certainly was not just pure coincidence."

Klimrod smiled; "They are simply the best." He raised his hand mischievously. "And I accept the invitation to lunch tomorrow that you are about to propose. I can very well understand that this evening you would rather celebrate within the circle of your family. My favorite Rumanian dish is *tocana de vitel*, veal stew, with *mititei*, spicy sausages. And, to finish, *dulceata*."

It was not so much Reb's knowledge of Rumanian gastronomy, including the crystallized fruit seasoned with vinegar, that surprised Tarras and Settiniaz. It was the breadth of the maneuver, which, for the purpose of acquiring sixteen oil tankers from under the noses of the largest fleet owners of the time, had within a few days mobilized Tarras and Settiniaz, the Petridis brothers, plus Diego Haas, Harlan, and only Marx knows how many Soviet ministers and high-ranking officials, including Beria and Stalin, plus Evita and Juan Perón, a probable secret agent from the East, an Argentine multimillionaire, who was Diego's uncle, and a second multimillionaire, this one an American, an impassioned collector of Russian art and a shareholder in one of the largest insurance companies in the United States. And now they had just learned that during this same time, Reb had also moved two other pieces on his chessboard, his two best Black Dogs.

Reb had said to Settiniaz, when he almost kidnapped him to go to London: "I hope that once, at least, you will be on the front line." In Settiniaz's eyes, the hope had been accomplished.

There followed strange weeks and months. Or at least they seemed strange to men who, with the constant exception of Diego Haas, were not used to seeing Klimrod at work, running fifty businesses or more at the same time, more often than not with different teams, who didn't know of each other's existence; using men who would probably have been most surprised to learn, if put in each other's presence, that they were all working for the same man. And then, once ideas were set forth and orders given, he would disappear, sometimes for long periods of time, and reappear suddenly, just when his presence was needed, like a chess player playing one hundred games at the same time.

From mid-July 1950 to the spring of 1955, after his purchase of the oil tankers (while at the same time he was conducting the Wall Street operations and was working with Lilian Morris on the expansion of Jaua Food, with Roger Dunn on the development of his publishing enterprises, and seeing to the installation of his restaurant chains, and more), Reb Klimrod retreated more and more into a hermitic anonymity. His name was still never used in any operation, and if it did happen that he had to appear in person, he always did so using another name or concealing his true position in the matter. He expanded his system of using trust agreements. He made amazingly few errors in the choices he made of those who were to help him, either at his side or in his name. For trustees, he usually chose U.S. citizens of recent

249

immigration, mostly from Poland. He was also one of the first to make full use of companies based in Panama and Curaçao.

Settiniaz calls this period the "breakthrough." For practical purposes, it was founded on the ever-increasing number of the men he called Black Dogs. The term might seem undignified, almost insulting. But he didn't mean it in that sense. For him, it expressed the fanatical devotion of these lawyers and their absolute ferocity when it came to defense of the King's interests. After Lerner and Bercovici, as years went by they became more and more numerous, coming from all over the world, secretly, and alone, to the offices on Fifty-eighth Street.

The first few days of 1951 in London were one of the rare times when several members of the future staff of the King were together at one time: Tarras, Settiniaz, the Petridis brothers, and Lerner and Bercovici. They formed a nucleus, which grew considerably.

Tony Petridis left for Argentina. His brother took over the freight operations needed to complete the transports to be carried out by the *Java Blue Rose*, whose cargo Klimrod had acquired thanks to the Roarke transaction.

Tarras left for the States, to do some prospecting in the naval shipyards of the East Coast, especially in Maryland and Massachussets. He also went to Liberia, and to Japan, to start preparing the Japanese operation.

Settiniaz finally returned home to New York. He resigned from Wittaker & Cobb and began setting himself up in the offices on East Fifty-eighth Street, where he is today, and started the recruiting for which Klimrod had given him a free hand.

One day in February, Reb Klimrod came for the first time to the new offices. In spite of the freezing weather and snow-covered streets of New York, he was wearing only cotton pants, and shirt and his old leather jacket with the fur collar. He was lucky to get through the door. As it was, he was made to wait almost half an hour, which he spent chatting pleasantly with the receptionist. Had Settiniaz not happened to come out of his office, he would not have known he was there.

"Why the devil didn't you say who you were? I was told a certain Anton Beck was waiting to see me."

"This girl you have here is quite charming," answered Reb

innocently, and Settiniaz was incapable of deciding whether it was feigned or not.

He added: "David, do you remember the night we went to London? I gave you a rundown of my activities. You were unable to take any notes then, But I think we can do it now. It will take a little time, so if you have any other engagements, perhaps you might cancel them, unless they are imperative. Can we get started?"

And with that, they worked for eighteen hours straight. Eighteen hours with no interruption other than to swallow down sandwiches and coffee. Reb would alternate between sitting across from David, his legs stretched out and his wide-open eyes staring at the ceiling, and hands deep in his pockets, pacing back and forth, with the annoying habit of straightening the frames of paintings or diplomas when he was actually disrupting their balance, knowingly.

Reciting all along. Reciting endlessly, quietly, never using notes, memos, or, apparently, any mnemonic system.

". . . Chicago, October 11, 1950, name of company: Shamatari Food System, Incorporated. Trustee: Anatoli Parewski, born on March 23, 1909, in Brest Litovsk. American citizen. Married, two children. Profession: electrical contractor. Address: 1096 North Kingsburgh Street. Assets of the company: ten thousand dollars. Earnings as of last January 31: six hundred twenty-three thousand five hundred sixty-seven dollars. Personal estate and real estate: three thousand one hundred fifty dollars. Lending bank: Naval Fairfax Bank. Amount of credit: fifty thousand dollars. Monthly payment, including interest: nine hundred sixteen dollars. Attorney: Moe Abramowicz, already mentioned, from Chicago. Responsible manager: Herbert Miewski, who can be reached at the company headquarters: 106 Roosevelt Drive or at his home, 985 Elm Drive West. Stock deposits, seal, and account books can be found at the Michigan State Bank, box number 45219 XC, combination number . . ."

And: "Detroit, November 9, 1950, name of company . . ."

And so on. At one point, Settiniaz, incredulous, pretended to have made an error.

"Excuse me. I am having trouble rereading myself. . . . What is the exact address of Beppard, the trustee of Reichenau in Baltimore?"

"He does not live in Baltimore, but in Frederick, also in Maryland. And his address is 67 Lincoln Place. David, please don't make me waste my time. . . ."

Two hundred and eighteen companies, run by one hundred and thirty-one trustees, men like Zbyniev Cybulski and Diego Haas (his was the only name Settiniaz recognized). Men, but also women; one of the things that surprised Settiniaz was the abundance of women trustees.

"As if you had recruited them out of a women's college . . ."

"They are usually not of college age. And I like working with women; they are usually more dependable than men."

Diego Haas alone represented almost twenty-five companies.

"Reb, this is crazy. Sooner or later, the Treasury Department will see a connection."

"So? All these companies pay their taxes. And it is your job to study the situation created by the juxtaposition of all these companies, and to draw legal and financial conclusions. I will pay all the taxes I am supposed to, as long as you and your team, and all the other financial specialists you wish to consult, tell me that I really must. You once said that all I needed was an accountant. You can see now that I expect you to do much more than merely collate my business affairs. It is your task to centralize everything, to examine the books of all these companies, to point out the slightest anomaly, of any kind. And you have to see to it that at no time, under any pretext, am I actually named. I don't want to appear, and you know it. Can you do that, David?"

"I can try, at any rate," answered Settiniaz, a little overwhelmed.

"You'll do it, David."

"Will you be forming other companies?"

"Most probably. We are trying to bring things up to date through today. From this point on, the lawyers will come tell you themselves of the companies they have formed, and they will give you the information. You must check everything, of course. Don't trust anyone, David, please."

"Not even Georges Tarras?"

"Not even Tarras. You will be told of each new business by two distinct sources: a lawyer like Benny Bercovici, Lerner, or Abramowicz, who will have drawn up the contracts and prepared everything, and my official agent. On all matters concerning maritime shipping, you will be dealing with the Petridis brothers and Tarras. There will be other Petridises, in other areas. Shall we continue now, David? Montreal, September 29, 1950, name of company . . ."

And the Black Dogs did begin to visit Settiniaz. They were all strikingly alike, Jews of Rumanian origin for the most part (especially during the early fifties and when the businesses were in Europe or the United States), alike at least in their furtive behavior, their way of saying only what was strictly essential, their mafiosi airs, their deadly seriousness, and their ruthless loyalty to Klimrod. Settiniaz never had the occasion, or the inclination, to establish any contact with them other than professional. Of Bercovici, for example, whom he saw often for more than a quarter of a century, he only discovered quite by chance that he was married, had four children, and was a collector of porcelain and a lover of literature. But only outside of work— and Benny Bercovici, especially during the early years he served the King, worked more than sixty hours per week.

The two Petridis brothers, Nick and Tony, were almost identical. They managed and made decisions and mostly appeared officially, heading all the trustees and the Panamanian and Liberian companies. But they were equal to a Lerner or a Bercovici as far as discretion was concerned, and they almost matched them as far as work capacity went. Their method of avoiding answering a question that, according to them, did not warrant one was slightly different: instead of retreating into a tomblike silence, they would smile beneath their identical mustaches and would start telling far-fetched tales completely unrelated to the subject at hand. The result was the same: they revealed only what was strictly necessary. In the organization set up by Klimrod in December 1950 and January 1951, they rapidly became specialized, taking care only of the King's maritime businesses, working in collaboration with other specialists, two Scots in particular, but controlling everything. They were not just Black Dogs; they were more like ministers or barons to whom Klimrod had entrusted a fief.

Other men appeared over the years, with similar attributes and responsibilities, but in other areas or in other parts of the world.

One of these was Paul Soubise, a Frenchman with whom Settiniaz, probably due to likemindedness, or maybe just their common language, struck up a friendship that continues today.

There was Tudor Anghel, a Californian in spite of his name, which was Rumanian, a regular Black Dog at the beginning, who eventually climbed up in the hierarchy to occupy a more important position, becoming the key man in Klimrod's West Coast operations until his death in 1976.

There was also the Mexican Francisco Santana, with whom Settiniaz also became friends, a specialist—and quite a specialist—in tax havens.

In New York, for all operations requiring a façade that would inspire confidence in the traditional WASP establishment, Klimrod, probably with Tarras's help, since many of these men had been his students at Harvard, called upon existing law firms whose principals had the right names.

Roger Dunn, for printing and audio-visual matters, and Ernie Gozchiniak, for the restaurant chains and the Jaua Food Organization, stood among the barons in the North American territory.

Outside the country, a few names emerged, for the very reason that they maintained their distance, and thus became, truly, King's Men. This was the case with the Swiss Aloïs Knapp, and his successor, Thadeus Töpfler, the Chinese Hang, the Lebanese Nessim Shahadzé, the fabulous specialist on the exchange market, who was also responsible for dealing with the Eastern countries. For hotel chains, there was British Ethel Court.

And there was the entire South American contingent, including the Argentine Jaime Rochas—not to be confused with Ubaldo Rocha, the Brazilian, who was, almost like Diego Haas, a special case—and two Brazilian lawyers, one from Rio, the other from São Paulo, Jorge Socrates and Emerson Coëlho.

Settiniaz discovered the existence of the South Americans only much later on. It was a parallel staff. None of these men knew each other. For Nick Petridis, for example, Klimrod was a shipowner and that was all. For Santana, he was an oilman who was involved in real estate. And so on. The same separation existed for the Black Dogs. Thus it happened that three or four Black Dogs appeared in Settiniaz's offices at the same time, or Nick Petridis and Tudor Anghel, and passing each other in the hall did not know they had been sent by the same man.

Above them all, occupying a special position, a most exceptional one, just like David Settiniaz's and knowing almost as many things about the King as he, but in other areas, serving up to the end as a sort of "personal and private counselor," there was Georges Tarras.

He arrived around April 20 and walked through the offices, spread out over two floors (a third floor was taken over only in 1964).

Coming back into David Settiniaz's private office, he shook his head and said: "What has happened to us, David? Six years ago, almost to the day, we made the acquaintance, under rather special circumstances, of a strange young fellow, who left quite an impression on us, even then. . . . Did you recognize him when he reappeared before you? When was it, anyway?"

Settiniaz hesitated, hating himself for hesitating, and almost ashamed of his mistrust.

"Last July 16. The day of my birthday and of my marriage. Yes, I recognized him immediately."

"For me, it was early in September. And I also recognized him right away. More than that: I immediately recalled his last name and his two given names. I could see him standing in my office at Mauthausen, looking at those horrible photographs I was stupid enough to hang all over my walls, and telling me in his calm voice: 'I don't feel as if I've been defeated by the United States of America. . . . What gives you the right to ask me these questions?' And the kid could hardly stand up!"

Tarras looked at Settiniaz, remained quiet for a moment, then suddenly burst out laughing.

"And here we are, six years later, you and I who have known each other for twelve or thirteen years, both of us afraid to open our mouths for fear of betraying one of the awesome secrets of His Majesty Reb Michael Klimrod! Have we gone mad, David, or have we contracted his madness?"

"I do believe you're right," said Settiniaz, who was also laughing. "I am happy to see you again, Georges."

"Me, too, young David. You were always my favorite student, even though you have no sense of humor. By the way—I say 'by the way,' but, of course it's totally unrelated—by the way, I have just returned from Japan. I did not go there to sightsee.

255

He sent me there, and he asked me to come tell you about it. I am supposed to tell you everything. I will tell you everything. Take notes, Master Settiniaz, please. Lesson Fourteen, or How to Form the World's Largest Oil-Tanker Fleet without Using One Penny from Your Own Pocket."

For the next hour, with exactly the same tone of voice he used at Harvard when he explained that law was never just a "group of underhandedly and deliberately contradictory rules having no purpose other than to give the appearance of reason to the most demented transactions," he told David of Reb's latest initiative and what they were hoping to gain from it.

"Onassis, especially, among the Greeks, had the idea of scrounging through the ruins of the German shipyards near Hamburg, Bremen, Kiel, to mention just a few. Of course, the Germans, things being what they were, gave him an exceptional welcome: they are going to build, and are currently building, loads of ships for the above-mentioned Greeks. Reb figured that another country, which had also taken a beating in the last war, might be in a similar welcoming position. Hence, Japan, Master Settiniaz. The place is called Kure. To the right of Hiroshima, if you were ever to go to Hiroshima, and why would you? Young David, in preparation for their war against us in the Pacific, the Japanese sent the largest ships ever built out to sea, the *Yamato* and the *Musachi*, about sixty-four thousand tons. I might mention in passing that we sank them, but the fact remains that they know what building a ship means. And they have agreed to do it for Reb, who ordered six oil tankers, two of which—listen to this—will have a capacity of fifty thousand tons. They will be the largest ever. Even Goulandris's seem small in comparison."

"And the money?" asked Settiniaz, with his ever-present practical sense.

"Nick Petridis will come see you and give you all the contracts. Without going into details, this is how it will work: Nick has obtained from Shell or Gulf, or maybe both, long-term charter contracts. Fifteen years, for the former Maiorescu oil tankers. Those represent hefty sums. And guaranteed returns, against which Reb has negotiated other moneys, additional moneys, to finance the Japanese construction. And since he had already signed other contracts, short-term ones, three to five years, depending on the case, for three of these six ships he is having built, he was able, thanks to this other series of contracts, to start a new series of loans . . . with which he will either repurchase . . . Why are you looking at me like that, Master Settiniaz?"

"This is crazy."

"What did you expect, with him? Let me continue. He will either repurchase or have more of them built, but next time here, in the States. There is talk of the naval yards of Sparrows Point and of Bethlehem Steel, if I understood correctly. All of this involving close to three hundred million dollars. He takes insane risks."

"I know," said Settiniaz, simply.

When Tarras was finished, Settiniaz could feel, on the tip of his tongue, sentences like "And you don't know the half of it, Georges" and "If it was only in one area that he took such phenomenal risks, I wouldn't shudder each time someone brings me a new file." As he learned of the hugeness of the growing empire, and of the conditions of its birth—almost exclusively founded on credit—his concern grew, however much he trusted Reb Klimrod's uncommon capacities and in spite of the strict adherence to the system of airtight companies.

But he revealed none of this and remained quiet, keeping his promise not to trust anyone, "even Georges Tarras."

"All right, David. And the jury is instructed to disregard this last question that I almost asked you: would you like to have lunch with me?"

"Not today. Perhaps next time."

Tarras got up. He was smiling but there was a slight tightness around his mouth.

"See you soon."

They parted, each feeling a first breach in their almost perfect friendship, a breach that never widened, but that, in the next four years, never had any reason to disappear.

During those four years, Settiniaz saw Reb only at intervals of several weeks or as much as months. In the beginning, he was concerned about these absences, as he was about the confidences that were entrusted to him, but as time went by he began to find them both normal, or, at least, ordinary.

Settiniaz has the figures. He is the only one to have them. And he points out that these figures do not represent the total of Klimrod's businesses that were in his charge, just as he points out that he has no way of knowing how many other businesses were run by the King. In the spring of 1982, trying to come up with a complete list, he arrived at the figure of one thousand six hundred and eighty-seven companies and Klimrod's name did not appear in a single one of them. Not one. Though there was indeed *one* company in the name of R.M. Klimrod. Tarras remarked to Settiniaz that there could very well exist somewhere else in the world, in Switzerland, in France, or elsewhere, another David Settiniaz, doing exactly the same work and feeling the same amazement faced by the same list!

In May of 1955, David Settiniaz wrote (without mentioning to whom it was addressed) a quick report that gave an overview of the areas in which the King was involved:

Jaua Food Organization and thirty-seven companies connected with it, with a value of one hundred and sixty million dollars.

Communications businesses, representing nearly four hundred and twenty million dollars. Included are:

advertising agencies
two weekly television-program publications (created in 1953)
travel and recreation organizations
the S.O.S. Migrants agencies;
19 radio stations broadcasting in nine languages (fall of 1952)
one television station (summer of 1954), a second one is planned

Roger Dunn is the official owner of all these businesses (sixty to eighty percent). In reality, the trust agreement binding him to Reb gives him ten percent (not so bad).

Newspaper delivery service, developed well geographically (California, winter of 1951) and vertically, with the necessary legal precautions. Garages for the maintenance of the vehicles, contracts with foreign companies, partial or total repurchases of these companies. Added to these are:

trucking and warehousing businesses
delivery business
industrial maintenance and emergency repairs (September of 1953).

Estimated value: three hundred and eighty million dollars.

Four restaurant chains. Geography: from Canada to the Mexican border. Organized competition. Suppliers: Jaua or one of its affiliates. West Coast exploitation projected for 1956; contacts made with a British group to break into the European market.

Supermarket chains (apparently independent of the restaurants). Trustee for both areas: Lillian Morris. Total value: four hundred million. Six hundred and thirty, counting the plants and co-operative farms (1953).

Real estate assets: one hundred and fifty million dollars. Wall Street operation not yet completed. Projects for 1957?

Ships. Twenty-nine different companies. Tonnage: three million six hundred and twenty-eight thousand, of which two million seven hundred are oil tankers, the rest ordinary cargo ships (source: Nick Petridis). One oil tanker of twenty-eight thousand tons: about two million dollars. Estimated total: three hundred and eighty-five million dollars (30 April 1955).

Liquid assets (speculations): one hundred and nine million one hundred and twenty-four thousand (30 April 1955).

Total evaluation? Cost of credit, costly organization to protect Reb, high number of associates . . .

Settiniaz concluded that in 1955, almost ten years to the day since Mauthausen, less than five years since he arrived in New York at a newspaper stand, Reb Michael Klimrod, not yet twenty-seven years old, was worth over a billion dollars.

And fewer than five people knew about it.

At the beginning of May 1955, Georges Tarras returned to New York, back from another job he had just completed. "Yes, David, for him. You turned down my invitation to lunch three or four years ago. Do you remember? How about today?"

They went to the Caneton, on Wall Street. Sipping his usual martini, Settiniaz recognized at least five of Klimrod's men sitting at neighboring tables and answered their salutations with a simple nod and a smile. Tarras's sharp eye caught these exchanges.

"Are you developing a secret sense of power, David?"

"In a way," said Settiniaz, embarrassed and slightly annoyed, because the remark had some truth in it. As a result of dealing with all these men, about whom he knew everything, whereas they knew almost nothing, he did in fact have a certain feeling of power.

"And you've even started using some of his expressions: in a way."

"Let's talk about something else."

They ordered, and after the captain left, Tarras said suddenly:

259

"I have some things to tell you, David. For starters, let's talk about your sister-in-law."

Settiniaz looked at him, surprised.

"Listen," said Tarras, "I know I must look like a busybody, sticking my nose where it doesn't belong, but don't always believe what you see. What does your wife's family think of Charmian?"

"I don't understand."

"When did you last see Charmian? And I don't mean just you, David. I mean Diana, and your in-laws."

"She spent Christmas in New York with us. As she does every year."

"And you didn't notice anything?"

David Settiniaz was a placid, peaceful man. To his own surprise, these last years, as he was organizing all of Reb Klimrod's operations, he had discovered that he had some undeniably useful qualities, as an organizer especially. Reb had said to him, in a hotel in London, that he had qualities he didn't suspect, and time seemed to be proving him right.

But Tarras's question elicited a flow of violent and contradictory feelings, almost overwhelming him. He was irritated by Tarras's nosy indiscretion and worried to see confirmed his own fears about Charmian. Moreover, he was, as often, feeling the pressure of the silent war waged against him by his mother-in-law and his wife, who both accused him of not having kept "this Klimrod at a distance."

"Notice what?" he asked, with a bitterness that was unusual for him.

"Charmian is unstable. She is probably the most beautiful woman I will ever see under the sun, but her family should have taken care of her a long time ago."

Tarras finished his martini, looking straight into Settiniaz's eyes.

"David, please don't get angry. It just happens that I know more than I should and more than I want to know. When did you last see Reb? David, please don't look at me that way."

"Last February 12, and the day after. We spent the night working."

"And since then?"

"No."

"David, he told me he had organized all his businesses, all of

260

them—though I am aware of only a small part of them—in such a way that they could develop on their own. Is that right?"

"Yes."

"So that it is not strange for several months to go by without your having any contact with him?"

Settiniaz frowned.

"What are you getting at?"

"This is one of the things I am supposed to tell you, David. He is going to disappear for some time. Don't ask me where or why; I don't know. I am simply supposed to let you know, although he should have taken care of this himself."

"For how long?"

"No idea. I asked him the question myself, with no result. . . . I think I wouldn't mind another martini."

"And the other things you're supposed to tell me?"

"They are about Charmian. You've probably known that she and Reb . . . "

He didn't finish his sentence. Deliberately. He was not sure of what David knew of the strange relationhip between Charmian Page and Reb Klimrod.

"I know," said Settiniaz, "that she and Reb have been seeing each other frequently during the past few years. But she has never spoken of him to us, and they have never appeared together."

He noticed Tarras's sharp glance.

"Has something happened to Charmian?"

"I really think we need two more martinis, one for you and one for me."

6

This had happened three weeks earlier.

Georges Tarras left London, where he had been, with Tony Petridis and one of the Scottish lawyers, on some shipping business, and had, via Paris, reached Marseilles. There, as a cable had indicated, a seaplane was waiting. After a flight of one and a half hours, the plane touched down on the sea, a few hundred yards from a rough reddish coastline, which was quite beautiful. Nothing happened for a while. Then a motorboat appeared from among the rocks and came alongside the float of the plane. Diego Haas was at the controls, and alone.

"You're just in time," remarked Tarras. "I was contemplating playing Monte Cristo."

"The island of Montecristo is not on this side of Corsica," answered Diego, "but on the other side. And besides, what would you do with the treasure?"

"Good point. Let's go, sailor."

Unlike Settiniaz, Tarras liked Diego. "A man who has that much humor and who hates the whole world to that point cannot be all bad."

And if Reb wanted to have this curious Argentine with him at all times, that was his business.

"Diego, do you know that W. C. Fields used to say, 'Anyone who hates children and dogs can't be all bad'?"

"I don't know anyone," said Diego, laughing.

"Where is Reb?"

"In Ajaccio. He will be back for lunch."

"Where the devil are we going?"

In answer, Diego slipped the twin engines into gear. It was eleven o'clock in the morning, and the Corsican spring sun was already strong. Tarras looked back: the seaplane was taking off, with unexpected grace, while their boat was passing a small promontory. Then the large beautiful Piana cove appeared, crowned with needle points and sharp indentations . . .

. . . and there was a black-and-white yacht.

"Reb's? I didn't know he had bought a pleasure boat."

No answer. But there was a strange expression in Diego's yellow eyes.

Tarras practically had to shout to be heard over the roar of the engines.

"I don't understand: Reb makes me rush down here from London, and now you tell me he's not even on board."

"The yacht is not his," said Diego in a normal voice, having just cut back the engines. "And it is not he who sent the seaplane for you."

He skillfully steered the boat up to the hanging ladder.

"Not him. Her. She wants to talk to you."

As soon as he reached the deck, a beautiful young black girl, golden brown actually, came toward him, smiling. Without saying a word, she directed him toward the stern. Charmian Page was there, sitting at a breakfast table. Near her were two other black girls, wearing blue veils that covered their bodies, revealing only their faces.

She put her hand out toward Tarras, offered him some coffee, which he declined, then some tea, which he accepted.

"The last time we saw each other," she said, "was at that dinner David gave for some of his former Harvard classmates. You were the guest of honor, and you were especially dazzling."

"In that case, our meeting today stands a good chance of being a total fiasco," answered Tarras. "I am never dazzling two times in a row, however hard I try. And I do try."

He couldn't help looking at the blue-veiled girls with undisguised curiosity.

"They are Danakils," explained Charmian, "Danakil in the singular, Danakils in the plural. Do you know Ethiopia? No? You should go there. It's a remarkable country, with thousands of years of history. These young girls come from Asmara; they are Christian and they speak French. Which you do also, I believe. Reb told me you speak an amazing number of languages. . . ."

"Five. And all badly."

He felt slightly nervous. He knew very little about Charmian Page. He had seen her two or three times, and had heard David Settiniaz mention her. He knew her to be rich, extremely rich, very independent, intelligent, and, also according to Settiniaz, "eccentric."

And of course she was beautiful, exceptionally so, even among these beautiful Ethiopian women with their pure profiles.

She continued to speak, about the Red Sea, where she had spent the last few months, going from one place to another, to Yemen, Aden, Saudi Arabia, Ethiopia, Djibouti, Egypt. Two weeks earlier, her black-and-white yacht had come through the Suez Canal. Then on to Alexandria, Crete, Malta, the straits of Messina and Bonifacio.

"Next, I don't know. Perhaps Switzerland? Or Paris? What do you think?"

She was looking at Tarras with her violet eyes, and one would have to have been blind not to see the extraordinary fever that burned in them. Tarras's discomfort grew. Only once had she mentioned Reb Klimrod's name. What does she want from me? he thought. I am not even sure what there is between them. . . .

"And why not Kalamazoo or Manchester?" he suggested, trying to sound relaxed, though already anticipating what was to come.

"Perhaps you and your charming wife will be my guests one day?"

"Shirley would love it. She has been after me for a yacht for the past thirty years."

And then there was a silence, just as Tarras had feared.

Charmian said, in French, to the Ethiopians: "Leave us now. . . ."

The girls left. It was getting warmer, and from the nearby shore came the intoxicating odor of the Corsican scrub.

"I would like to speak with you, Mr. Tarras. About Reb, of course."

She lit a fresh cigarette from the one she had just finished.

"How long have you known him?"

He hesitated, not knowing what to answer, and she immediately interpreted this hesitation.

"Oh, my God!" she exclaimed. "I asked David the same question and he also didn't answer. He began stammering, as if my curiosity were shameful. Mr. Tarras, I have been Reb's mistress for the past . . . for over four years. I even went to that horrible room he has in Greenwich Village. I lived there with him, when I could have bought the entire neighborhood. I don't understand anything about his life; I don't know what he does, or what he wants to do, or where he wants to go. He never says anything, ever. I wait for him, and sometimes months go by before he reappears, coming from I don't know where. Money . . . money does not seem to have any value to him. And yet, he has some. He has given me extravagant gifts, and I'm sure that if I asked him for—I don't know—a castle in France or an island, or anything at all, that he would give it to me. Who is he, Mr. Tarras?"

What can I answer? thought Tarras.

She crushed her half-smoked cigarette, and automatically lit another one.

"As far as I know," she said, "there are three men who must

know more about him than I do. There is this Diego, who would probably kill someone if Reb told him to, and it would be foolish and pointless to question him; besides which, he frightens me. . . . There is David, my very own brother-in-law, who turns red and starts sputtering like a pimply schoolboy. . . . And then there is you."

She was looking at him intensely, and Tarras could see in her dilated pupils such a look of despair that he turned away, ashamed of himself.

There was silence.

"I see," she said finally, with infinite bitterness.

He didn't dare look at her. She went on in a very soft voice, which shook a little.

"I am young, rather pretty, I think, rich, and I love Reb the way I didn't think it was possible to love someone. But that's not enough, apparently. I have asked him to marry me, or just to let me live constantly with him; it wouldn't make any difference to me. I begged him. I want children from him. Is that too much to ask?"

"You are placing me in a horribly difficult position," said Tarras in a hollow voice.

"I know, and I am sorry about that. One of the rare times Reb told me a little about his life, he mentioned your name and he told me you were the man for whom he felt the most friendship."

"Please," said Tarras, in pain.

Then, very suddenly, without moving, she began to cry, not bothering to brush away her tears.

"Mr. Tarras, each time he comes back to me, he is extraordinarily tender. He is very gentle . . ."

She was sobbing now, but, although her whole body shook, she remained sitting there, her hands stretched out and inert on the arms of her chair.

Tarras jumped up, feeling what was almost rage and also moved as he had never been before, thinking: To hell with Klimrod and his monstrous egocentrism! He went to the railing and grabbed hold of it furiously. As he was about to turn around and speak, finally, he felt another presence to his right. He turned his head, and there a few yards away, having silently appeared, was Diego, who was smiling, with a demonlike gleam in his eyes.

"Reb will be here any minute," he said.

They ate lunch on the stern deck, the three men and the young woman, served and surrounded by the graceful Ethiopian women, who looked as if they were dancing. Reb spoke the most, at least at the beginning of the meal, with, it was true, a great deal of softness, and, as far as Charmian was concerned, the unquestionable signs of a deep, comforting tenderness. Books and paintings were, as far as Tarras can remember, the main topics of conversation, which Reb directed with ease, managing even to get the former Harvard professor started on one of his pet peeves: high-seas piracy, a subject about which he had completed a second book, a miracle, considering how few readers he had. And it took Tarras two hours, carried away as he was by the topic, to notice that Klimrod had tricked him into doing the talking.

"I have been horribly talkative!" he exclaimed when he finally realized he alone was speaking.

"But thrilling," said Charmian, all traces of tears completely gone from her face, and seeming to be perfectly in control of herself.

The sea was warm, although it was only April. The young woman and Reb went for a swim, as did the Ethiopian girls, who wore a sort of sarong which, pressed against their taut bodies, revealed more than it covered, which was fine as far as Tarras was concerned. Diego, pretending that he could not swim unless the air temperature was above ninety degrees and the water at least eighty-five, remained in one of the large wicker chairs painted bright green, smoking one of these nauseating cigars.

Someting struck Tarras then. "Each time he comes back to me, he is extraordinarily tender," the young woman had said about Reb. And the facts were there, certainly: towards Charmian, Reb behaved with a disconcerting gentleness. On two or three occasions, Tarras noticed gestures that did not permit any doubt: his hand or fingers brushing her shoulder or the back of her neck, and also the intensity of his gray eyes when he looked at her. If it were anyone else but Reb Klimrod, Tarras thought, I would believe he is madly in love with this woman, desperately so.

As is normal in that season, night fell quickly and brought with it cooler temperatures. Tarras returned to his cabin and began dressing for dinner, just as the yacht—which had a crew of six men, Greeks, he recalls, all showing exemplary discretion—began its journey. He had just finished his shower and was putting on his shirt when there was a knock. Reb's tall figure appeared at the door.

"Does it bother you to spend the night at sea?"

"Not in the least."

"Tomorrow morning we will be in Marseilles."

The gray eyes slowly looked around the cabin. And came back to Tarras, who thought, suddenly, He knows, of course. This devil of a man is probably capable of reconstituting word for word everything Charmian told me, including my most minute hesitation. Even without the help of Diego, who probably overheard our conversation.

"Georges, I really did have something to tell you, which justifies, to a certain extent, your trip from London to here. I am going to disappear for a time."

"Disappear?"

"There is a place that I need to go to, from time to time. And that time has come."

He smiled.

"You can close your mouth now. That look of stupefaction does not suit a former Harvard professor whose intellectual acumen and verbal agility are justly recognized. Georges, there is nothing dramatic about this. I am simply going to join some people who are friends, whom I have not seen in a long time, and whom I miss."

"In Europe?"

"No," Klimrod said simply.

And you can forget it, stupid! thought Tarras. He isn't about to tell you.

"And how long will you be gone?"

"A few months, perhaps more. I don't know yet."

"Can we get in touch with you?"

"Yes and no. I have made plans in case of an extreme emergency. David will know. But you know very well that these few companies I have set up can function perfectly well without me. I wanted them to be that way."

"Does David know about this?"

"You will tell him about it. Tell him not to worry. That is

267

really his only fault: sometimes he is too scrupulously careful. Georges, please, do not say what you feel like saying to me."

Taken aback, Tarras shook his head furiously.

"I can also jump overboard and swim back to shore. And I will say whatever I please, Reb. Have you told Charmian about this coming absence? Have you prepared her for it?"

"I don't think you should worry about this, Georges."

"Perhaps she is going with you?"

But Tarras knew the answer had to be no.

"No," said Reb.

Klimrod's clear eyes shone with an absolute and terrifying ferocity.

Terras felt a chill. But nevertheless he said: "Speak to her, Reb. Please. *Please* . . . Or, take her with you. . . ."

Silence. The gray eyes were once again covered with that dreamy veil that made them inpenetrable. The cabin door opened and closed. Tarras sat down on the bed. He felt completely overwhelmed and uncharacteristically sad.

More than the gunshots, which he did not hear, it was the noise of running in the hallway that woke him. He automatically checked his watch: one-forty-three in the morning. He slipped on a bathrobe and went out. An Ethiopian girl passed by at that moment, with a bloodstain on the long white tunic she was wearing.

"Sir, you must come," she said in French.

He followed her, and walked past her when they reached the doorway of a sitting room at the end of the hall. He walked into a large, lovely cabin beneath the stern deck. He saw Charmian Page, standing, eyes wide open and staring into space, her long hair undone, holding in her right hand a small gun, barrel pointed toward the black carpet. She was wearing a negligee, almost transparent, beneath which she was naked.

Reb was seven or eight feet away, sitting on the floor, with his left leg folded under him, his shoulders and neck resting against a white sofa. His torso was naked, and, though blood was running freely, the two holes made by the bullets in his chest were perfectly visible. Another Ethiopian girl was leaning over him, trying to get him on the sofa.

Reb said, in a calm voice: "Georges, help me, please."

Tarras took three steps forward, and still remembers today the feeling he had at that moment, a feeling that was the result of his rancor and his anger toward Klimrod.

"You asked for this Reb. . . . "

He didn't have the chance to think further. A crazy madman flew into the cabin, understood what had happened in one instant, and threw himself on Charmian with a ferocious animal-like rage.

"DIEGO!"

Reb's voice snapped like a whip.

"Diego, leave her alone! *Do not touch her*! Diego! Move away from her, Diego!"

There was a moment of silence.

Then Reb said: "Please, Georges, take the gun away from her, gently. Very gently. Diego, come help me . . ."

A coughing attack shook him, and a pinkish foam appeared at the sides of his mouth. But he opened his eyes again.

"Charmian? Give Georges the gun, please. . . . Give it to him, my love. . . ."

Tarras was standing in front of the young woman. She didn't seem to see him; she was panting slightly as he circled her wrist with his fingers, dislodged the weapon, and slipped it into the pocket of his bathrobe. When he turned around, Diego, who was crying, was trying to get Reb's big body up on the white sofa. He was talking in Spanish, hurriedly and in a low voice, looking hysterical. Reb was answering him, in the same language, in monosyllables.

Tarras returned to the wounded man. Of the two bullets that had hit him in the chest, one was rather high, at the level of the heart but too much to the left to have reached it; the other one, lower down, had just missed the pancreas, as they found out later.

"Georges?"

"Don't talk, Reb."

"Georges, take good care of her, please. I am putting her in your hands. And do . . ." A new coughing attack made his face turn white. " And do whatever Diego tells you."

A few minutes later the noise of the engines suddenly changed, and it was clear that the boat was heading toward the coast at full speed. The Ethiopian girls had Charmian in hand. They made her lie down and had probably given her some medication, because when Tarras went to check on her, he found her sleeping soundly.

When he came out of the cabin, he found Diego waiting for him.

"Just to make sure everything is clear," said Diego, "*I* shot Reb, accidentally, of course. You didn't see anything. You were sleeping when it happened, and she was sleeping also. Neither one of you was there. We had been drinking, Reb and I, and were having fun shooting out the porthole at what we thought were flying fish. At one point, I tripped, and two bullets accidentally hit Reb in the chest. That's all you know."

"The Ethiopian girls?"

"They also were sleeping, and they won't say anything. The sailors will say even less. It's all taken care of. Mr. Tarras, this is what Reb wants and this is what we are going to say, all of us, without any exception. And now, give me the gun, please."

He was hospitalized in Toulon, in the naval hospital. The doctors said that his life was not in danger, that he was too strong for that, and that, besides, the small caliber of the bullets and their weak impact had caused little damage.

The police investigation was routine. The French detectives apparently were satisfied, and their choice was slim, with Klimrod's version and Haas's. Tarras stuck to the story he had been assigned.

He wondered how Charmian would behave with the policemen and with him. But during the days following their docking in Toulon, he never saw her. The yacht had been taken to the small port of Mourillon, and Charmian remained cloistered inside, with the Ethiopian girls her only company. Two policemen went on board, but left after twenty minutes, politely, impressed by the wealth of the ship and, therefore, of its owner, but apparently satisfied with the answers they had obtained.

Tarras went to visit Klimrod, who, after the first few days, had been taken to a private clinic in Mourillon. He found him on the phone, speaking in Spanish, discussing figures. He finally hung up after giving a last set of instructions and leaned his head back on the pillow.

"Georges, I am sorry you became involved in something that should not have concerned you, much less affected you."

Then he continued as if it had been an unimportant incident. He wanted Tarras to return to New York as soon as possible. "I was on the phone with Nick an hour ago, and there are some problems he wants to discuss with you. . . ."

He went on, with his amazing and abnormal memory, remembering each detail of every operation, including the names of the people in charge of the different shipyards in the United States and in Japan.

"Georges, please tell Nick that I want a detailed breakdown of everything concerning the containers. The Japanese have changed their prices for certain items, and I would like to know why. Numata and Kameichiro had quoted us . . ."

His slow, grave voice recited exotic names and figures with a bewildering, almost nerve-racking precision.

Tarras got up from his chair. Through one of the windows, he could see a white mountain, a naked rock under the clear blue sky.

"Georges?"

Tarras checked the movement that would make him turn around. He had no desire to have eye contact with Reb. But he couldn't remain silent any longer.

"One of the things Charmian told me about," he said, "was this friendship you bestow upon me, apparently. I am the man for whom you feel the most friendship."

Silence.

He finally had to turn around. And was hit, right between the eyes, as if by a fire, by the gray stare—which he held. An inconceivable thing happened next: it was Reb who looked away.

"I love that woman, Georges. No, let me finish, please. . . . I am not used to this sort of confession. Did she tell you how long she and I have been . . . have been seeing each other?"

"About four years."

Red nodded. He was looking at the white mountain now.

"Did she tell you she wanted me to marry her, or for us to live together?"

"Yes."

"Have my children?"

"Yes."

271

"And you think you know why I so obstinately refuse to give her what she wants? You think I am indifferent, or an egoist, preoccupied, as I am, in the pursuit of my private dream? That is what you think, isn't it, Georges?"

"Yes."

There was a short silence.

Then Reb said in his faraway voice: "She has already been hospitalized four times, Georges. I will furnish you with the addresses of the establishments and the names of the psychiatrists who have treated her. We have already had a child together, two years ago. She killed it, a month and a half after its birth. She strangled it. The nurse was in the next room and didn't hear anything, and couldn't do anything, in spite of all the safeguards we had set up. After that, she was again hospitalized, and when she came out—the doctors thought she was well—she had an operation, and can never have children again. She has tried to kill herself three times. Now we're going to have to hospitalize her again, and try again to cure her. . . . Must I go on?"

"I will check on each fact," said Tarras in a hoarse voice, shocked by his own determination, but torn.

"Do it."

There was a knock at the door. Diego stopped in the doorway.

"In a minute, Diego," said Reb softly. "We are almost finished."

Diego closed the door and again there was a silence.

Tarras, who had lowered his eyes, exhausted, looked up and saw Reb leaning back against the pillows, his eyes closed, his face thinner, drawn, pale. And suddenly an overwhelming feeling of pity, shame, and sadness came over him, and his eyes filled with tears.

"One more thing, Georges. We *are* married, Charmian and I. We were married on January 19, 1951, in Reno, Nevada. You can check on that also. And I would like you to check it, like everything else. I would like . . . "

He stopped, took a deep breath, and that was the only visible sign of the great emotion that was tearing him apart.

"Georges, I want to be sure that I simply haven't been having a nightmare."

Before returning to Boston, to the Victorian house where he

lived with Shirley when they were not in Maine, Tarras went to New York, to see Nick Petridis, but before that he went to Lausanne and to Zurich, to London and to San Francisco. And to Philadelphia and Reno.

Even before he started checking, which he did, not without feeling ashamed, he knew Reb had told him the truth.

As, of course, he had.

In April of 1955, Charmian Page Klimrod was once again hospitalized in Switzerland, her hospitalization having been planned five weeks earlier, after a terrible crisis in Cairo. And Tarras had not been able to tell, when she asked him where she might go at the end of her cruise on the Red Sea and in the Mediterranean, whether she was really conscious of her actual destination, which she did know about.

When Tarras saw her, she didn't recognize him, having forgotten even his name, having forgotten everything, even Reb. Otherwise, she seemed completely normal, and talked about a trip she was planning, to the Celebes Sea and to New Zealand. She seemed happy, funny, and heartbreakingly beautiful.

7

Diego slapped the naked buttocks of the two mulatto girls he had packed with his suitcases, to occupy his nights and his siestas, along with thirty-six bottles of the finest whisky. After blowing a kiss to the yellowing picture of Betty Grable that a preceding passenger had pinned to the wall, he walked out into the corridor, knocked on the door of the next cabin, and walked in.

He found Reb reading, as always.

"Are you coming up?"

"No."

"We have, as they say, sighted land."

"Good," said Reb, without looking up.

Diego went out on the deck of the small steamship, which was filled with a noisy and merry crowd, mostly black, and among whom several improvised bands were making a tremendous racket. You couldn't hear a B-29 flying overhead, thought Diego. He climbed a ladder and joined the captain, master on board after God, who was not a Brazilian but an Irishman.

"Are we stuck?"

"We are waiting."

The heat was diabolical; the decks were burning beneath their feet, and precautions had to be taken before leaning against the railing. Diego did so anyway. He leaned over. Directly ahead was a wall, almost seven feet high, and stretching as far as the eye could see. This wall was brownish-gray, moving, supple, crowned at the top by a golden froth, fluttering above the swirl that every so often clouded with muddy stains, which quickly disappeared, the intense blue of the Atlantic Ocean.

Diego leaned over farther, fascinated, enjoying the excessive, sometimes gruesome taste he had for uncommon phenomena. And this meeting, this mute, reptilian, ferocious confrontation, in which the Atlantic and the most powerful river in the world faced each other, and which had resulted in a draw since the beginning of time, had everything to satisfy him.

Looking up, he could see that the duel was not just between the waters. Almost directly above the brown wall of water, the sky also was divided. On the side of the mist-covered earth, the sky was swollen with purple clouds, which were advancing as a united front, looking like guards standing elbow to elbow, as if to prevent anyone or anything from getting past them. On the other side the sun was shining brightly over the ocean.

"And what are we waiting for?"

"The fucking pilot."

Who didn't arrive until six hours later, and quite nonchalantly.

Only then could the steamship start its journey through the gigantic estuary of the Amazon River.

In Belém, Ubaldo Rocha was waiting. At first Diego disliked him intensely, because of his somber appearance, his almost total silence, and what Diego called his "man of the woods who knows everything" air. But rapidly, having convinced himself that Rocha had the same fierce devotion to Reb that he had, he came to see him in another light. From that point on, the two men got along famously.

Rocha had a large boat and three men to work it. He took them up the Amazon. They reached Manaus at dawn on May 14, 1955. Reb had not left his bunk once during the entire trip from Belém. When they passed Santarém, Rocha, abandoning himself in an exuberant verbal folly, told them in a few laconic words the story of Henry Ford's final failure here, between 1927 and 1946, when the American multimillionaire had invested twenty million prewar dollars to create hevea plantations in Amazonia, planting close to four million trees from roots imported from the Philippines. Ford had even created a town, Fordlândia (in all modesty), of three thousand inhabitants, with its own schools, churches, hospitals, atheletic fields, tennis courts, swimming pools, and golf courses, and stores supplied by special planes. But the sites had been badly chosen, and when a new attempt was tried elsewhere, taking into account that it takes a hevea eight years to begin producing latex, the man from Detroit who dreamed of being his own tire manufacturer discovered that his Amazonian rubber was costing him more, unmanufactured, than that which was delivered to him at home in the form of tires, prepaid. And Ford, discouraged, had sold, for a quarter of a million dollars, what had cost him at least forty times more.

"What a deal," said Diego.

But he had listened to Rocha's story with an uneasiness bordering on anguish, and this uneasiness grew as the days went by on the never-ending river. Plunging into this unknown world, he felt oppressed and experienced once again, eight years later, that same feeling of despair and tragic abandonment he had felt when, after their escape from Bogotá, he had seen Reb Klimrod walk away, on the start of his solitary journey of one hundred days and nearly twelve hundred and fifty miles.

At Manaus, he nevertheless insisted on continuing. Through Rocha, he knew that the boat would be going on to Moura, where Rocha was born, and then up the Rio Branco.

"That would serve no purpose, Diego. And you have things to do, for which I am counting on you. We agreed."

"Two or three weeks won't make that much difference."

He almost had to implore, feeling all the more strongly because

275

he could see that something, unexplainable to him, was happening to Reb. He was experiencing a sort of mutation. He spoke less and less, his pupils grew larger, and he seemed to be changing physically. At times, he would retire within himself totally. Two or three times in Manaus, where they spent three days while Rochas busied himself with incomprehensible preparations, he had spoken, in unknown languages, with Indians he met. But otherwise he had withdrawn to the point where he, who was usually so polite, didn't even seem to hear when he was spoken to. He had never been inattentive, however dreamy he may have looked. Now he was, and unbelievably so.

"Let me come with you, as far as possible."

"All right: Caracaraí. But you won't go beyond that point."

Caracaraí

If to Diego's ears the word had a vaguely alien musical sound, it meant nothing to him. He didn't bother to check a map. The boat left Manaus. They reached Moura, a small agglomeration of no apparent interest, to Diego at least.

Then came the trip up the Rio Branco, with its dark waters, free of mosquitoes, or almost. I am in the middle of the jungle, thought Diego, worried. Me, Dieguito Haas, Mamita's favorite son (she has no others), a regular of palaces, adored by women and the terror of butlers all over the world, here I am going into the swarming and enigmatic Green Hell, being watched from both banks by Indians who are certainly cannibals and who are licking their chops covetously at the sight of my juicy buttocks. . . .

Actually, he had no other choice but to retreat into humor, and to talk to himself. Reb, crouched at the front, no longer spoke at all, at least not in any civilized language. On several occasions, looking out toward the curtain of the forest, he would call out bizarre sounds, and, immediately after, naked Indians would spring forward with frightful features and bows that measured seven or eight feet.

Ubaldo Rocha was not any more talkative. As for the crew, they were not those from Belém. At Manaus there had been a change, and Indians had taken over. Just the thought of having them as his only companions on the way back worried Diego in advance.

"Here."

The sun had just risen. Diego did the same, extricating himself from his hammock. It had rained all night, but the rain had stopped, and the swollen river flooded large areas of the forest with its calm waters, forming a pefectly smooth mirror, which reflected every shadow in the sky with such precision that Diego had trouble discerning the image from its reflection.

He looked in the direction that Rocha had just indicated, and saw a burned-over area, already almost ingested by new vegetation, with nothing that could distinguish it from the thousand others. They were probably no longer on the Branco, for this river was too narrow, too eaten up by trees and foliage. The boat, pulled by hooks, berthed along a kind of dock, a simple rotting tree trunk whose worm-ridden humus hid the roots of another majestic tree. Behind it, and all around, was an impenetrable wall of greenery.

Reb had jumped from the boat. To Diego's great horror he removed the cloth shoes he had been wearing since Rio, threw them away, and began wading, barefoot, with visible pleasure, in the muddy water, wherein reigned very disquieting animal life.

As for Rocha, he performed a tightrope walk over the tree trunk until he reached firm ground, if there is such a thing as firm ground in this aquarium, thought Diego.

He called out, "Reb!" exactly as he had eight years earlier.

Reb didn't even turn around. He was undressing until he was completely naked, and he was talking to the wall of greenery, behind which indistinct movements were occurring.

"Now, you had better go away," said Rocha to Diego. "Otherwise, they won't come out. It's possible they won't recognize Reb right way after five years. No point in taking any unnecessary risks."

As an added measure of precaution, he yelled out an order to the Indian crew, who pushed on their hooks and thus made the boat slip back into the current. Diego sat on the bulwark as the distance grew between Reb and himself. It grew to eight hundred yards, and only then, out from the wall of shining leaves, gleaming from the rain, did figures appear.

"Guaharibos," said one of the crew, in a low, respectful voice.

All around Reb, immense and naked, the figures multiplied. It looked as if insects had come to feed on a large wounded animal.

Just as a bend in the river was about to separate them for good, Diego thought he saw Reb make a gesture with his arm, intended for him, as if to say everything was all right. At least Diego hoped he had made the gesture, and for his sake. Afterwards, he went back to his hammock and huddled there, miserable as never before.

In Manaus, he found the two Brazilian lawyers, who had been waiting for him for several days, with whom, according to Reb's directions, he had so much to do . . .

. . . and with whom he did so much.

The King's Men

1

Tudor Anghel left Los Angeles on September 14, 1957, at dawn. He reached Barstow at nine o'clock and stopped for some coffee and a piece of apple pie. Anghel was a massive man with a strong square jaw; in his youth, he had been an amateur boxer and had fought about thirty times, winning eleven times by a knockout. His Rumanian ancestry could be seen in his very shiny, very black eyes, in his volubility, and in his consummate ability to talk and say nothing, especially when he really had nothing to say.

Just under fifty miles out of Barstow, following the instructions he had received in the letter, he left the Interstate and took the road to the left, which runs to the east of Death Valley.

The letter had said: Just be in Tonopah by four o'clock. Six miles past Tonopah, to the east, on Route 6, turn left onto 8A, go about thirteen miles to 82, which is a dirt road . . . "

It sounded like a treasure hunt.

He crossed over from California to Nevada at around one o'clock in the afternoon, had a spicy hamburger at the Devil's Hole, and continued north, bypassing Las Vegas; "Do not go through Las Vegas, please," the letter had said.

It was three minutes to four when he drove through Tonopah. He drove straight through, without stopping, then onto 8A, which went to Battle Mountain and to Elko. Then onto 82, the dirt road . . .

It was a winding, climbing road, which made its way between the double chains of the Monitor and Toquiman ranges, reaching an altitude of about ten thousand feet and entirely covered by forest. "Twenty-seven and a half miles farther, on the right, you

see a stream, and an even narrower path, with a sign: MUD
WELLS."

Anghel turned in. "Go about two miles. There will be a cabin
on your left." He found the wooden cabin, a shambles, solitary,
perched on a rocky platform, right next to a grotto.

"Please wait there."

He turned off the ignition, and a crashing silence fell on him.
Just opening the door caused a tremendous noise. He walked up
to the cabin, which was empty and seemed abandoned. But he
noticed that a fire had recently been made. He visited the grotto,
where some water was trickling through the stones. Back at the
car, he turned on the radio, but shut it off almost immediately,
sensing the incongruity of the noise in the heart of this solitude.

Half an hour later, he sensed a presence. He got out of the
car, looked up, and felt his pulse quicken. A tall, thin figure was
coming down the path, without disturbing a single stone, with
the light footsteps of a hunter.

He recognized Reb Klimrod.

"First, the mines," said Reb.

He spread a map out on the hood of the car, and Anghel noticed
innumerable crosses, circles, lines, and triangles drawn on it.
"Look closer, Tudor." He did, and realized that next to each of
the signs were squares and letters that were underlined.

"Tudor, the crosses stand for Lovelock, the circles for Circle,
the three lines for Three Fingers, the triangles, of course, for
Triangle West, the squares for Chess & Wilson. . . . The rest
is easy: H for High Hill & Western, G for Goldman, and so
on. . . ."

The names of the companies were familiar to Anghel. Somewhat. Then he remembered.

"Those were the ones you asked me to set up five years ago."

"Those and eight others. Take this down, please."

He recited the names, addresses, and telephone numbers of
the trustees, the lawyers who had been involved, the banks that
had been used, mentioning each time the name of the banker
who had been involved, his address and private telephone number. When he had finished, he asked: "Did you get it all down?"

"Yes."

"I would like you to keep this map and use it to establish a
list of mines and lodes for each company. You will take all nec-

essary steps to check on the trustees and the trust agreements, and to collate secondary trust agreements in your name. Please see to the registration of the title deeds. Once you are finished, please be kind enough to give everything to Settiniaz, as usual."

"By hand?"

"By hand."

Anghel looked at the map, fascinated and astonished at the same time.

"For heaven's sake, how many mines have you bought?"

"Three hundred and fifty-three. I am still missing one."

"Only gold mines?"

"Yes. When you finish with the map, please burn it."

"Of course," said Anghel. He was looking at Klimrod, who had a beard, long hair, and a green snakeskin band across his forehead. Had it not been for his eyes, so light, which shone so brightly in his thin, tanned face, he would have looked like an Indian.

Thinking rapidly, he said: "Five years ago, you bought some gold mines throughout the Rockies. Their characteristic then was that they were unprofitable. One ounce of extracted gold was worth thirty dollars, or forty, with an official rate, which has remained unchanged till today, of thirty-five dollars. Do you expect something to happen?"

Instead of an answer, he received Reb's icy glare, and precipitately said, managing a weak smile: "I take back my question."

"I didn't hear it," said Reb. "Now for the land. Are you taking this down?"

It was getting dark. Anghel had to get a flashlight from his glove compartment.

"I'll hold it for you," said Reb.

Anghel didn't stop writing, but he became increasingly bewildered.

"That's it," Reb said finally.

He handed the flashlight back to Anghel and began pacing in front of the old cabin, which, at that time of day, was almost invisible, giving the whole scene a feeling of unreality.

Anghel rapidly looked over the notes he had taken, and came up with a rough estimate.

"Approximately thirty-four thousand five hundred . . ."

"Thirty-four thousand one hundred twenty-two."

283

"Plus what you bought in 1951, and two years ago."

"Forty-one thousand one hundred forty-nine. Seventy-five thousand two hundred seventy-one in all. Spread over one thousand four hundred and twelve plots and sixty-four companies."

"God Almighty!" exclaimed Anghel.

From the now dense darkness came the calm, slow, amused voice of Reb.

"I don't believe He had much to do with this. Tudor, once you finish the collation, and have checked on everything, make sure you get it to Settiniaz. Tudor?"

"Yes, Reb?"

Where the devil did he go? Anghel wondered. He could no longer see a thing in front of him.

"Thank you for coming. Thank you for your help, for the past six years. Recently, I went by this house you bought in the hills of Santa Monica. It's lovely and is well worth the hundred and twenty-two thousand dollars you paid for it. I also saw your children, and you have every reason to be proud of them. I seem to remember that on October 2 you will be celebrating your twentieth wedding anniversary. Am I right?"

"Yes," said Anghel, at the mercy of contradictory feelings: boundless admiration, respect, and friendship, and fear before the implicit threat he thought he detected in this display of precise facts that Klimrod knew about him.

"Are you still fond of Rumanian painting, Tudor?"

"That is how we met."

"Fate has put me in possession of a beautiful painting by Theodor Pallady, who is at the same level as Matisse, or nearly. I would be very pleased if you accepted it. It should arrive in about two weeks—the morning of October 2, I believe. Now, Tudor, leave, please."

"This place is lost in the wilderness. Don't you want me to drop you off somewhere?"

"No, thank you, Tudor. Go to Las Vegas, as planned. The suite at the Flamingo is in your name. I suppose your team is already there?"

"As you asked me."

There was a silence. And suddenly, without the slightest noise to signal his approach, the Indian with the light eyes was standing next to the open car door.

284

"Now, beat it, Tudor, please. I am invited to eat some beans with a local gold prospector named Fergus MacTavish. If he sees me getting out of a fancy limousine like yours, he will think me a millionaire and will charge me one hundred dollars more than his mine is worth."

Tudor Anghel went from Black Dog to King's Man as a result of hard work, intelligence, and absolute faithfulness to Reb Klimrod.

The gold-mine operation was carried out according to a tested plan: each small company, owning one or several mines, was run by a trustee. As the apparent and official owner, this trustee actually owed everything to a primary trustee, who controlled several secondary trustees. This primary trustee was himself subordinate, by another trust agreement, to one of the King's Men, in this case, Tudor Anghel. He was the only one to know Reb, to whom he was linked by yet another trust agreement, and who controlled by himself all the primary trustees in a given area of activity.

Until the end, each one of the King's Men thought he was alone, and considered Klimrod to be an eccentric millionaire who wanted to remain anonymous for personal reasons. Some thought Klimrod was himself an agent for someone else or for a group or even a state. Nick Petridis, for example, still thought he was a shipowner; Anghel took him to be a clever speculator in land and gold mines; Santana saw him strictly as an oilman; Nessim for a long time believed he was a rich man who didn't want to speculate for himself.

The operation of the gold mines in Nevada, Colorado, and other areas of the Rockies was certainly the simplest one ever conducted by the King.

From 1951 to 1957, his successive purchases, handled with complete discretion, involved an investment of three million two hundred and ninety-six thousand dollars. This for mines that were actually unprofitable, that had for the most part been abandoned for forty years. The gold that could be extracted didn't even cover the cost of the exploitation, given the official value of the metal: thirty-five dollars an ounce.

The number of three hundred and fifty-four gold mines mentioned by Klimrod to Anghel represented the exact number of concessions recorded by Anghel when he finalized their acquisition. But another team was working parallel to Tudor's and these three hundred and fifty-four mines were only one part of the gigantic wave of purchases undertaken by Klimrod from 1951 to 1957—which eventually made him the owner of two thousand two hundred and eleven lodes.

On January 21, 1980, after successive increases, gold, which was worth thirty-five dollars an ounce in the fifties, hit the astronomical price of eight hundred and fifty dollars an ounce.

Two years before, in February of 1978, all the mines had been reopened and made operational.

What's more, Nessim Shahadźe, in Klimrod's name, made regular yearly gold purchases, ranging from two hundred thousand dollars to one million and a half, at thirty-five dollars an ounce to begin with, then at eighty, then, as of December 1974, when gold transactions were being handled in the United States, at one hundred and eighty dollars.

The profit realized by the King in January of 1980 can be put, without error, at four billion three hundred and fifty-five million dollars.

2

Diego Haas, completely naked, was happily splashing about in a round bathtub measuring nearly ten feet across, with little spurting jets on all sides, in the company of three girls wearing only their modesty and their earrings. The telephone rang. He crawled over a sea of breasts and rounded buttocks (he liked them *very* rounded) and answered on the third ring, saying, with his usual good humor: "Sheik Abdul ben Diego here."

Then he said "Yes" seven times in a row, and, for a change, once, *"Jawohl."* He hung up. Six weeks had gone by since he had arrived in Las Vegas, and he was becoming unbearably bored, notwithstanding the girls, whom he indulged in prodigiously. Gambling left him cold. He had played, to be sure, using the twenty-five thousand dollars Reb had given him for that purpose, but bad luck had stuck with him throughout, with sardonic irony: he kept winning. No way to get rid of this lousy dough, he thought. Even the croupiers start snickering when they see me coming. I have become the laughing stock of this place. Not once am I ever able, at craps, to shoot anything but a seven or an eleven. And he thus formulated a theory according to which, in order to win money in a casino, you simply had to try to lose it, all the while praying sincerely to Nuestra Señora de Guadelupe.

But the waiting was coming to an end. He looked at the girls. And that sarcastic, crazy, and frightening flame started shining in his golden eyes.

"All hands on deck," he screamed. "Time to get to work, clew up all and everything, hoist the main capstan, the large topsails and the royal sails, the staysails and the foretopmost sails, hard a starboard. In other words, ladies, out you go. And quickly."

He threw them out without giving them time to get dressed, to the great delight of the bellboy. And for the next three hours was very busy.

In those three hours, Diego carried out, step by step, all the maneuvers for which he was responsible. He made no fewer than forty telephone calls, mainly within Las Vegas, but also throughout the United States.

Each call consisted of a few, strictly necessary words.

After completing this first task, he left his suite in the Flamingo, making sure on the way out that Tudor Anghel was setting himself up there as planned, along with the five lawyers of his team who had come from Los Angeles, and went out, unbothered by the unbelievable heat of the Strip.

He went to the Sands. There also, everything was in order. The two lawyers from New York, Harrison Quinn and Thomas McGreevy, had checked in the night before and had their documents ready.

Same thing at the Desert Inn. But to get there, Diego took a taxi. If the heat didn't bother him, any physical exercise was abhorrent to him, except with the ladies. Steve Pulaski, from

Detroit, was staying there, with two of his associates and his documents.

He completed his tour by a visit to the Dunes—the lawyers from Chicago, Moses Bern and Louis Benetti, were staying there—and to the Sahara, where he visited the group from Philadelphia, headed by Kim Foysie.

To each of them, he repeated the instructions and confirmed the schedules of the meetings.

He derived the greatest satisfaction from all of this; the craziness of it enchanted him. And also, he probably experienced what Settiniaz felt all the time, that is, being the only one to know (with one exception) what was going to take place, when, and why. This knowledge, added to the fact that Reb was finally coming back, was enough to make him very happy.

None of the teams of lawyers who had come to Las Vegas had any idea that they were not the only one. They had no knowledge of each other's existence.

By the time Diego was finished, it was five o'clock in the afternoon.

Just in time, he thought. He returned to the Flamingo by taxi. The car he had rented a week ago was waiting for him. He got in and drove down the Strip. Reaching Jones Boulevard, he went north, along land he knew belonged, for the most part, to Reb.

He came to a point when the only thing in front of him was a straight road, which undulated to the north and went on forever, and the only thing to left and right was burning desert, while behind him the orgy of lights of Las Vegas was still visible. He began singing at the top of his voice, having cut the engine, giving a violent interpretation of "Ramona."

A truck stopped ten yards away, on the other side of the road. Reb got out, with his bag on his shoulder. He smiled and shook hands with the driver, who left. As the truck drove off, Diego recognized the name on the side as that of a trucking company of which he had been the president for some time. Then, I sold it, he thought. I don't know to whom, or why, or for how much, but I sold it. I remember very clearly the day Reb told me to sign.

He sang as loud as his lungs would permit him to.

Reb opened the car door and sat down.

"How about lowering it a little? I'm sure they can hear you in Alaska."

They had not seen each other for forty-three days, and Diego's happiness was immense.

"Everything all right?"

"Yes. Almost. How are you doing?"

"Everything is ready. We are set to start tomorrow morning at eight."

Diego's suite at the Flamingo was not in the name Haas. He had rented it under the name Luis de Carbajal, an identity that, according to Settiniaz, he used at least a dozen times, and which Settiniaz thought was fictitious, because he used it in towns and hotels where his missions did not call for a passport. It took Settiniaz twenty-five years to discover that Diego's real name was Luis Diego Haas de Carbajal. Through his mother's line, he was almost an authentic Spanish nobleman.

"Which room do you want?"

Reb shrugged. His large tanned hand picked up the telephone, dialed a number. He began to speak, in French. Probably Settiniaz, thought Diego, who understood one word in twenty. He was looking at Reb, and his disappointment was considerable. He had hoped that being back in the United States, where they had been for the past four months, traveling back and forth between the coasts, would have changed Reb back to the man he used to be. But no. He was more distant than ever. Ten months had passed since Reb had plunged into the Amazonian jungle, near the Caracaraí waterfall, and the merciful day when, while he was in Rio with Socrates, the telephone had rung and he heard the usual "Diego, I need you." This stay in the Green World had again changed Reb Klimrod. Although he maintained polite attention to whomever he was addressing, what Diego called his "absences" were becoming increasingly frequent, and lasted longer.

The phone conversation ended with "*A bientôt*," which even Diego understood.

"Reb? Why 'almost'? I asked you if everything was all right and you answered, 'Yes. Almost.' "

The gray eyes turned toward him slowly. Reb smiled suddenly.

"A certain Fergus MacTavish. His bacon and beans are excellent but his whisky is hideous. And he said no to me."

Diego didn't have the slightest idea who Fergus MacSomething was. And of course he did not ask.

"But I haven't finished with him yet," Reb went on.

And he had that amused and malicious expression on his face. He undressed and took a shower.

Diego asked: "Hungry?"

"Yes."

"Hamburgers and eggs?"

"Yes."

He doesn't care, Diego thought.

"Diego, did you arrange for the barber?"

"He will be here in thirty-three minutes and twenty-four seconds. And your suit is ready. As for shoes, I bought three different sizes, just in case. As a result of playing Indian, your feet may have grown. As for the ties . . . *Dio mio*, such ties! I bought you a dozen. This one?"

"Too loud."

"It's green. They are all green, by the way. This one is almost mute."

"Fine."

Fifteen minutes later, a waiter brought the eggs and the hamburgers. He didn't see Klimrod, who was in the next room, on the telephone once again, this time speaking in German, to another anonymous party. The barber arrived after that, and started tending to the hair and beard without saying a word. He was Mexican and probably thought the two men were what they were pretending to be: South Americans up for a good time in Las Vegas. When he left, Reb resumed making phone calls, but he was so transformed physically that even Diego might have had trouble recognizing him. His hair was very short, he was clean-shaven and was wearing steel-rimmed sunglasses. He seemed younger (he was about to turn twenty-nine) and looked exactly like he wanted to: like a young business-school graduate. The glasses, especially, changed him, since they almost completely concealed his eyes.

At exactly seven-thirty, there was a knock at the door, following a call from inside the hotel. Two men came in, Lerner, whom Diego knew well, and a certain Abramowicz, who was less familiar. They went into the other room with Reb, while Diego stood guard, for one hour and a half, then left.

Reb started telephoning again, and during one of the rare pauses, Diego asked: "Do you want a girl for tonight?"

Reb shrugged his shoulders, indifferent, eyes lost in the distance.

"Just in case," said Diego, "I got two. Tall, dark, and reading Aldous Huxley and Rabindranath Tagore, as you like them. Shit, it will relax you! Linda or Terry? Or both?"

Telephone. Diego answered and recognized Abie Levin's voice, though he didn't identify himself. He handed the telephone to Reb, and out of discretion went for a walk in the hall, stopping to play with the ice-cube dispenser. Thus he witnessed the arrival, a few minutes before nine o'clock, of the man who, of all the King's Men, remained the most enigmatic.

He was an average-sized man, of average appearance, averagely dressed, with glasses and an insignificant face, impossible to describe.

The man, who was carrying a leather briefcase, stopped in front of the door, without knocking on it, and looked at Diego, who came forward, ready to send him away. The man smiled.

"Mr. Haas? Would you be kind enough to tell him that Jethro is here?"

"Jethro?"

"Simply Jethro. He is expecting me."

Diego walked into the suite and delivered the message.

Reb nodded without saying anything.

"And he knows my name," said Diego.

"Yes."

He was staring into space. "Have him come in, Diego, and, as of this moment, I don't want to be disturbed. No more phone calls. I will be about two hours. And it will be Linda, finally. Eleven-thirty. If she doesn't mind waiting until then."

He smiled.

Jethro came in, and he and Reb locked themselves in the room.

Diego made the necessary arrangements to have all calls held for the next two hours. He turned on the television and found an old James Cagney movie, *Blood on the Sun*. He would have preferred Shelley Winters. He loved Shelley Winters: blonde, and rounded, with a devilishly mischievous mouth. When the film was over, and not hearing any sound from Reb's room, he went and took a bath and a shower, shaved, washed his hair, cut his fingernails and toenails and the hairs in his nose.

He heard, but did not see, Jethro leave. Reb appeared, with a look in his eyes that expressed great satisfaction, even triumph.

"Now for this Linda. Tall and dark, did you say?"

"Who knows Tagore and others by heart, as you like them."

"I am ready."

He was really in a good mood.

"So," said Diego. "except for Fergus What's-his-name, everything is all right?"

"Everything is all right, except for him."

Wearing a bathrobe, Diego went into the sitting room to call Linda, who was waiting in a room two floors below. While he was at it, he also invited the other girl, Terry, even though she was neither blonde nor rounded. He would make an exception, for once.

"Now that I am all clean and handsome, what a figure I cut!"

It was by chance that he noticed the four files, just as Reb was about to put them away. They had obviously been brought by Jethro. There was nothing extraordinary about them, simple cardboard folders, undifferentiated from each other . . .

. . . except by their color: one was black, one red, one green, and one white.

Jethro worked for the King for at least thirty years.

Until 1976 he was paid regularly by the King through a Panamanian account. After that the payments were handled through a bank in the Bahamas.

The transfers were never justified in any way, and it was Reb himself who personally gave Settiniaz the order to proceed.

The amounts, which were semi-annual, varied little, never less than three hundred thousand dollars, but with certain exceptional peaks. Such as one in 1957, when the amount of the transfer was over one million dollars.

Jethro was at the head of a formidable information and espionage network, which was at the sole service of the King. Tarras believes that Yoël Bainish played a role in setting up this network.

As for Jethro's presence in Las Vegas at that time, and a Jethro who took the risk of showing himself to Diego, it only served to underline the importance of the maneuver undertaken by the King on September 16 and 17, 1957—a real financial St. Valentine's Day massacre.

3

The black file was in the hands of Harrison Quinn, the lawyer from New York who was staying, with his associate Tom McGreevy, in a suite in the Sands Hotel.

Both were in Las Vegas for the first time. They were not used to negotiating with vagrants, but the idea did not frighten them especially. They were business lawyers, known for their dangerous incisiveness and their love of well-prepared documents, and, if that failed, for the implacability with which they defended their client's interests.

The file they had been given earlier satisfied them completely. They found it remarkable. Having worked on it relentlessly, they could not find the slightest fault. This Lerner knew his stuff, clearly, although he didn't look it, with his hurried, almost painful delivery and his errand-boy-dressed-for-a-Sunday-funeral attire. Lerner had not made a good impression on them when he had come to solicit their services. They had almost turned him down, in spite of the considerable retainer he had offered. And then Lerner had said: "The clients I represent are not thieves. They are respectable. You can be assured of this: Call David Fellows, at Hunt Manhattan. Do it, please, now." They had. Fellows had burst out laughing. Yes, he knew Lerner's clients; yes, he would vouch for them, on all counts; no, he could not reveal their names; yes, Quinn and McGreevy, respectable as they were, could without regret or remorse take on Lerner and his clients. . . .

Quinn opened the black file. It contained two pieces of paper, typed, without a signature or a letterhead. He read them and shivered. Without saying a word, he passed them to McGreevy. After that he turned around and examined more closely the young man with the steel-rimmed glasses who was sitting behind him. Quinn knew, from Lerner, three things in all about the young man: "His name is Beck; he is one of my assistants; he represents me. Please abide scrupulously by all the instructions he will give you in my name."

And this was the same young man who had discreetly handed him the black file a few minutes earlier.

McGreevy had now finished reading the contents of the folder. He also remained impassive, but Quinn noticed that his hands were trembling a little. It was exactly eight-twenty-nine in the morning of September 16, 1957.

Quinn slowly looked around the room of the Sands, where the meeting was being held.

He said out loud: "Everyone is here, I believe."

There were murmurs, and heads nodded in answer. They were fourteen in all. Quinn had McGreevy to his right. Behind him were his two associates and young Beck. Then there was this disquieting person whose name was Abie Levin, flanked by two less attractive individuals, a certain Moffatt, who alone represented several syndicates, and a lawyer named O'Connors; across from him, five men: Manny Morgen and Sol Mayer, the official owners of the two casinos and the development licensees, the main gambling director, Joe Manacacci, and their legal counselors.

Quinn looked at Levin and said: "Mr. Levin?"

"You are making the offer," replied Levin. "You begin."

His black eyes were slightly slanted and they were as hard as they were impenetrable. Quinn had heard of him; it had even been said that Levin was the plenipotentiary ambassador of the crime syndicate—if it really existed, of course—to the unions. According to this same informer, Levin was, at the same time, a former lieutenant of the "old guys," like Genovese, and the new man to call for the young generation of Gallos, Persicos, and others. All this without breaking a solid friendship with Meyer Lansky. And, in spite of all these interesting connections, without having ever been called to appear before any court in the past twenty years.

Quinn looked at Morgen and Mayer.

"You are the owners of two casinos, one on the Strip, the other a little further back. The receipts from the first average out to approximately four hundred and twenty thousand dollars. For you, Mr. Morgen, the figure is substantially less: three hundred and forty thousand dollars. Per day."

"Where did you get this kind of information?" asked Morgen, suddenly furious.

"It is correct," McGreevy said calmly. "And besides, that is not the point."

"What is?"

"The problems you are currently having," said Quinn. "And the problems you will be faced with in the near future."

"In the very near future," said McGreevy, smiling pleasantly.

"Which will force you to sell," said Quinn.

"Sell to our client," specified McGreevy.

"There was never any question of selling anything," said Mayer. Unlike Morgen, it was not the two New York lawyers Mayer was watching, but Abie Levin.

That being said, thought Quinn, Mayer has already understood. He is smarter than the other one.

"Mr. Mayer," said Quinn, "you are having problems in your establishment. With the Gambling Commission. Irregularities have been found in your casino seven times during the last four months; you have already been fined once, one hundred and twenty thousand dollars. Tomorrow, or in any case very soon, you will be faced with two more fines, if not three, which could add up to five hundred thousand dollars."

"We will pay it," said Mayer.

"That's a point to which we will come back, Mr. Mayer," said McGreevy, smiling more than ever. "As for you, Mr. Morgen, your situation is no better than that of you associ—Oh, excuse me, of your colleague."

"You also are clearly faced with a few problems with the Gambling Commission," said Quinn.

"But in your case they are less serious," said McGreevy, as if to say: Don't worry about it.

"In your case," said Quinn, "it's the IRS that would pose serious problems."

"The IRS," said McGreevy, "has proof that the receipts you have reported do not exactly correspond to the actual receipts."

"Concealment of income," said Quinn.

"And, in any event," said McGreevy, "there is also the fact that the state of Nevada . . ."

". . . through its Gambling Commission . . ." said Quinn.

". . . intends to carry out a systematic cleanup of the gambling establishments . . ." said McGreevy.

". . . by eliminating the disreputable people," said Quinn.

"In God's name, what is this circus!" exclaimed Morgen. "You are accusing us of what, exactly? And besides, who are you to accuse us of anything? We came here because Abie Levin, who is a friend, asked us to come. . . ."

He went on protesting. Someone touched Quinn's elbow. Without looking, he took the piece of paper, folded in half, opened it on his lap, and read the three words written in very small, tight handwriting: "Faster. Kill them."

"Let's not waste any time," said Quinn. "You mentioned paying the fines, Mr. Mayer? With what money? What you have in the cash register? I have some bad news for you, Mr. Mayer. Mr. Levin?"

"Alas!" said Levin, impassive.

"Mr. Mayer," said McGreevy, "you have built and furnished you casino with . . ."

"That is also the case with Mr. Morgen," said Quinn.

". . . with loans granted through the financial services of certain syndicates, represented here by Messrs. Levin and Moffatt. That is correct, is it not, Mr. Levin?"

"Correct," said Levin.

"Now," said Quinn, "your moneylenders themselves are having problems."

"The contributions are not coming in well," said Levin. "Bad times."

"What's more, the federal government, rightly or wrongly, is worried about syndicate organizations financing gambling operations . . ."

". . . especially when they are run by people they consider to be . . ."

". . . rightly or wrong . . ." said Quinn.

". . . disreputable," said McGreevy.

"In short," said Quinn, "your moneylenders are very soon going to present you with their notes, Messrs. Mayer and Morgen. For you, Mr. Morgen, the sum to pay will be, roughly, one million four hundred and eighty-three thousand six hundred and twenty-two dollars and fifty-three cents, including interest. Mr. Mayer? For you, the figure is approximately two million ninety-four thousand five hundred and seventy-one dollars even, including interest."

"We have friends," said Morgen, whose eyes were glaring with fury and hatred.

"Let's talk about these friends, then," said McGreevy, smiling.

He took out one of the sheets from the black file, and Quinn took the other.

"Frederic Morgen, born March 14, 1912, in New York. Two years in prison for armed robbery. Killed Charlie Basile on August 11, 1939. Sentenced to twelve years . . ."

"I am not Frederic Morgen."

"You are his brother. And the Kefauver Commission accused you, seven years ago, of having received money, not only from your brother, but also from two other men, who, the same commission discovered, drew the major part of their income from prostitution rackets."

"They were never able to prove anything. I was never prosecuted. They never convicted me."

"If they had, you never would have obtained a license to operated a casino. But we are in possession of this proof that the Kefauver Commission was not able to bring forth, Mr. Morgen. Account number 165 746 K, in the name of Frank Grabenher, in the Royal Britannia Bank. Shall I read you the dates of the deposits and the amounts? I am sure that the United States Senate investigators would be more than pleased to know about these . . ."

"Mr. Mayer," said Quinn, "I believe it is your turn. . . ."

"I can go on," said McGreevy. "I still have many things to tell Mr. Morgen. About a certain Leslie Muro, who was found dead on . . ."

"I think Mr. Morgen has understood by now," said Quinn good-naturedly. "Mr. Mayer?"

He began to read the from the second piece of paper.

"It is stated here that you were in close collaboration with a certain John Mandris of Los Angeles. Also with Joe Bagna and Mike Levy. You were almost indicted for murder, Mr. Mayer. Had it not been for the testimony of someone called Eddie Sage, the California police would certainly have looked more closely into the schedule of your activities at the time of the late Mr. Siegel's death, so honorably known in Las Vegas as the founder of the Flamingo Hotel and Casino. Shall I go on, Mr. Mayer?"

"Can I see that paper?"

"Certainly."

Mayer read through the typewritten sheet of paper, which was all about him. Without emotion, he put it down in front of Quinn and asked, in a calm voice: "Who is your client?"

"A man named Henry Chance," said Quinn. "He is a man whose respectability is more certain than that of the late Mr. Siegel, and, what's more, he has had a great deal of experience with casinos. Naturally, the Gambling Commission will give him the necessary license to operate."

"And what is he offering?"

"He will take care of the fines, settle with your creditors, and offer an additional six million nine hundred and seventy-five thousand dollars. Cash."

"As for you, Mr. Morgen," said McGreevy, "the offer is, co-incidentally, the same: the discharging of all liabilities, the take-over of the debts, and the payment of five million two hundred and ten thousand."

"Cash," said Quinn.

"Those are reasonable figures," said McGreevy.

"And you know it," said Quinn.

"Of course, you have a certain time within which you can study our proposals."

"And to discuss them with, let's say, your friends from Los Angeles," said Quinn.

"Whose names, addresses, and the number of shares they hold in your respective establishments are all on the sheets of paper we have right here. Shall we read them to you?"

"That will not be necessary," said Mayer.

"The time limit is two hours, exactly," said Quinn.

At ten-forty-four—they were running a little behind schedule because Morgen delayed things by presenting a counterproposal of five million five hundred thousand, which was rejected—the first papers were signed. Mayer and Morgen left with their little staff, who hadn't had the chance to utter one word.

"Now for our business, Mr. Levin," said Quinn.

McGreevy grabbed the papers that his assistant was handing him. He read them again. The agreement foresaw that the syndicates, which were officially represented by Moffatt, would receive full payment for the notes on the two casino-hotels formerly owned by Manny Morgen and Sol Mayer.

In addition, in association with Henry Chance, a steering committee would be formed by these same syndicates, which would oversee both establishments. This committee would be in charge of furnishing all technical equipment and food supplies for the casinos.

To do this, it would set up agreements, which were already drawn up, with several companies, the most important of which was the Jaua Food Organizaiton.

The papers were signed. Levin, Moffatt, and O'Connors left.

Quinn then turned to the young man with the steel-rimmed glasses, whose eyes were hidden behind the tinted lenses.

"Was it absolutely necessary to badger me with that note you passed me?"

"I am truly sorry," the young man answered, rather timidly. "I was just following Mr. Lerner's orders."

The red file had arrived in the hands of Steve Pulaski, in a suite in the Desert Inn Hotel, on September 16, at 2:00 P.M.

Its contents did not surprise the lawyer. As soon as Moe Abramowicz had begun explaining to him, in his Detroit office, what his "clients" expected of him, he understood the maneuver that was being set up: a battle between two factions of big-time criminals. Not ordinary criminals, but the other kind, the invisible kind, those who could buy congressmen and other political figures in Washington and abroad.

The contents of the red file, a single page, informed him that the man he was facing, whom he had to persuade, within two hours, to sell his casino, had had a murky past. Nothing official though, no charges had even been brought against him. But the succinct information, which was typewritten, revealed that he had been involved in some rackets; it mentioned names, dates, and figures; there was enough there to warrant twenty years.

And that was what surprised Pulaski most: the way the information was set up. It was not in the style of the big criminals. He thought it was more in the manner of the Secret Service, or the OSS, with whom he had worked during the war, or the FBI. Perhaps even a very large private-detective agency directed by some former intelligence people.

As for the "buyer," whose name was Andrew S. Cole, Pulaski was absolutely certain his name was an assumed one.

There was only one person he had no doubts about, and who didn't particularly interest him: the tall young man with steel-rimmed glasses, who had brought him the red file. As far as he was concerned, he was an errand boy, sent by Abramowicz, and he didn't look especially bright.

The final result, along with a most satisfactory fee, put Pulaski totally at ease. The transaction was completed, and the casino changed hands, without any difficulty. Caught between the threat of the frightening Gambling Commission and that of federal agents, having suddenly lost the support of the syndicates, represented by Levin and a leader of the syndicates by the name of Maggio, the man who was until then the owner of the casino gave in quite rapidly when, following Abramowicz's instructions, Pulaski presented him with the contents of the red file.

It served its purpose beautifully.

Ditto for the green file.

It came into the hands of a lawyer from Philadelphia by the name of Kim Foysie. The interesting thing was that Foysie himself was a gambler, a poker player, to be exact. He had a taste for capital punishment—in the figurative sense, of course—at the gambling table when a player went beyond his limit and got massacred. Foysie was not a man who felt any pity, in this area at least: "When you lose, you pay. Or else you don't play."

He had been contacted at the beginning of July, two and a half months earlier, by a colleague from New York whom he had known at Harvard, Philip Vanderbergh. He was not overly fond of Vanderbergh, who was as warm as an iceberg at the height of the Ice Age, but he appreciated the efficiency of his former classmate. Foysie examined his game as he would have a poker hand. He discovered three master cards: the danger faced by the "potential seller" of an imminent joint investigation by the IRS, the FBI and the narcotics boys, who were all equally convinced that narcotics money had been laundered through the casino-hotel in question; the attitude of the syndicates, which until then had been financial backers and which suddenly seemed determined to disinvolve themselves from the business (they were even prepared to take back their interests in another form, that of a council and supply committee, in association with companies operated by member of the Gozchiniak family); and, finally, the buying price, which was very reasonable for an establishment of that size: eight million six hundred and sixty-five thousand dollars, the firm and definitive price.

Once he was in Las Vegas, and in presence of the potential seller, who, during the first minutes, didn't even know he was selling anything, Foysie realized he had two other winning cards.

One was the threat, thinly veiled but real, and clearly expressed by a certain Abie Levin, who, with a man named Kramer, represented the syndicates, of a strike by the employees of the casino, which would have forced the owner to close his doors for several weeks and would have taken him to the edge of bankruptcy. His management would no longer be taking in receipts but would nevertheless have to keep paying the interest on the loans he had made for the purchase and improvement of facilities.

The second was the green file.

This contained proof, or at least strong evidence, of some questionable banking manipulations and transactions.

That was more than enough to win him over. And to make of Maryann Gozchiniak, the potential buyer, an actual owner.

Kim Foysie was probably the only one to have some doubts about the young man with the steel-rimmed glasses.

With his poker player's eye, he looked over the tall, thin young man, who remained almost silent, and who, during all the time he was in his presence, never removed his sunglasses.

He sat in on the negotiation as Abie Levin's assistant, and gave his name as Berkovich. It was he who had handed Foysie the green file. And the Philadelphian, by pure instinct, sensed some kind of pretense. He discussed it with Philip Vanderbergh, who shrugged a cold shoulder.

"I don't know any Berkovich."

"He was part of Levin's team, but I would swear that he is more than one of Levin's assistants. I had the feeling there was more to him than that."

"Why don't you ask Levin himself?"

"*Very* funny."

The five children of Simon Gozchiniak, who had been assissinated in 1950 by Finnegan, were taken in charge by Reb Klimrod, starting with the youngest, Ernie, whose schooling he paid for, and whom he eventually appointed as the official president of Jaua. If Reb Klimrod had any friends, they were the Gozchiniaks, who always showed him a faultless loyalty, although they were not actually King's Men, except for Ernie, of course.

He never forgot to thank anyone who had ever helped him in any way.

Maryann Gozchiniak's role in the casino operation was that of figurehead for Henry Chance, the King's Man for all matters pertaining to gambling. Just like Andy Cole and Roger Dunn, who participated in the fourth operation, the white file, and joined forces with Chance.

The last of the four files Diego had seen was the white one.

The two lawyers who used it, Moses Bern and Louis Benetti, had the advantage over Quinn and McGreevy, and over Pulaski (they were unaware of the existence of the other teams, of course), of knowing the middleman who had come, two months earlier, to offer them his proposal: a Jew of Rumanian origin named Benny Bercovici.

Bern and Benetti were all the more prepared to come into the picture because they also knew Abie Levin, for whom they had already officiated, two or three times, in some dry-cleaning enterprises. And they knew that Levin had some interests in several communications ventures.

The name of the man whose interests they were defending in Las Vegas—in other words, the buyer of two casinos—was even a familiar one. It was a certain Roger Dunn, a New York publisher and printer who, for the past six or seven years, had accumulated quite a fortune, thanks to a group of foreign-language newspapers geared to recent immigrants. For some time, this Dunn had diversified his activities by buying radio and television stations, and he was also publishing magazines. That Dunn should now want to extend his investments into the gambling field with the purchase of two casinos was not so surprising. Especially with the help of Abie Levin, who, during his negotiations with the "unwilling seller," used all his weight at the right moment. Levin was accompanied by two other leaders of the syndicates, Guarda and Bauer.

There was nothing extraordinary, either, in the presence of Dunn's younger brother, Jack, a tall, awkward, ungainly fellow, with a mustache as blond as his hair, and wearing thick glasses. "I would like to have my younger brother there," Dunn had said, looking somewhat embarrassed. "You can just say he is one of my assistants. He is a nice boy but I can't seem to get him interested in my business. Besides girls and cars, few things hold his attention. Maybe sitting through a negotiation such as this one will spark some interest in him. You can't choose your family.

Also, he will be giving you a white file that I suggest you read, and which will help you to convince the man you will be dealing with."

The transaction was successfuly concluded by Benetti and Bern, in a suite rented by Dunn in the Dunes Hotel. The only thing that surprised the Chicago lawyers was the time of the meeting: three o'clock in the morning, on September 17, 1957. "It is entirely my fault," Dunn had said. "I have some appointments in New York that I could not postpone, and I will not be able to reach Las Vegas before the end of the evening at the earliest. Begin without me if I am not there on time. After all, that jerky brother of mine will be there!"

A minor detail for Bern and Benetti. Given the amount of money they would be earning, they would have been prepared to work at any time of the day or night, with or without the "jerky brother" on their backs. For that price, they would have agreed to the presence of Dunn's dog, if the publisher had insisted.

And then, there was the white file. In truth, when Bern read the contents to the person Dunn had referred to as "the man you will be dealing with," he almost had the feeling that he was committing murder, so utterly crushing was the effect.

"We couldn't have done better with a gun," he later said to Dunn.

Just as Quinn and McGreevy, Steve Pulaski, and Kim Foysie had done before them, on the morning of the sixteenth, the afternoon of the sixteenth, and the evening of the sixteenth, in the same way, Bern and Benetti concluded their commando operation with the signature of agreements with syndicate representatives, foreseeing the creation of four steering committees and of four other committees, which would supply the casinos that had just been bought back, for a five percent guarantee for the syndicates of the gross receipts of the establishments, and this for a thirty-year period.

Thus, each of the four teams of lawyers was absolutely convinced that it was the only one in Las Vegas to be conducting such a transaction.

Each time, Levin was intermediary, during the second phase.

303

But, changing hotels four times in twenty-one hours, he also changed partners four times, never having the same syndicate leaders at his side.

He, therefore, was the only one to have noticed the presence of the young man with glasses at each meeting. He almost never spoke to him except when he was called Berkovich and was his assistant. On that occasion, Levin had asked him to get him some cigarettes and Berkovich had readily obeyed.

So Abie Levin was the first, aside from Reb, of course, to appreciate the extraordinary extent of the operation: in a period of twenty-one hours, from September 16 at eight-thirty, to September 17 at about five-thirty in the morning, six casinos changed hands.

All of these casinos were attached to a hotel, the smallest consisting of four hundred rooms and three restaurants.

Reb Klimrod's total investment in the Las Vegas St. Valentine's Day massacre was thirty-six million two hundred and forty thousand dollars.

The revenues from the two casino-hotels in Puerto Rico, the two in the Bahamas, and those later on in Atlantic City were added to those administered by Henry Chance.

Without including the two hotel chains and the three motel chains, which at that time were run by Ethel Court, and were in the United States, Canada, the Caribbean, South America, Europe, and elsewhere, an estimation of Henry Chance's fief, before taxes, would be eight hundred thousand to two million dollars. Per day!

4

"Happy birthday," said Diego, walking into the room. "Twenty-nine, that's practically senility, *amigo*."

"One moment, please, Diego," said Reb softly, with a smile. "And thank you for your wishes."

He was holding the telephone.

Diego was about to leave.

"Diego? Take care of her, please. Nicely. She was lovely. Except that she thinks Rabindranath Tagore is a baseball player." He had spoken in Spanish.

Diego leaned over the girl, who was sleeping and whose charming naked breast was pointed toward him. He kissed her on the lips, and signaled her to follow him. Picking up her scattered clothes, he carried them into the next room.

"This is the way out, *querida mia.*"

He watched her get dressed, thinking. "Nicely. How much did 'nicely' mean?" He decided on one thousand dollars, with the absolute indifference he had toward money, an indifference that bordered on contempt. He could just as easily have given her one hundred thousand.

"There must be some mistake," said the surprised girl. "This is a thousand-dollar bill."

And honest, too, thought Diego. Maybe I should marry her, after all. Mamita would be pleased.

He pretended to examine the bill closely.

"My, you are right! Please forgive me, *señorita.*"

He handed her a second thousand-dollar bill and delicately led her out the door this time. Enough was enough. One day, just for a laugh, he thought, I will make a big pile of two or three hundred million dollars, and I'll set it on fire. Just for a laugh.

Through the closed door, he could hear Reb's indistinct voice, speaking German or Yiddish or French—or Italian, Spanish, Hebrew, Polish, Arabic, even, perhaps—why not?—English.

He ordered breakfast.

Tudor Anghel arrived at the same time as the bacon and eggs.

"It's not a well-known law," said Anghel, "but my guys went through the books with a fine-tooth comb, and it is perfectly applicable."

"Who will do it?"

"Thomas Perry, Del Moran, Tex Haynes, James Olivero."

"But with Perry in charge?"

"Yes."

"And with the help of?"

"The firm of Kinkaid & Nelson, in Las Vegas. Perry has contacted them, and they have agreed to take on the case. They are good; I have used them before."

"Three years and ten months ago," said Reb. "In the Salt Lake City case. Fifty-two thousand six hundred and fifty dollars in fees for four hours of actual work, at the time. I would like them to be a little less greedy this time."

He was eating his eggs hungrily. According to Diego's calculations, he had slept six hours in all during the past three days—and he was including, in those six hours, a few tumbles with the pretty and very honest Linda—but Reb's face was so thin and drawn that fatigue, if there was any, did not leave its mark. He smiled at Anghel.

"I am not critizing you, Tudor. I agreed to those fees, at the time. Tell me about this law, please."

"It permits the exchange, within specified amounts, of a sizable piece of desert property for another one, a smaller but better-situated one."

"Which means what in this case?"

"Tom Perry, who is tied to me by a trust agreement, is the official owner of thirty-one thousand one hundred thirty-five acres in Nye County. In 1952 you paid . . . well, he paid one dollar thirty for each acre. Which comes to . . ."

"Forty thousand four hundred and seventy-five dollars and fifty cents."

"I'll take your word for it. So, under this law, we can exchange this property for another one, in our case some land just north of Las Vegas, about seventy-five square miles."

"Do you foresee any problems?"

"No. The law will cover it and the governor of the state of Nevada will not oppose the exchange. They have their own reasons in the governor's office in Carson City. The U.S. Air Force wants to enlarge the size of its nuclear-testing site. These thirty-one thousand one hundred thirty-five acres the state would be obtaining would enable them, in turn, to collect some revenue from the flyboys, and to collect it now, not seven years from now, when the land will be worth gold. Seven years from now, there could be another governor, and another administration."

"What is this land actually worth?"

"Three hundred thousand. But it will be worth ten or fifteen times that much in ten years."

Reb's gray eyes were lost in the distance.

"Diego," he said, "call Nick in New York, please. Tudor, take this down please: account number 62396 AT 17, at Sheridan, in their Westwood branch. The account is in your name. The money is already there. Pay Tom Perry the twenty-five thousand dollars you agreed on, and give whatever bonus you think appropriate to your guys. As for you, two possibilities: either you collect your seventy-five thousand dollars now or you take five percent of the future profits, when the land is resold. Your choice."

He bit into a piece of bacon. Anghel was dumbfounded.

"Reb, what a royal gift! I would prefer to pay my guys from my own pocket and take the five percent. I am not crazy."

"New York on the phone," announced Diego.

"All right, Tudor, you've made your choice. The Moran, Haynes, and Olivero deals are the same as the Perry?"

"Same principle. But the lots are smaller."

"Do it. End of discussion. Take care of all the details. I will be in Los Angeles next Wednesday at eight-thirty in the morning, at the Panamex Motel, under the name Beck. Thank you for coming."

Anghel left, still in a state of shock. Five percent! That could mean two hundred thousand dollars!

"It's his birthday, today," explained Diego. "He is becoming a little senile, with age."

Behind Diego, Reb's voice.

"Nick? Yes, thank you for your wishes. What's the story with the freighters in Abadan?"

Later, in 1977, the Nevada land, purchased for forty thousand four hundred and seventy-five dollars and fifty cents, eighty-six thousand with all the expenses, fees, and commissions, was sold for twenty-four million five hundred thousand dollars.

Tudor Anghel's wife and children (he had died in the meantime) received one million two hundred twenty-five thousand dollars, the five percent share of the land resale.

They left Las Vegas around six in the evening, on this same September 18.

"Now what's the point, I wonder. We slept what—three hours? If that. That Terry had legs that never ended. A boa. It gives me the shivers just to think of them. I'd be surprised if we slept two hours and forty-three minutes. And now what do we do? Hit the road. It's six o'clock, the sun is setting, exhausted; it's going to be pitch black. We won't know where to sleep, or where to eat. We will probably die in the desert, and our skeletons will scare the little children who will come upon us after the nuclear war . . ."

"Diego."

"I know: shut up, Diego. But the revolution is coming."

"Stop, please. I mean the car."

Diego stopped. They were in the heart of the desert; it was certainly beautiful, especially with the lights of Las Vegas beginning to glow in the distance as night fell. But Diego was exhausted.

"I'll drive," said Reb. "You get in the back and go to sleep. There's a blanket there."

Diego burst out laughing, and said, with the utmost sarcasm: "I'm not that crazy. You are the worst driver on this side of the Rio Grande. On the other, also, probably. And I wouldn't want to see you die like an ass just because you missed a turn. Reb, you are really a terrible driver."

"I know," said Reb. "But I'll drive anyway, and you can sleep a little. I'll go very slowly."

"You swear it?"

It was absolutely true that at the wheel of an automobile, perhaps because he had learned late, Reb was a public danger. He sometimes had disquieting lapses of attention. Usually, it was Diego who did the driving.

"I swear," said Reb, with his right hand lifted. "On Settiniaz's head."

"What a joke! You know I can't stand him."

"Go to sleep."

The car was a kind of Jeep, which, in Diego's opinion, must have been used during the war in Korea after serving in the Pacific; after which a horde of bodywork specialists must have taken it apart and put it back together ten or fifteen times, before they started banging on it with steel pipes. It was intimidating. But Reb had said to Diego: "Find me something that doesn't look like much."

And he had found something, clearly, that didn't look like

308

anything. And as for paying for it, well, he had bought it for fifty-one dollars from a gold prospector who was broke, at the door of the Last Chance Casino at the southern end of Las Vegas. Fifty-one dollars: fifty for the tires, which were almost new, and the steering wheel, which was encrusted with pyrites, the gold of madmen, and one dollar for the rest.

It was also true that they had slept very little. The final phase of the Las Vegas St. Valentine's Day had ended during the previous night. Reb had spent the afternoon on the telephone, making calls throughout the world, having, at times, two people on the phone at once. Then, at about eight-thirty, Abie Levin had arrived, discreetly. He and Reb had locked themselves up for hours, until well past midnight. Levin had then left. Reb was on the telephone once again, especially to Europe, where, because of the time difference, it was already the next day, though early. This went on until two in the morning at least.

After that, Diego had pulled Linda and Terry out of their own beds and brought them back upstairs.

At six o'clock they had to get up, once again to telephone, and to see Anghel, who had come as requested.

And for the rest of the day, without a stop, the telephone again.

And now, they were on the road. *Madre de Dios!*

Diego fell asleep under the stars.

The jolts of the Jeep woke him up. When he opened his eyes, he could see hardly anything, other than a few rocks and trees in the light of the single headlight that was still in working condition.

And he was cold.

"I understand: you had one of your moments of distraction, we went off the road, and we are dead. Right now, we are on the road to heaven. It's a fucking steep road, isn't it? They could pave it a little, given the amount of traffic that must go by here. . . ."

"There's some coffee; it's almost hot. And a cheese sandwich."

Reb explained that they had stopped in a place called Tonopah two hours earlier, and that although he had tried to wake him, there was no hope.

"You were screaming: 'Terry, stop strangling me with your fucking legs!' "

309

Diego drank the coffee: cold, without sugar and American. "I am really leading a miserable life."

He got back into the front seat, shivering.

"Shall I drive?"

"Don't bother. We are almost there."

But after that they went on for about another hour on this mountain road . . .

. . . and the gunshot tore into the silence of the night, as well as into the trunk of a nearby pine.

Diego opened his mouth but didn't get the chance to utter a word: two more bullets flew by his ears, one of them going between him and Reb.

"Take it easy, Diego," said Reb calmly. "As long as you don't move, there is no reason for him to get you."

Three more shots, one after the other, and this time the windshield was shattered. But the Jeep kept climbing the mountain road.

"I hope," said Reb, "that he found his glasses. He aims a little less accurately without them."

The seventh bullet hit the rim of the windshield, the eighth reached the back, ripping the seat.

"We are almost there," said Reb. "I think I told you this already: he makes the best pork and beans. Actually, that's all he does."

"Stubborn, aren't you?" said MacTavish roguishly.

"In a way," said Reb. "I see you found your glasses."

"With or without glasses, I can shoot you in the eye, the one of your choice, from four hundred yards. Even if I am below you and it's night. We can try whenever you want."

"Maybe some other time. Fergus, I've been thinking about that counter-offer you made me, and I don't think I can accept it. Two thousand eight hundred and twenty-five dollars—it's much too much."

"Three thousand," said MacTavish. "Don't try to put anything over on me. I may be seventy-three . . ."

"Seventy-seven," said Reb. "Do you have any beans left?"

"What do you think?" snickered MacTavish. "With the thousand or so pounds you had sent to me yesterday, it would be surprising if I didn't. As for the six frying pans and the twelve mules, you wasted your time. I already have a pan and a mule. Who the devil needs seven pans? I can heat some up for you, if you want. And I am not senile, even though I was born in 1884."

"In 1880," said Reb. "On September 2, 1880, at nine-thirty in the morning. Your father's name was Angus MacTavish, and he was born on January 6, 1851, in Carson City, a product of Fergus Athol MacTavish, born August 23, 1825, in Chillicothe, Ohio, and of Mary MacMurtrie, born June 13, 1830, in Cleveland, Ohio. Your mother's name was Kathleen MacIntyre, born March 14, 1862, to Jock MacIntyre, who was born . . . Put a lot of bacon in, please. If you have enough, of course. I wouldn't want to drain your supplies."

"The supplies consist of tons," said MacTavish. "The six and a half pounds I still had, plus the two tons you had delivered from Pennsylvania by special plane. It should last me a while. And my grandfather MacIver, where was he born?"

"MacIntyre, not MacIver. He was born in Neenah, Wisconsin, on April 30, 1831. He married Maeva MacAllister, who was born on February 8, 1840, in Mackinaw City, Michigan . . . and the spices, please, don't forget the spices."

"Are you going to teach me how to prepare pork and beans? It's just like those damn radios and televisions you sent me. And that lousy enormous antenna you had set up. It ruins the scenery. And the refrigerators keep me from sleeping. They hum. Besides, I'll bet you don't know when the first MacTavish set foot in this country."

"Calum Fergus MacTavish, born March 22, 1612, at Kinloch Rannoch, Scotland. He arrived in Boston on October 9, 1629. He came over on the *Angus Stewart*, whose captain was MacIlroy. He was a carpenter, then a caretaker at Harvard College, as of 1636. Two thousand six hundred and thirty, that's my last offer."

"Listen here, young man," said MacTavish. "How many times have you come to see me in the last few weeks? Six?"

"Five. Six counting today."

"And each time I said three thousand. What's said is said. And by the way, I've cut those damn telephone wires you had put in. My stupid daughter and that idiot of a son-in-law of mine didn't stop calling me. They are very happy with the service

311

station and the motel you gave them, along with the garage. But that's no reason to call me every single day to tell me so. Good God, it didn't stop ringing! Just yesterday, there were two calls. One of which was some banker who wanted to talk to me about an income of one thousand dollars a month some jerk has set up for me. Who is this other idiot next to you with the yellow eyes who can't stop laughing like a jerk?"

"His name is Slim Zapata," said Reb. "It just so happens I have a proposal to make to you concerning him. I cannot go beyond two thousand six hundred and thirty dollars, and you refuse to come down from three thousand. How about if we play poker for your gold mine? Slim Zapata could play for me. A man named McCabe in Tonopah told me you are the best poker player in all the Rockies."

"Before or after the beans? They're almost ready. It's better to eat them now, or they're going to get cold. It's always the same: around midnight or one in the morning, the air gets cold around here. We're almost at twelve thousand feet."

"*After* the beans," said Reb. "Why do you think I came?"

"I always knew I was going to beat him," said Diego. "Even when he was winning by one million eight hundred and twenty-three thousand dollars. His downfall was inevitable. It only took me fourteen hours. The hardest part, in the end, was those lousy beans."

There was no answer. He turned around and saw that Reb had fallen asleep, in the rear of the Jeep, where they had simply ripped out all the bullet-torn parts, including the remaining fender. To Diego's surprise, the Jeep was still running, valiantly. And it was crossing through an admirable landscape, in suffocating heat, where the lights were playing games, running through the whole range of reds and yellows, from burning shades to blinding white ones. Diego felt an overpowering and joyous exaltation.

"Slim Zapata!" He burst out laughing.

. . . But stopped the next second.

"Reb? I don't even know where I am supposed to go."

No answer. He took one hand off the wheel and shook the leg of the sleeping man.

"Reb, where are we going?"

"Reno airport. New York plane."

Diego hit the brakes. The Jeep swerved, in place, on two wheels. It turned its back on Montezuma peak and headed north.

"I didn't understand one thing," said Diego, a few minutes later. "Do you think you might articulate?"

"It would really have bothered me to leave Nevada with a failure behind me," Reb repeated, half asleep. "Even for some beans."

5

Diana and David Settiniaz had their third child in 1957, and, after two girls, they finally had a boy (the third of their six children), whom they named David Michael.

Reb Klimrod had emerged from the Amazonian jungle at the beginning of the summer of 1956. Settiniaz found him changed, transformed. Not extraordinarily so, at first glance. He had always manifested an incredible, abnormal, almost inhuman calm and an extreme, almost excessive courtesy toward everyone. Settiniaz said later: "I never heard him raise his voice or show the slightest bad temper. He wasn't a saint, though; in fact, a few of us often wished he was more . . . more like us. This control he had over himself always made me very uncomfortable. Georges Tarras saw it as a form of paranoia, but I think that is a little excessive."

Reb had built up his first fortune with magical rapidity. That he was able to disengage himself completely from his businesses for thirteen months shows the solidity of the organization he had set up.

"On his return," said Settiniaz, "he was even more extraordinary. He came back with a sort of ferocity and cold-bloodedness he had never shown until then. He was almost thirty; he had matured. In any case, he moved faster and higher than ever before, in all areas. The expansion was in full force."

Klimrod arrived at Settiniaz's office on June 30, 1956. He said he had come to see "how things were going." Settiniaz explained how the merest transaction had been recorded, and the precautions he had taken to ensure the most complete secrecy.

"I would like to look over your files for three or four days, David. Even if it means giving your staff some vacation. July 4 is a holiday in the United States, is it not? Tell them things are going so well that you are giving everyone three extra days off."

"Don't you want me to stay and help you?"

Reb shook his head.

"Thank you very much, David. But I don't want to deprive you of the presence of your young son. Michael, is it?" His pale eyes gave him a friendly, amused glance.

Settiniaz felt like a perfect fool: he had had to fight with his wife to impose Michael; "Reb Settiniaz" would have seemed far-fetched, and Diana would have divorced him had he suggested Reb.

Reb said simply: "Have a good vacation, David."

Settiniaz, his wife, and the children went to their summer place. On July 2, he called the office, getting no answer. On the morning of the fifth, upon his return, he found everything in perfect order. The keys were in the vault, along with a note: "David: Thank you and bravo. From now on, one percent." And, as a signature, an *R*, written firmly. He had just doubled Settiniaz's percentage on his own profits, and that represented tens of millions of dollars.

Two months later, Sotheby's in London shipped to David Settiniaz a magnificent Gauguin. "For Michael. Especially," said the unsigned card.

Nick Petridis met with Reb Klimrod on July 5, 1956, during the afternoon. The telephone call had come six hours earlier, at around nine-thirty in the morning that same day: a certain Major Beck was asking to speak to him. One of three code names. Petridis cleared his office and took the call.

"Nick? Can you leave New York for a few days?"

"Sure, if Tony can stay and take my place."

"I need only you. Ideally, you could meet me at three o'clock today, at the Algonquin Hotel, room in the name De Carbajal. With whatever you think you have to show me. And plan to have someone come by at five-thirty to pick up the files and take them back to your office. We can leave together for the airport. The plane for Paris is at ten minutes of eight."

Within an hour (he was always ready for this kind of emergency), Petridis had assembled "whatever you think you have to show me," that is to say, the complete balance sheets for a thirteen-month period of a shipping company owning over three million tons.

It took Reb one hour to go over the enormous file, and another hour to draw conclusions from it and establish new directives.

Petridis himself went down to the lobby to hand the files back to his two assistants who had come to pick them up.

He was again at Reb's side when they were flying over the Atlantic.

"And it happened just like that," Petridis said later. "He suddenly began telling me about his past, or at least a little bit about his past. He spoke of the two times he was in Tangiers, right after the war, and told me he had spent some time in Cairo, in France, in Sicily, and in Italy. I was rather surprised: at that time I had known him for seven years, we had traveled together often, and never had he made any allusion to his younger days. I still thought he was Argentine. When we arrived somewhere, he would never say whether he had been there before. His taste for secrecy was more because he felt indifferent toward the dead things of the past than due to the any fear or mania. Except for business. In that area, there never was the slightest ambiguity: I was paid, beyond all my expectations, by the way, to preserve his anonymity, which I did until the end. At the beginning, my brother and I were intrigued: this man had more ships than Onassis and Niarchos put together, more than Ludwig, and, except for Settiniaz, we, the Petridises, were the only ones who knew how rich he was. It was a curious sensation. . . .

"As for drawing any conclusions from the situation, one would have to be crazy. Especially after the Harper affair . . ."

"John Patrick Harper," said Reb very softly, "was recommended as an agent by your brother, Tony."

"I would also have recommended him."

"And the investigation conducted at the time confirmed that he was reasonably trustworthy. As much as you can trust a human being."

"Reb, he only made a little mistake. Which I took care of."

315

"But which you did not tell me about, Nick."

It was night over the Atlantic, but for a long time Reb nevertheless looked out the window. But, for that last remark he slowly turned his head, and his eyes rested on the Greek attorney, who shuddered. The sort of haze that usually filtered Klimrod's gaze was gone, and from his eyes came a startling expression of ferocity.

"Harper is an all-right guy who did something stupid," Nick said, feeling very uncomfortable.

"He misappropriated twenty-six thousand three hundred dollars."

"It wasn't really misappropriation. And he reimbursed it all two days later. Reb, what did you want me to do? Kill him?"

"I took care of it this morning, Nick. It's done."

Petridis stared at him, stunned.

"You mean you . . ."

"Harper is alive. And will remain so, for as long as I choose. But a certain safety device, which was planned a long time ago for this sort of circumstance, was put into effect this morning. Of course, Harper, from this day forward, ceases to exist for you and me. That is not all, unfortunately for him. His financial situation will become extremely difficult, and that will not be his only problem. He is going to have a great deal of trouble finding work worthy of the name. And, therefore, trouble paying back the twenty thousand dollars you lent him, last May 26, after you both had lunch at the Seven Seas, at table number 18. Even if he were to sell his house outside Philadelphia. Which is mortgaged, always annoying in a situation like his, and it creates other problems. At least you won't be out the cost of the lunch, since I understand that that that particular restaurant, as well as the entire building, belongs to you, although it is officially in the name of one of your cousins. Nick, as far as Harper is concerned, you behaved correctly, and I am not criticizing you, except for the fact that you didn't feel you had to tell me about it. Do not commit that sort of error again, please. But enough said about Harper."

He smiled, his eyes once again lost in a dream.

"Let's speak of something else, Nick. For example, of the Frenchman and of this other man with whom we will be working . . ."

The Frenchman's name was Paul Soubise. He had been George Tarras's student for two years, until Tarras gave up teaching.

His name appeared for the first time in files that reached Settiniaz in the fall of 1953, and at that time Soubise was already playing an important part in the administration of a large French shipping company. The way in which he became a King's Man was typical of the methods used by Klimrod.

Except for direct intervention on his part (and as of 1955 that was extremely rare), new names of those who figured in the upper echelons—a total of three thousand four hundred men and women earning an annual income of more than fifty thousand dollars, at the time—were subject to a particular procedure. Generally, on the same day a person was added, but sometimes two or three days before, an anonymous messenger would bring David Settiniaz a file: "Strictly confidential. To be delivered to addressee in person." Should Settiniaz be absent, the messenger would leave without having made his delivery. There was always a connection between the "strictly confidential" file and the new name. The file contained an extraordinarily detailed curriculum vitae of the newcomer.

Files like these also existed for the Black Dogs.

And they were continuously updated, by subsequent information, on an acquisition, for example, or a change in status, such as a divorce.

The higher up in the hierarchy of the organization a person was, the more complete his file.

In certain files, the word "SPECIAL" in red would appear on the top left corner of the first page. That was a sign that the individual in question was already or was about to become a King's Man, meaning he would have direct contact with Klimrod and receive orders directly from him. In the case of Tudor Anghel, for one, a Black Dog file was set up for him in 1951. The red caption appeared on it four years later, symbolizing his rise in the hierarchy.

There were never more than eighteen red captions.

In Soubise's file, it appeared the first day. The first report stated that, besides having an impressive collection of diplomas, the man possessed a "very remarkable intelligence" as well as "political ambitions and the right social and family connections to, sooner or later, lead him to a high position in his country."

This last remark, which came from Jethro's organization in 1953, proved to be premonitory: Soubise, during the sixties, became a member of the French government.

Also in Soubise's past: a rather clumsy speculation in 1950, probably the result of inexperience; a private life that was not exactly immaculate; a few tricks to hide some income in two Swiss bank accounts.

"Nick Petridis, Paul Soubise," said Reb.

The meeting took place in Cannes, in a large hotel on the Croisette, on July 6, 1956. It was afternoon.

It was Soubise's third meeting with Reb Klimrod. As far as he knew, Klimrod was an Argentine, apparently quite rich, who was trying to make a place for himself in the shipping business, competing with all those Greeks, and succeeding with *brio*.

"I foresee certain changes," said Reb. "But before we get started, I think Paul should understand the entire situation. Nick?"

Following the exact instructions Reb had given him, Nick began lining up figures, on hotel stationery, which was later burned. And as he was noting the incredible outline of the companies and their respective tonnage, he was deriving a malicious, almost arrogant pleasure as he saw the astonishment growing on the Frenchman's face.

"That's it," he said finally.

Soubise removed his glasses, rubbed his eyes. He began to laugh.

"And Lloyd's? Are you sure you don't own Lloyd's?"

"I may have overlooked it," said Reb. "Nick, do I own Lloyd's?"

"Not as far as I know," said Nick. "But that doesn't mean anything. You may have bought it without telling me."

He smiled at Soubise.

"He is capable of that."

Soubise picked up the sheets of paper, read them over again, and made an approximate calculation.

"Close to three and a half million tons."

"Three million six hundred and twenty-eight thousand," said Reb quietly. "Two million seven hundred and fifty-three thousand of which are oil tankers. Owned by seventy-four companies. It is concerning these tankers that I wish to make some changes. . . ."

And it was, to use his own words, "extremely simple." It was now the beginning of July, which gave them six months. . . .

"At most. Ideally, the maneuver should be, if not completed, then at least well under way by . . . let's say November 15."

As to the maneuver, it consisted of a giant redeployment of the entire fleet of tankers, under cover of the seventy-four companies, whose shares belonged to Reb, through trust agreements between himself and the Petridis brothers, Soubise, and Tarras, who in turn controlled the seventy-four secondary trustees, who were the official owners.

"Nick, I want you to study each ship and determine precisely which ones will be free of any contract on November 15. As a first step. And for each one, I would like to have an indication of the possibilities of a one-time trip."

"There are quite a few long-term agreements that cannot be canceled."

"I know that, Nick," said Reb. "And that is why I want a ship-by-ship breakdown. Even going beyond November 15."

"So that you can do as many one-time trips as possible as of November 15?"

"Exactly."

"For how long after November 15?"

"One year."

The same question was burning on the lips of both Soubise and Petridis: what was going to happen on November 15?

Neither of them asked it.

For two reasons. First, they realized that if Klimrod had wanted them to know the answer, he would already have told them. Second, they knew that Klimrod would never speak "in front of a third party." The way the two men eventually recalled this story showed the amusing duality and the perfectly identical reasoning followed by the New Yorker and the Frenchman.

"Another thing," said Reb, "and it would be best if Paul handled this: I would like a report on all the oil tankers currently in service, in construction, and on order."

"Including Japan?"

"Including everything. Including the ships that are being built for our companies—and in those cases, everything should be done to accelerate the work—and those that others are having built.

"And in their case, everything should be done to slow them down."

Reb smiled.

"Don't suggest any pirate ships, Paul, please. . . . You should also include all the oil tankers currently at sea, whoever the owners and whatever their flag, and find out whether they are currently leased or when they could be, and at what cost. This for the next twelve months. Can you do that, Paul?"

"It's a monstrous task."

"Exactly sixteen months ago, on March 25, 1955, I asked you if, when the time came, you would agree to come work for me, full-time. You answered yes. I asked you to weigh your decision. You confirmed it to me at our following meeting, on April 11. The moment has come, Paul. Come and play with us."

"All right," said Soubise, feeling feverish. "When do you want all this?"

"Yesterday," said Reb. "You can set up your own company today. We will arrange financial and legal matters later on. For these transactions, you will work with Nick and his brother, Tony, whom I trust implicitly and who will be in charge of this area. With them, and with another man, who will join us this evening . . . I would rather you did not smoke, Paul, unless you're really desperate to."

"It can wait," said Soubise, slipping his pipe back into its pouch.

"One more thing," said Reb. "I would like a list of all the oil tankers in the world that we can charter between today and December 31 of next year. I don't suppose I need to caution you that this should be done with discretion. Use all the companies at our disposal, and, if necessary, more companies, which we can create for this purpose."

"And shall we draw up charter agreements?"

"Yes. With no other limitation than that of discretion. I don't want anyone to suspect anything."

To charter ships as of this month of July for actual use beginning November 15 was going to entail astounding investments, and, mostly, perfectly unproductive ones over a period of several months, Soubise pointed out.

"This point did not escape me, Paul," answered Reb. "Study each charter separately, and limit the unproductive periods as much as possible. You know as well as I that we have several options. And, if need be, I am prepared to take some losses."

This operation involved around fifty million dollars. The money, which was channeled through a multitude of banks, came essentially from an insurance company, three banks, one of which was Hunt Manhattan and another an establishment in Hong Kong, and a group of financial investors assembled by Nessim Shahadzé.

From the start, in August of 1951, a special procedure had been arranged between David Settiniaz and Reb Klimrod for emergency calls.

Klimrod's frequent and sometimes long absences, like the one lasting from May 1955 to June 1956, made such a procedure absolutely indispensable. The first time it was put to use was in May of 1956. The code words were "Brazil" followed by "Hawaii" and "San Francisco," to be used in the same sentence.

Settiniaz took a long-distance call, coming from Rome, and the voice he heard had a heavy accent.

Settiniaz replied: "You must call Mr. Diego Haas in Rio. *H,* two *as, s.* The number is . . ."

"Please," said the voice, "I would rather not do it myself. Could you please convey a message?"

"Certainly."

"Just two words: Shenken Dov. I will spell them. . . ."

"That's it?"

"That's it. Thank you."

He hung up. Settiniaz called Rio himself, and Diego Haas answered. He repeated the two words to him. There was no reaction from the little Argentine, who simply made a few sarcastic remarks about what the fucking weather in New York must be, and who then invited Settiniaz to come spend a week or two at his house in Ipanema. Settiniaz, who was not far from thoroughly despising Haas, answered that he would love to come, as soon as his schedule permitted it. He hung up without mentioning Reb's name.

And this was the only clue he had, this phone call from Rome, that led him to believe that the informer in this matter was an Israeli by the name of Yoël Bainish.

He had no proof, of course.

But it also convinced him that Reb's reappearance at the beginning of the summer of 1956 was not a coincidence.

The Israeli attack on the Sinai took place in October 1956, at five o'clock in the afternoon. The French and British paratroopers unfolded their corollas on November 5, at seven-fifteen in the morning. Eight days later, the heads of the Arab states, who had gathered in Beirut, confirmed their wish to close the Suez Canal, which, incidentally, was obstructed by the wreckage of the ships sunk on Nasser's orders to interrupt oil exportation to France and Great Britain. In both those countries, the supplies from the Middle East, their main source, fell by eighty percent, leaving them with two to three months' worth of reserves. On November 27, when the pitiful retreat of the French and British troops was announced, an oil rescue mission was put into effect, arranging for the shipment of five hundred thousand barrels of oil a day, coming from wells in the United States, the Caribbean, and Venezuela.

The canal remained closed for six months. In order to reach Europe from the Persian Gulf, tankers were obliged to make a detour around the Cape. Only those of large tonnage were capable of such a trip, a distance of eleven thousand three hundred nautical miles.

Reb Klimrod had been, along with Goulandris, the first to foresee what would be called "supertankers." The Suez affair made a fortune for most of the Greeks—Livanos, Kulukundis, Embiricos, Goulandris, Vergottis, Onassis, Niarchos. They held a wild celebration one evening in the Café Royal in London, where they used to meet. Daniel Ludwig realized a net profit of one hundred million dollars.

As for Reb Klimrod, who had, as of November 29, 1956, and for the following year, until 1968, in fact, obtained a tonnage of more than four million in oil tankers alone, under eighty-one different names, his profit passed the half-billion-dollar mark in less than one year.

Yoël Bainish later said that he was part of the first phase of the Kadesh operation, which had a double objective: reduction of the Palestinian pocket in Gaza and taking Sharm al-Sheikh, at the extreme tip of the Sinai. He had had to insist on obtaining access to one of the sixteen Dakotas called to drop paratroopers over the Mitla Pass, only about twenty-five miles from the Suez Canal. Having touched ground without any difficulty, he had had to walk for nearly two hours to reach the memorial to Colonel Parker, who was the British governor of Sinai from 1910 to 1923. The following night, October 30, he watched the arrival of the 202nd Brigade, which had covered the one hundred eighty-six and a half miles separating Mitla from the official Israeli border in twenty-eight hours.

He returned to Tel Aviv on November 6, his vacation being over.

In 1956, he was thirty-one years old and held the rank of captain, but his real work was for the Israeli government or with the secret service.

In Tel Aviv, he learned of his next assignment: Adolf Eichmann.

He had left for Rome around November 25 or 26. He met Reb in the Italian capital at the beginning of December, and, according to him, it was a reunion "after a time of separation." Bainish gave no indication as to when, why, or how he and Klimrod met between this date and their last known meeting, before Klimrod's departure for South America and the execution of Erich Steyr.

Settiniaz never knew Yoël Bainish other than by name.

Tarras, on the other hand, went to the Middle East on several occasions and saw the Israeli twice. Bainish even visited him during the summer of 1978, when an Israeli government delegation went to the United States. He spent a weekend at the house in Maine. Years had gone by since the Suez affair, and perhaps Bainish knew of Klimrod's confidence in Tarras. In any case, he answered a few questions.

He said he had been "in contact regularly" with Reb, since about 1950. "I like him very much, and I think he feels the same way about me."

Tarras didn't ask him about Suez.

Nor about Jethro, whose remarkable secret organization, Tarras believed, may very well have been conceived by an authentic specialist in secret-service matters.

On the other hand, he did ask him whether Reb had played any part in the capture of Adolf Eichmann.

At first Bainish shook his head. Then he said: "Not directly."

The other man Reb Klimrod wanted to bring in with Nick Petridis and Paul Soubise, but only for this pressing oil-tanker operation, was a twenty-nine-year-old Lebanese by the name of Nessim Shahadzé.

Inasmuch as Soubise, with his obvious, almost ostentatious intelligence, had immediately impressed Petridis, when it came to this new choice of a lieutenant, Nick thought that Klimrod had, for once, made an error.

Nessim Shahadzé was a young man whose nonchalance bordered on parody, with a high-pitched, almost feminine voice, apparently more interested in women and in sweets than in finance; he was the type of individual you can imagine at the age of fifty being potbellied and bald.

Petridis had another reason for not being too enthusiastic about the arrival of the Lebanese: he and his brother had been Klimrod's men for shipping matters from the beginning. Not without good reason, he and Tony felt that they had done a good job. In an incredibly short period of time, they had gone from one cargo ship to sixteen oil tankers, then to a fleet surpassed in tonnage only by that of Daniel Ludwig, who had begun in the thirties; and the time would come when they would surpass Ludwig. Nick and Tony felt that some of the merit for such an amazing expansion was theirs. The fact that Reb had already brought in Soubise had irritated Petridis, until the Frenchman's apparent aptitude had soothed his wounded pride.

Besides, the enormous project Reb had disclosed warranted an enlargement of the staff.

"But to fling some sticky Arab on us!" Nick said to Tony.

Shahadzé arrived in Cannes in the early evening. Fate had it that Soubise was standing at the window at just the right moment. The four Rolls-Royces pulling up in a row had already caught his eye. The battalion of statuesque bleached blondes that descended from the cars with the ease of a commando force landing at Port Said aroused his interest even more. He burst out laughing and said, "You must come and see this!" Reb and Nick got to the window just as Shahadzé appeared, looking imperial, nonchalant, and a little sullen. He walked into the hotel with the air of someone who had just bought it.

Soubise caught the mischievous look in Klimrod's eyes and said: "Didn't you mention a Lebanese?"

"Yes, and that's he," answered Reb, obviously enjoying all this. "He should be here any minute."

It actually took him thirty seconds, but finally there was a soft knock at the door of the suite where the meeting had been in progress since five o'clock. Soubise went to the door. Nessim came in, a pudgy fellow wearing on his left index finger a diamond of several carats. He greeted Soubise in French, which he spoke without the trace of an accent. Petridis in English, with the precious intonation of a Harrow student whose voice has not yet changed, and Reb in German. He sat down and didn't say one word for the next two hours, during which time his eyes would close every so often, as if he were suddenly irresistibly weary, and with a serene indifference toward the surprised glances of the American and the Frenchman.

Reb, impassive, continued the business discussion. He went over one of his major ideas concerning the transportation of oil, which was to fit out as many ships as possible in such a way as to permit the eventual transportation of something other than oil, in order to avoid empty and thus nonprofitable return trips, a new idea at the time.

They turned to terribly complex calculations, involving numerous areas, including exchange rates. Soubise, who had attended the Polytechnic School, among others, tried his hand at the calculations.

Shahadzé then said, in his high-pitched voice: "Don't waste your time. The exact figures are . . ."

And he began spouting out an astonishing array of calculations, made on the spot.

Of all the King's Men, Nessim Shahadzé was assuredly the

most original, but his spectacular indolence concealed a mind that was actually diabolical. He was the only one to use the familiar *tu* form with Reb—besides Diego's familiarities, but Diego was not a King's Man; he was his shadow—and the only one also who could calculate faster than Reb, and in that area he was a pure genius. He had other talents, as hidden as the first. Two men, in the oil field, tried to get around the exorbitant monopolies set up by the large companies by dealing directly with the producing emirs. One of them was Ludwig, and if he was partially successful, he also incurred many problems, among them a general boycott, which did him a great deal of harm. The other one was Reb, and in his case everything went along without the slightest difficulty, with the harmony of a chamber orchestra, formed by the Petridises, Soubise, and Nessim Shahadzé. With, at the cello, a Swiss banker by the name of Aloïs Knapp.

Knapp was a man Reb Klimrod would never have met had it not been for an extraordinary and tragic incident that took place in Zürich.

6

The couple walked in at ten o'clock sharp. The bank was on the Bahnhofstrasse, a main thoroughfare of Zürich.

It was a sumptuous but austere establishment. It caused one to speak in a low voice, surrounded, as one was, by expensive paintings, a profusion of white marble, boxes of red geraniums, and the exposed vault, which looked like a shrine offering the entire range of gold coins ever minted and the colors of foreign currencies, some of them quite exotic. The simple noise caused by a lighter dropped to the floor would probably have caused a cataclysm, or at least set off a general alert.

The couple was extremely striking.

But incongruous.

She was wearing a white Christian Dior outfit and, around her neck, a fabulous emerald-and-diamond necklace; she was the most beautiful woman ever to have set a Charles Jourdan-clad foot in this Swiss bank. The mere sight of her took away the breath of Thadeus Töpfler, who at the time was twenty-six years old and held the position of assistant director.

In a less understandable way, Töpfler was equally impressed by the young woman's companion. The man was very tall and very thin, and he moved in a way that gave the impression of tight self-control. He had surprising eyes, light and very deep. But mostly, he clashed with the young woman, who was so miraculously beautiful. He was wearing a faded blue cotton shirt, with epaulettes and pockets with buttons, pants of the same color and fabric, and black loafers, which were carefully polished but far from new. Over his shoulder, he carried a khaki-colored cloth bag.

Töpfler remembers that it was the young woman who first approached a teller's window. She rested her elbows on the ledge and flashed a glorious smile at the man behind the counter.

"Do you speak Shamatari?"

"No, madam," he answered. "I am truly sorry." Wolfgang Müller had never even heard the word.

"Not even a few simple words?"

"None at all. I am extremely sorry, madam," he said.

She smiled again, more gloriously than before, if that was possible.

"It doesn't matter," said the young woman. "I only wanted to know."

The man approached then, one eyebrow raised in a mute question.

"Not a word," said the young woman. "It's amazing, but that's how it is."

The man also rested his elbows on the ledge, put his cloth bag down next to him, and asked:

"But perhaps you speak English?"

The conversation was taking place in English.

"Yes sir," said Müller, showing the first signs of nervousness.

"And German?"

"I also speak German," answered Müller.

"French?"

"Yes, sir. French also."

"Italian, perhaps?"

"Some Italian, sir."

"But not Spanish? Or Yiddish? Or Hebrew? Or Portuguese? Or Arabic? Or Polish?"

"He doesn't look like someone who would speak Polish," said the young woman. "That's obvious."

She smiled for the third time.

"Please don't take offense. I find you very attractive, actually. It's just that I would be most surprised if you spoke Polish."

"No, sir," said Müller. "I don't speak any of those languages. And I am truly sorry about that."

Thadeus Töpfler noticed the worried look of his subordinate and decided it was time to step in. He reached the teller's window just when the man was saying in a kindly voice: "In spite of these preliminary difficulties, I nevertheless am sure that we can do business together."

"Can I be of any assistance to you, madam, and to you, sir?" asked Töpfler. "Mr. . . . ?"

"Slim Zapata," said the man with a straight face, politely. Immediately, with a long index finger, he signaled Töpfler to come closer, and whispered in his ear: "Actually, that is not my real name. I am here incognito. I would be most grateful if you were to protect my anonymity."

He's a madman, thought Töpfler. Or a Cuban. In the last few months many Cubans had been appearing in Switzerland, now that Batista was out and a certain Fidel Castro had taken his place, bringing with them money that was being eyed hungrily by the new masters of Havana.

"I would simply like to cash a check," said the man. "Make a withdrawal, in a way."

"Nothing could be simpler, sir," said Töpfler, with an ease he would remember during sleepless nights. "As long as you have honored us with an account here . . ."

"Which I have," said the man. "But I do not have any checks. Might I trouble you for a teller's check?"

Töpfler mentioned the few formalities that would be necessary. After which, he, as well all the employees of the bank, if not the entire Swiss Confederation, would be at Mr. Zapata's service. Especially if his was a numbered account. Was that the case?

"Yes," said the man.

They moved on to a nearby office, which was more discreet. The formalities were taken care of. Slim Zapata graciously offered the secret number of his account, his initials, RMK, and even agreed to show his passport.

The name was completely unknown to Töpfler. He went to get a check, after having rapidly consulted with his superior.

"Everything is in order," he felt he had to say upon his return. "You can simply write down the amount of your withdrawal."

"I don't have anything to write with," remarked Zapata-Klimrod suavely.

Only at that moment did Töpfler again notice, with bewilderment, the young woman. She had sat down on a soft low sofa, evidently intending to take a little nap. She had already removed her shoes and her stockings, and was now removing her Dior outfit.

She was now wearing a brassiere and a pair of lacy panties.

"Anything wrong?" asked the man.

Töpfler swallowed and turned his full attention to the desk.

"Nothing," he said. "Nothing at all, sir."

On the desk was the check. He saw it upside down, but of course he could read the numbers on it. He saw the large dark hand write a miniscule one, then a zero that was not much larger.

"By writing small," explained Zapata-Klimrod seriously, "I have the feeling that I am spending less."

A second zero, then a third . . .

"I would like a blanket," said the young woman. "I am a little cold."

Töpfler automatically looked up, and wanted to kill himself for having done so. She was now completely naked, with her neck resting in the palms of her hands, and her right heel crossed over her left ankle.

"This man will take our check to be cashed and will be kind enough to bring you a blanket, my darling," said the man. "Isn't that right, sir?"

"Absolutely," said Töpfler. "Absolutely, absolutely."

He was beginning to lose his grip. He returned his attention to the check.

A fifth zero, a sixth, a seventh . . .

Mein Gott! thought Töpfler. I really am dealing with crazy people.

An eighth zero, then a three, then a period, then forty-five.

"There," said Zapata, spinning the check around ninety degrees.

His gray eyes looked straight at Töpfler and expressed nothing. Töpfler began to cough.

"Excuse me," he said, "you have neglected to spell out the amount. And you also forgot the commas."

Zapata-Klimrod, looking surprised, took back the check.

"Not at all," he said, "the comma is there. 'Three comma forty-five.' The European way. No doubt about it. It is there. Darling? Would you come over here for a minute?"

Töpfler dove forward and began studying his own knees with fascination.

"It's a very lovely comma," said the young woman's voice. "I don't see anything wrong with it. These bankers are unbelievable quibblers. They are all the same: they are happy to take your money but when you want it back . . ."

Töpfler, still leaning forward in contemplation of his knees, said, in a somewhat muffled voice: "Excuse me, sir, but if you leave just that comma, where it is, that would be over one billion Swiss francs."

"It's not Swiss francs but U.S. dollars," answered Zapata-Klimrod. "And the exact amount is one billion and three dollars and forty-five cents. I am quite sure that the three dollars and forty-five cents are in my account. As for the rest, I wonder. You had better go and check, sir. And don't forget the blanket when you come back."

Something surprising then happened to Thadeus Töpfler.

He was Swiss, the son, grandson, great-grandson, great-great-grandson of bankers. The Töpflers had been in banking for over three hundred years. "When my grandfather spoke of the bank," he used to say, "we usually observed a moment of silence."

Yet, as soon as he had walked out of the office, he was overcome by uncontrollable laughter. Nervous laughter, clearly, but nonetheless unstoppable.

The second strange thing he did that same day was to walk into the office of the man he hated most in the world, that of

Othmar Brockman, the head of the Credit Department, without knocking.

"There is, downstairs, a man wearing loafers and no jacket who is presenting us a check in the amount of one billion dollars."

With that, he was once again overcome by laughter, and almost fell over. It was, now, the detail of the clothes that set off his hysterics.

"You are drunk, Töpfler," said Brockman.

Töpfler managed to place the check on the desk. He wanted to say something like "See for yourself," but he couldn't control his laughter long enough to do so.

Brockman glanced at the check and shrugged his shoulders.

"A madman. Make a discreet call to the police."

Then, something must have struck him. He picked up the check again and examined it. He got up, went to open the little vault in the wall, and took out a notebook, which he looked through.

He came back to the desk and picked up the telephone.

The same day, at ten-twenty-five in the morning, Aloïs Knapp, as vice-president, was taking part in the monthly meeting of the Swiss Bankers' Association. The fact that he was being called to the telephone annoyed him. He did not show it, however; as a man and as a banker, he was as cold as death. In 1960, he had just turned fifty.

"What's wrong with you, Brockman?"

He listened, then asked: "You have checked everything?"

Then he said: "I am on my way."

He arrived at eleven o'clock. Brockman and young Töpfler were discreetly waiting for him.

"Where is he?"

They led him to the office on the ground floor.

"It might be wise to knock before going in," suggested Töpfler, who had, if not lost his urge to laugh, at least enough self-control to obtain it in the presence of Knapp, who had descended from his Olympus.

Knapp knocked, was invited to come in, did so, and closed the door behind him. He remained inside for ten or fifteen minutes. When he came out, he looked a little pale and had the recognizable red imprint of feminine lips on his right cheek. He looked at Töpfler.

"It's you he wants to deal with. Only you. You are Töpfler, aren't you? Well then, go ahead. Go in."

Walking into the office, completely flabbergasted, Töpfler heard Brockman's question and Knapp's answer.

"One billion dollars! This is madness. What do we do?"

"We pay."

In the office, Töpfler discovered the young woman standing on the sofa, wrapped in the blanket he had brought her. The man was no longer wearing a shirt and his face was smeared with lipstick, like a Sioux ready for war. The man smiled pleasantly.

"What is your name?"

"Thadeus Töpfler."

"I adore Thadeus," said the young women. "He is really so sweet."

"May I call you Thadeus?" asked the man. "Please call me Reb. Ah, one more thing, Thadeus: I would like the billion dollars in hundred-dollar bills. No larger bills, please. You can just pile them up somewhere."

"For the three dollars and forty-five cents," said the young woman, "we will leave it up to you: either one bill of three dollars and forty-five cents, or all in change. No, wait. Make it change; these toilets where you need change before going in, when you are a woman—but not when you are a man, if you see what I mean—are absolutely exasperating."

Töpfler sensed that something was wrong, and this feeling increased during the following hours. That someone should come and present such a check was extraordinary; it was exceptional. All right. But Knapp's reaction showed that this man with the gray eyes could really walk into any Swiss bank, the largest, anyway, and demand the extravagant sum of one billion U.S. dollars. Fine. That proved he owned a considerable fortune. But several men throughout the world were as rich; they were few, perhaps, but they existed. So there was something else.

Such as the fact that this man was unknown. Töpfler had been taught by his stern grandfather to read the financial newspapers. He knew the names and faces of Howard Hughes, Hunt, Getty, Gulbenkian, Onassis, and of others, like Niarchos, who were multimillionaires, one rank below. He also knew of the existence of the less-known Daniel Ludwig. But Klimrod? Who in heaven's name had ever heard of Klimrod?

He asked: "Is there anything else I can do for you?"

"A large martini, with a lot of ice," said the woman. "Then, some champagne and caviar. For the caviar, call the Shah of Iran on my behalf; he has a few tins of good quality. Tell him you are calling for Charmian Page, and he will do anything."

"Any particular champagne?" asked Töpfler.

"Dom Perignon 1945 rosé, please. Three or four magnums to begin with. Nothing larger: no jeroboams or anything larger, please. They lose their bubbles. Reb?"

"Yes, my darling."

"You should give this young man ten or fifteen million dollars. He is so sweet."

"I will think about it," said the man, with great gentleness. "As soon as they have cashed my check. Which might take a while, it would seem. Thadeus?"

"Yes, sir."

"I would like a hamburger, if it's not too much trouble. There are excellent ones in Frankfurt, made for the American soldiers who are stationed in Germany. Could you take care of that, Thadeus?"

"Most certainly, sir," said Töpfler. "With pleasure."

He tried to hold the flamboyant gray gaze but finally had to look away. A thought struck him that would soon be reinforced: This man is not crazy, not really. He's having fun, perhaps. But she, on the other hand . . .

For, as extraordinarily beautiful as she was, there could be no doubt: she was abnormal. In her fiery cheerfulness and her actions, Töpfler could discern a demented fever.

In Aloïs Knapp's office, which he entered for the first time that day, Töpfler discovered what looked like a war council. The full staff was present, and, what was more, within the next hour the old and venerable Jacob Füssli, who was seventy-eight years of age, and who had retired three years ago and been replaced by Knapp, arrived as a reinforcement.

"Tell us what is happening, Töpfler. Without mentioning his name."

"They want champagne, but not just any champagne, caviar, but not just any caviar, and also hamburgers, but not just . . ."

"Stop behaving like a fool, please," said Knapp. "Sit down, Töpfler. Listen. Our client wants to deal only with you. You are, therefore, as of this minute, discharged from all your other responsibilities and obligations. You will remain in permanent contact with your client, on the one hand, and with Mr. Füssli or me on the other. Your instructions are simple: comply with all your client's wishes, as long as they do not exceed one hundred thousand francs. For any expense over that limit, check with Mr. Füssli or with me. Are you married?"

Töpfler was only engaged. Knapp nodded, as if that piece of information, at least, was good news. He went on.

"It will take us some time to get that amount of money together. . . ."

"He doesn't want any bills larger than hundred-dollar bills," said Töpfler, daring to interrupt the Big Chief.

Knapp shut his eyes. Opened them again.

"In that case, it will take us two days longer. Three days in all. During these three days, Töpfler, you will be permanently available. If our client, yours, insists, as he seems to be doing, on remaining inside the bank until we have honored his check, try to see what their intentions are. If they want to sleep here, we will have the William Tell room set up as a bedroom, and a cot will be provided for you."

Töpfler looked at Knapp with stupefaction. The idea crossed his mind that perhaps Knapp also had gone mad, as well as Füssli the Venerable, and all the staff members, everyone except himself.

"Sleep here? In the bank?"

Knapp's icy glare shot through him. Then he announced: "Mr. Füssli and I would like to be alone with Töpfler."

The others left. Töpfler remained alone to face the Big Chiefs.

"Töpfler . . ." the Venerable One and Knapp said at the exact same time.

Then Knapp said, with deference: "Please, Mr. Füssli, go ahead. . . ."

"No, no, no, no, Aloïs," said the Venerable One. "You are in charge now." And, after a few seconds, he added: "Thank goodness."

334

"Töpfler," said Knapp, "you realize that we are faced with a unique situation, which has never happened in the annals of Swiss banking . . ."

"And probably not in world banking either," said the Venerable One.

"We will meet this challenge and all its demands," said Knapp, "with the rigor, the efficiency, the celerity, and the discretion— the discretion, Töpfler—which are our glory and pride, and which have made the fortune of this establishment."

Töpfler raised a respectful finger.

"May I ask a question, sir?"

"Yes, my boy."

"Does our client really have one billion dollars in his account?"

I should not have asked that, he thought immediately. The two Big Chiefs were glaring at him.

"Do not make us question your mental state, Töpfler. What's more, do not give us the added concern of worrying about the consequences of the choice made by our client in having you as the only link between him and us. Nobody in the world has one billion dollars in a bank account, Töpfler. It just happens that our client has a line of credit that surpasses that amount, and because of the special arrangement we have with him, we have to meet his demand."

Knapp took a deep breath.

"Töpfler, we will close the bank to the general public next Friday at three o'clock, giving as an official reason some rearranging of interior matters. Until then, the bank will function normally—at least, we hope so. Except for the fact that seventy men and women will be working day and night to find these bank bills. We do not have one billion dollars in one-hundred-dollar bills, Töpfler. We are frightfully far from that. We will have to contact all the banks in the country, and banks in other European countries, and, most probably, American institutions. We are going to have to implement a gigantic apparatus, with special planes and convoys, on a worldwide scale. And if we reach our goal in three days, it will be with the help of divine intervention. And you will be part of it, Töpfler, part of it. Your first name is Thadeus, is it not?"

"Yes, sir."

"Thadeus, there is one last point that we wish to emphasize,

Mr. Füssli and I: five other people, who represent the management of our bank, were here in this office a few moments ago, besides Mr. Füssli, you, and I. They do not know the name of our client. There are only four of us, with Brockman, who know it. So, Thadeus, should anyone, within the bank or, worse yet, outside of it, through your fault, for any reason, even if you talk in your sleep, learn of this catastrophe that has befallen us, and especially of the name of the man responsible for it, I swear to you on the Bible that I will see to it that you never find another job in Switzerland. And I will do so personally, Thadeus, if it takes me the rest of my days. Am I making myself clear, Thadeus?"

"Yes, sir. Very clear."

"Now, go, my boy. And do your best."

And they did set up the William Tell room. Beds and bedding for two complete rooms were loaned by the Dolder Grand Hotel and set up there. They had to drill through a wall so that access to the created suite could be accomplished without drawing anyone's attention, through an adjacent building and through the back rooms of the bank.

During the next few hours, there were great doings, in several areas. They had to set up a bathroom, of course. And a kitchen to reheat the meals ordered from outside, and also for the hamburger specialist who had been brought in that day from Frankfurt, with all his supplies and equipment.

And telephone lines, five in all.

"I will need to make a few telephone calls," the man had explained to Töpfler. "And I wouldn't want to tie up the bank's usual lines. It would make me feel bad. And, while I think of it, could you set up a small screening room, if it's not too much trouble. Mrs. Zapata loves movies, especially Humphrey Bogart films. Can you take care of it, Thadeus? That is really very kind of you."

And, indeed, the man made countless telephone calls. Several times, Töpfler overheard parts of these conversations, which occurred in many languages. The man spoke at least ten languages, and he went from one to the other with disconcerting facility.

As for what he was saying, Töpfler didn't understand any of it, and rapidly suspected that the man was having fun, or, rather, was doing all this to amuse his wife, if she really was his wife.

The young Swiss refused to be taken in; if he had, he would

have had to believe in the existence of a man who, by telephone, was running hundreds of companies throughout the world, in all areas of human activity, without exception. And doing so by using codes, bewildering, incomprehensible figures, and never mentioning one name.

All this made no sense at all. Obviously, it's only to amuse the young woman that he does all this, he thought.

As far as she was concerned, Thadeus Töpfler's initial intuition proved to be correct: She was mad. He felt no desire to smile about it. On the contrary, it made him surprisingly sad. One could not help but notice the immense tenderness and love that the man felt for her. And his infinite patience.

The first day was, therefore, rather hectic, with all the comings and goings that took place, without ever attracting the attention of the public or even that of the employees, who were not aware of anything unusual.

But in the evening, after closing time, things calmed down. The William Tell room was on the second floor and was usually used for receptions. Now, it was cut off from the rest of the building, and two extra guards were posted, although neither of them ever saw the couple and they were not aware of their presence.

Knapp's orders, as received by Töpfler, were very clear: "Thadeus, you stay with them. I am asking you this as a personal favor. Afterward, you can take all the vacation you need, and we will discuss your future in this establishment. But stay with them, Thadeus, and be as helpful as you can. If need be, serve them dinner, be at their beck and call. Thadeus? You can trust our client; he has his reasons for acting as he does."

Töpfler believes that Knapp realized from the beginning that the young woman was mad, and that this three-day comedy was conducted only "to allow this man named Klimrod—and at first I suspected even that was not his real name; I even suspected that he might be Daniel Ludwig, since I had never seen a photograph of him, but he was too young to be Ludwig—anyway, to allow him to—how shall I put it?—put on a little show for this woman he loved hopelessly. And maybe even to share her madness for a few hours . . .

"This so-called Klimrod knowing all along how it would end . . ."

337

The second day was less hectic, at least in part. Everyone settled in, extravagantly. The entire second floor was closed to everyone except Knapp and Töpfler. The latter had, the night before, catering to the young woman's wish, called a number in Teheran. To his great surprise, when he mentioned Charmian Page's name, he was greeted most pleasantly. His surprise turned to shock when the Shah himself came on the line, delicately asking how she was. "I think she is fine . . . uh, Your Majesty," answered Töpfler, bewildered. "She simply wanted some caviar and asked me to . . ."

His Imperial Highness said that he fully understood the situation, that he would give the necessary orders, and that he would be most grateful to Töpfler if he were to convey to Miss Page his very best regards.

The caviar did arrive, flown in on a special plane and brought to the bank, and through the service door, by two solemn, taciturn Iranians, visibly diplomats or secret agents.

"I was living a crazy dream," Töpfler recalled twenty-two years later.

The crisis occurred during the evening of the second day. As had been planned, a cot had been set up for Töpfler, in a small office two rooms away from the William Tell room. He heard a scream at around nine o'clock, following a loud noise of breaking glass and thudding sounds.

He hesitated, then ran. He knocked at the door, and the man told him to come in. He found the man restraining the young woman by her wrists, which he had behind her back. With her eyes rolled up, she was panting, drooling, and fighting back in a rage.

"Help me, please," said the man. "We will carry her over to the bed."

Töpfler asked whether he should call for a doctor.

The man answered: "No. This is just a nervous crisis, which my wife is sometimes subject to. I know what has to be done."

He was unnaturally calm. Töpfler helped him hold the young women down on the bed, and a shot was administered. Its effect was almost immediate.

"She will sleep now."

The gray eyes suddenly took on an infinite, overwhelming expression of sadness, and Töpfler thought the man might begin to cry. He turned away.

338

"Thadeus?"

"Yes, sir?"

"Thank you."

Töpfler nodded. He didn't quite know what to say or do.

The man said softly: "Tell me about yourself. Do you have any brothers or sisters. Are you married?"

They spoke, or at least Töpfler spoke, for about half an hour, in the great silence of the empty bank. He spoke about many things, but specifically about his terrible grandfather, Anton Gustav. The man hardly seemed to be listening, with his dreamy look and his eyes staring into space, but the questions he asked showed that he was actually paying close attention, which, according to Töpfler, the subject matter was not worthy of.

Töpfler finally took his leave and returned to his cot. But he was not able to fall asleep. Through the doors, which he had left open in the event that he was needed, he could see that the lights in the William Tell room were still burning. So two hours later he got up and went back to see if there was anything he could do.

"Nothing, thank you," said the man in his soft, polite voice.

He was sitting next to the bed where the young woman was sleeping, and he was reading, in German, an edition of Homer translated by Johann Bodmer, which had come from Aloïs Knapp's personal library.

"He spent the whole night that way; I am sure of it. In the morning, he was still there."

And in the morning, when he saw the couple again, Töpfler found the young woman—Charmian Page was apparently her name—almost normal, a little languid at first, which only added to her beauty, but then, as time went by, her quickness and abrupt humor returned. She seemed normal except for the feverish gleam that shone deep in her violet eyes.

For the past two days, armored trucks had been arriving, some from Zürich, from other banks, which had, to the maximum of their ability, parted with their U.S. bills, but most coming from the airport. The activity increased on the third day, but fewer people witnessed it, since the bank closed earlier than usual.

The money was piling up.

No one had actually been able to figure out how much space a billion dollars in bills would take up. To play it safe, rather than choose a single room that might prove too small, they decided to pile up the bills in the middle of the hall, on sheets.

Töpfler, to occupy his spare time, had tried to figure it out.

One stack of ten one-hundred-dollar bills, with the band, measured one thirty-second of an inch in thickness—slightly less if they were new, and slightly more if they were used—so he took an average. He calculated that one million dollars in packs of hundred-dollar bills with bands would make a pile measuring twenty-four and a half inches.

He tried to figure out how many piles six and one-eighth by two and one-half by twenty-four and one-half would fit into one square yard.

The answer was ninety. Ninety million dollars a square foot. Sweet Jesus! How much would a five-room apartment hold?

. . . Now, there are one thousand million in one billion.

Or one thousand divided by ninety . . .

Twelve point fifteen square yards.

Still figuring with the same height, of course. It was madness. Even if the height of the ceiling permitted, as it did in certain places, the access to the top of such a structure would be impractical, to say the least. Should our client want to count it, Töpfler thought, he would need a helicopter, or at the very least an ice ax.

He calculated that rather than have nine hundred and ninety-one piles, it would be preferable to reduce the size of the aforementioned piles. For example, by cutting them in five parts. Which made for easy calculation.

The answer seemed reasonable and plausible to him: piled in this way, one billion dollars would be represented by a pile measuring almost five feet in height spread over an area of, approximately, sixty-one square yards.

In any event, he thought, it will fit in the hall. That's already something. Nowhere else but in the hall.

Thadeus Töpfler's clever calculations proved to be wrong. Not by much, but by enough.

The colossal pile of bills covered more than sixty-five square yards, and, in certain places, measured over six feet in height. For the simple reason that they had not been able to gather enough one-hundred-dollar bills and were forced to make up the difference with packs of fifty-dollar bills, and even of ten-, five-, and one-dollar bills.

This considerably increased the overall size of the structure.

At around seven o'clock in the evening of the third day, the telephone rang in the William Tell room. Töpfler, who had been anxiously waiting for the call since the departure of the last armored truck, picked up the receiver.

Knapp's voice said: "Now."

The three of them went downstairs, the young Swiss following the couple, who were walking arm in arm.

In the large deserted hall, besides one billion dollars' worth of bills, were Aloïs Knapp and the Venerable Füssli, leaning on his cane.

The man who called himself Klimrod, at least to Thadeus Töpfler, didn't even go near the fortune. He stood still, his eyes lost in the distance, all trace of humor or enjoyment having long since disappeared from his face.

The young woman, on the other hand, slowly walked around the heap.

"One billion dollars?"

"One billion, three dollars and forty-five *cents*," answered Knapp. "Please accept our apology for the delay in honoring your check."

She disappeared behind the bills. But her voice rose under the echoing vault.

"It's all yours, Reb?"

"Yes," said the man, who remained unmoving.

"And you have this how many times?"

"I don't know."

"Two times, Reb? Five times? Ten times?"

"I don't know."

She reappeared in the four men's field of vision.

"And if I set it on fire, Reb? Can I burn it all, Reb?"

"Yes."

"I can, really?"

"Yes."

But he smiled and said, with fascinating softness: "Only, you would also set the bank on fire."

341

"Buy the bank."

"What would we do with a bank, my love? It's a rather sad place, don't you think?"

She was looking at him, and suddenly tears appeared in her eyes.

"You are wonderfully sweet and tender, Reb. I love you."

"I love you, too, Charmian."

She leaned against the wall of bills and began to cry, without making a sound.

Töpfler first, then Knapp, and finally Füssli turned away, not daring to look at her, or at Klimrod, whose face was that of a crucified man.

"Take me back there, Reb, now. Let them lock me up again."

The several armed guards posted all around, but outside the room, let them pass on a signal given by Knapp.

Even after the doors closed, Töpfler didn't move.

Knapp said to him: "Go home, my boy. It's all over."

"What are we going to do with all these bills?"

"Put them back where they belong. What else can we do?"

Töpfler nodded. Of course.

He began walking toward the door.

"Thadeus?"

Töpfler simply said, without turning around: "I know: I must not talk about this."

He left. He didn't want to talk to anyone at all. He actually felt more like crying.

7

Charmian Page died on January 17, 1961.

As she had always done, she had come to spend the Christmas holidays with her family in the United States, accompanied not only by her Ethiopian girls but also by another woman, a Swiss, who turned out to be a doctor and who was never far away from her. During the two weeks she spent in New York and Connecticut, she seemed playful and even happy, although every so often the disquieting fever would appear in her eyes. At these times, the Swiss woman, whose name was Martha Hodler, would draw closer, very discreetly, ready to intervene. But things never went any further, and Charmian would smile and say, "I am all right, Martha."

She adored David and Diana Settiniaz's children, and this year, like the years before, she arrived bearing incredible numbers of gifts. One of them was an authentic Swiss chalet, made of wood, consisting of six rooms, completely furnished, including even a hilarious clock with a cuckoo that would jump out at the most unexpected times, screaming in an inebriated falsetto: "It's the children's time! And the children are good if the parents are crazy!"

The entire thing was at a scale of two-fifths, including the chimney.

So when the Settiniaz's Hawaiian servants tried to clean the inside of the chalet, which had been set up at the end of the garden, they had to do so on their knees, and sometimes had to crawl in. (A team of carpenters had come from Zürich on a cargo plane to assemble the chalet.)

The kids adored it. Of course, they had insisted on spending their vacation in their own house, along with their cousins and allies, locking themselves inside. To get them to come out for their evening bath required patient negotiations and the use of go-betweens. Naturally, they idolized their aunt, who was capable of such inventions . . .

. . . Just as did David Settiniaz's in-laws, even his wife. When he ventured to bring up what he timidly referred to as Charmian's "nervousness," they would shrug their shoulders. They probably felt like criticizing him for bringing it up so often. Charmian was eccentric and had been since childhood, so why all the fuss? They had heard of her marriage to "this Kimrod," whom no one had ever seen, except for Diana, who saw him once or twice. They had even heard the story about the shots she supposedly fired at her ghost of a husband, on her yacht somewhere in the Mediterranean in the spring of 1955. (David, who had been told the true story by Georges Tarras, had confided in his wife.) But that

343

wasn't much to go on; there had been no actual police investigation, and, besides, who knew what had really happened anyway? "This Kimrod or whatever his name is" was just a dowry chaser, for sure, who had been attracted by her ten million dollars, and she must have married him as a lark and tried to get rid of him for the same reason. "She is by far the most intelligent member of the family, and no man, whoever he may be, could ever force her to do what she doesn't want to do." This Kimrod had probably come asking for more money, and they would not have been surprised to learn that it was he who had tried to fire those shots at her, and Charmian, with her usual generosity, had probably decided not to turn him over to the police.

Moreover, if Charmian really was unstable, it would show. She had been to see doctors in the United States as well as in Europe; she had never made a secret of that. But had they ever decided to hospitalize her? No. She lived in Switzerland, on this huge and luxurious property she owned near Zürich, and if she chose to surround herself with one or two doctors, that was one of her whims, the way other people have mind-readers or astronomers.

"Really, David, look at her! . . . Does she seem abnormal in any way? She lives alone—I mean without a husband or children—but is that forbidden? Why can't a woman remain single? You men are all alike: if one of you refuses to get married or have children, you all think he is practically a hero. But if a woman chooses to do the same thing, you think she is crazy."

The telephone call came during the night of January 16, at around two o'clock in the morning, eight o'clock in Europe. Settiniaz answered, and the voice, in a German accent, said: "Something has happened, sir. It's serious."

In Zürich, he and Diana rented a car, followed the road toward the southeast. The property was on a beautiful elevation overlooking the Walensee.

Martha Hodler was waiting at the gate, her eyes red and swollen.

"I will blame myself for the rest of my life, Mr. Settiniaz. For the rest of my life."

And she cried again. She had been with Charmian for seven years, and she was not the only doctor who was constantly present; two others worked with her, in shifts, day and night, along with nurses. The property, which was so luxurious, with an abnormal number of servants and supposed secretaries, was nothing more than a private psychiatric clinic, for the use of only one patient, whom they protected against herself.

"We watched a film last night, as we often do. She was extremely calm, more so than usual, and lucid, extremely so. That is precisely why I feel so responsible: that very lucidity should have alerted me. . . ."

She had had a crisis, a brief one, upon her return from the States. As she always did. "Because of the children she saw there. It always had the same effect on her. Had it been up to us, we never would have let her go."

But very quickly she seemed to come out of it. That was what was most difficult in her case, those periods when she became normal again. "These last two years, she was having fewer and fewer of these absences, which made her forget even the names of those who were closest to her. Including her husband, whom she didn't recognize. . . . But she seemed to be feeling better, and last year they spent three days in Zürich, and he told us it had been all right. Except that when she returned, she had another crisis, which lasted one month. . . ."

Charmian had gone to her room at eleven o'clock. The Ethiopian girls had put her to bed. One of the two other doctors had come to administer her medication, which made her sleep and reassured everyone, "because we were certain then that she would sleep soundly for at least eight hours.

"We found the pills under her pillow. She pretended to swallow them, pretended to fall asleep. . . ."

Two Ethiopian girls always slept with her when her husband was not there. They didn't hear anything, for the good reason that Charmian had drugged them. "She premeditated her death, prepared everything for it. . . . She went out of the house, in her nightgown. We found the trace of her footsteps in the snow. She would have died of the cold, if nothing else, since the nights are very cold at this time. It was well below freezing. We believe it must have been around one o'clock in the morning. . . ."

She had walked in a straight line under the trees, and had gone to the very end of the garden, into the gardeners' shed, and the dogs had not barked because they knew her. She sat directly on the ground, which was hardened by the frost, and first she slit her wrists. But the blood was freezing, so she also used a scythe, which she plunged into her stomach. . . .

"It must have taken her an hour to die, at least. . . ."

Diego Haas was there, having arrived at least two hours before the Settiniazes, who had taken the first plane leaving for Europe. And not only was he there, but also he was giving orders as if he were the master of the house, and everyone obeyed him very naturally. In this time of intense emotion, David Settiniaz let loose the antipathy he had always felt for the small Argentine.

"What gives you the right to meddle in everything?"

The yellow eyes glared at him coldly.

"I am following Reb's orders."

"Charmian Page is part of our family," said Diana, shaking with indignation. "She was my sister."

"She was Reb's wife," Diego answered calmly. "And only that. Nothing else counts beside that."

In his golden pupils, David, right or wrong, thought he saw a sarcastic irony, which literally enraged him, a feeling he had not experienced before that day.

"You get the fuck out of here, right now," he said. "This is Charmian's house."

"This is Reb's house," said Diego. "Everything here belongs to him. Me, first of all, and you, too, Settiniaz. And I will do what Reb has told me to do, even if I have to kill you, you and your wife, to do so. Is that clear? Now, since it appears that you still have certain doubts, the lawyer's name is Karl Siegwart. Here are his address in Zürich and his telephone number. It would be my pleasure to dial the number for you. They are expecting your call; just mention your name. They speak English."

He had dialed the number, said a few words in German, and handed the receiver to Settiniaz, who took it. The voice on the other end told him that the entire house, each thing it contained, the merest object, was the property of a Mr. Haas, of Buenos Aires; that Mr. Haas was also the one who paid the doctors, the nurses, the servants, the entire staff. Siegwart added that we would be extremely grateful to Mr. and Mrs. Settiniaz if they could, as soon as their painful obligations were met, come by his office, so that they might settle some details of Mrs. Klimrod's will.

David hung up.

Diego had not moved, but he said: "The ceremony will take place tomorrow morning at nine o'clock. Mrs. Klimrod wished to be cremated, and therefore will be. Everything has been arranged."

"Her family will not have enough time to get here."

"That does not concern me in the least."

Georges Tarras arrived during the afternoon of the same day. He explained that Diego had called him to tell him the news, which had devastated him.

"David, I beseech you: don't let your animosity get the better of you with Diego. He obeys Reb in everything, and by law Charmian was Mrs. Klimrod. You know that. Taking it out on Diego doesn't make any sense."

Charmian's mother and father, and David Settiniaz's mother arrived that evening, with three or four other relatives. So that, the next day, there were ten at least, besides the staff who had taken care of the young woman, to go to the cremation site.

But not Reb.

Settiniaz once again confronted Diego Haas.

"Where is he?"

"Where he wants to be."

"And he won't even come?"

Settiniaz had almost shrieked these last words.

"He will do whatever he wants, Settiniaz."

The yellow gaze, which was perpetually sarcastic, revealed more than ever during those days the amazing hatred and violence that inhabited this pudgy little man, who at no point before, during, or after they burned the body of the young woman showed the slightest emotion. He looked at the others, the tears of the women and the emotion of the men, with a half-smirk on his face.

"You are even crazier than he is," Settiniaz had finally said to him, when he had run out of arguments.

Diego smiled with a thin, almost cruel smile.

"No one is more anything than Reb."

After which he added: "This afternoon and tonight I will be taking care of everything concerning the people and the house. Reb said that if there is anything that you, your wife . . . or they"—he pointed with his chin to the group formed by the Page

347

relatives—"would like from the house, go ahead and take it. Take whatever you like. Everything has been planned. I have suspended the insurance."

"Go to the devil," said Settiniaz.

"I certainly hope to meet him someday, without really believing in him though," answered Diego. "It's a meeting from which I expect a great deal."

Actually, it was the way he had said "tonight" that aroused Settiniaz's irritated curiosity. He and Tarras went back to the property on the hilltop near the Walensee toward the end of the afternoon, on January 20.

Earlier, Settiniaz and the Page family had attended the reading of Charmian's will. The young woman left approximately twenty-three million dollars. Her beneficiaries were her nieces and nephews, for ten million dollars—the very amount she had received when she turned twenty-one in 1947—and the rest was to go to the International Children's Fund. "At least that Klimrod didn't manage to wheedle her money away from her," Settiniaz's mother-in-law had remarked.

The entire staff had been dismissed, and with an undeniable generosity.

The house was a beautiful white three-story building, in the center of a garden of about thirty acres, with outbuildings and stables. Having stayed there two or three times in the summer and in the spring, Settiniaz knew it blossomed with flowers during those seasons. It had thirty rooms, all of which were sumptuously decorated.

It was dark when Tarras and Settiniaz turned their car into the long path bordered by giant trees. But there was not one window, one opening in the house that was not illuminated. At first, they thought perhaps a party was taking place. They stopped by the double-columned porch. The black lacquer door was wide open, so they walked in.

The smell hit them right away. They exchanged a look of concern. This concern grew when, running slowly down the black carpet that covered part of the white stairway, the spilled gasoline appeared.

Almost immediately Diego himself looked down from the top of the stairs. He was holding a can of gasoline in his hand.

"You are just in time," he said. "In a few minutes, it would have been too late. Reb said: 'If they want anything from the house, let them take it, anything at all. . . . ' "

He smiled. "Go ahead, then. But be quick."

"What are you going to do?" asked Settiniaz.

Diego raised the can of gasoline he was holding and spilled the little left in it over the banister. The liquid splashed the bottom of Tarras's trousers.

"Excuse me, Mr. Tarras," said Diego. "Of course, you can guess what I am doing."

"It's pretty obvious," said Tarras.

Settiniaz took two steps toward the stairs.

"Tttttt," said Diego. "Look."

He raised his right hand and revealed a gold lighter, which he flicked. The small flame appeared. Diego smiled.

"There is enough gasoline in this house to set all of Zürich on fire. I myself am wading in it. One more step, Settiniaz, and we'll both burn together. Come closer if you want to see . . . "

"David, for heaven's sake, come back," said Tarras.

Settiniaz did, reluctantly.

"Now the two of you will go out and move your car away. I wouldn't want it or you to burn. Reb didn't tell me to set you on fire."

He was laughing, still holding the flame over the sheet of gasoline.

"Come, David."

Tarras dragged his companion outside, to the snow that had been packed down by all the comings and goings of the last few days.

"Start the car and park it a little farther away, David, please."

"He has to be stopped," said Settiniaz, trembling with anger. "We have to call the police. . . . "

"Shut your mouth and get this fucking car out of here, please, Master Settiniaz," Tarras said, calmly, departing, for once, from the polished style that was usually his.

He waited for the car to pull away, then ran back up the steps. He came nose to nose with Diego, who was coming out, with two more cans of gasoline in his hands. Tarras raised his hands.

"I have no intention of stopping you."

"I know," said Diego. "Reb said so."

He brushed past him, unconcerned.

"Watch your feet, Professor."

The gasoline was pouring out. Diego finished emptying the cans by flinging the remaining liquid onto the wood shutters. Then he walked toward the outbuildings that seemed almost in daylight because of the lights blazing in the main house.

Tarras saw him wetting down, with more gasoline, the single-story buildings and the stables. He went to lean against the trunk of a larch tree, fifty yards away. He was shivering, or trembling, not knowing what caused him to do so, the cold or the excitement he was feeling. He heard the crunching noise of the snow under Settiniaz's footsteps, as he came and stood to his left without saying a word.

"Have you calmed down, David?"

"Yes."

"Do you understand now?"

"Yes, I think so. But it's horrible."

"Who the devil ever said it wasn't?" said Tarras. And he was thinking: Reb might be very close to us, hiding in the night, impassive, with his dilated nocturnal eyes, burning inside with all the fires of hell. Lord, that man will have suffered more than anyone. . . .

The first flame appeared, with a sort of timid furtiveness.

It ran, bluish, along the railing of the wood balcony of the building where the staff had lived. Quite suddenly, it turned into a blazing fire, in a blinding yellow light. At the same instant, in such an incongruous way that Tarras thought he was dreaming, there came the rumbling sound of horses' hoofs and neighing.

But those noises were real. Diego reappeared, riding bareback a chestnut horse with three white stockings, pulling behind him eight other horses, by a long halter. He galloped away from the flames, but quickly pulled the animals back when he reached the two men.

"Reb didn't say anything about the horses. But he knows they are the only thing I care about."

He turned slightly to look back at the white house. He raised his arm and threw the lighter toward the porch.

A blaze broke out instantaneously.

Upon which he gave a savage scream, and the horses took off at a gallop in the snow, and were rapidly engulfed by the night.

8

After that, there was only Diego Haas, who confided more or less in Georges Tarras, to tell what happened to the King.

Even if many others saw him and spoke with him. People like the Petridis brothers, Aloïs Knapp, Paul Soubise, the Chinese Hang, Roger Dunn, Ernie Gozchiniak, Francisco Santana, Henry Chance, and Ethel Court, and, of course, Settiniaz and Tarras, who each saw him on several occasions and sometimes for periods of a few days. During the five years following Charmian's death, Reb Klimrod traveled a great deal, turning up in the most surprising places, where his presence would never have been expected. Hang, for example, who worked out of Hong Kong and Singapore, was visited by Klimrod at least a dozen times in the early sixties, in 1963 especially, when Klimrod was setting up textile plants in Southeast Asia, and later plants for electronics.

He continued to expand, for at least five years, until 1966, the intricate network of his companies. At the same time, Settiniaz had begun a new classification system for his files, using a computer. This was the time when he increased the working space of his Fifty-eighth Street offices by taking over additional space on another floor, where he installed the computer.

"To a certain extent," he said later, "I could follow Reb's traces. On the rare occasions when we met, or when he called, he would never tell me where he had been. He began operating more and more through the intermediacy of the Black Dogs, whose number increased considerably, reaching twenty-six in 1965 and 1966.

"For the Black Dogs, he merely perfected the system he had used from the beginning, which had worked so well. The majority of these men, exactly fourteen of them, were of Rumanian descent, often but not necessarily Jewish, and often but not necessarily U.S. citizens. I don't know much about the Rumanian diaspora or about the reasons that led these natives of Walachia, Moldavia, and Transylvania to emigrate to other countries during the period between the wars and after 1945. But, in following Reb's path, one gets the impression that these Rumanians had dispersed all over the world. One day, I even had a visit from a fellow named Dimistris—not his real name—who came to my office on an Australian passport to tell me about three new companies Reb had created, an airline and two mining companies, in New South Wales and in Perth, that is to say in Hang's fief.

"Whatever their origin or their nationality, however, these men had certain traits in common: they were fiercely and fanatically devoted to Reb, and if, one minute after they had delivered their messages to me, I had asked them to tell me about Reb Klimrod, they would probably have looked at me blankly and asked 'Who?'

"But as to Reb's daily life, we only have Haas's testimony."

Or that of Ubaldo Rocha, of course. And of the South Americans. But during Klimrod's second offensive, and until 1967, David Settiniaz never knew of Rocha. Just as he was unaware of the existence of Jorge Socrates and Emerson Coëlho, and therefore of the titanic thing silently taking shape on the South American continent.

Thus, it is through Diego Haas, and then through Georges Tarras, that the Waco adventure is known.

In Dallas, Reb spent two days in discussions with oil magnates and bankers. Following his usual method, he did not lead the negotiations himself; that was done by two lawyers, a Texan named Gary Morse (who never knew Klimrod's name) and a smooth and sophisticated Mexican by the name of Francisco Santana.

Santana was a King's Man, and in 1964, in July, the date of the Waco operation, he had been working with Klimrod for nine years. At least, his name appeared in Settiniaz's files in the spring of 1955, when a new file revealed the man's status: the first page carried the word SPECIAL. In red.

In spite of his physical appearance—he was long and lean, handsome, with slightly slanted eyes indicating some Indian blood in his veins, and looked like the heir of an aristocratic Spanish-Mexican family—he was of extremely modest origins. Born in a remote pueblo, he had obtained his diplomas as the result of good fortune and extremely hard work. Georges Tarras nicknamed him the Matador, the Killer. And with his wily ways, the easy precision of his speech, his icy intensity during negotiations, he did have something about him of an Ordoñez or, even more, a Dominguin in the arena. Francisco Santana was a King's Man for all matters concerning tax havens, oil deals in

352

Venezuela, the United States, and the Caribbean, and, surprisingly, the desalinization of sea water.

At the Dallas negotiations, he appeared as the representative of a U.S.-Mexican group that owned, within the city itself and on its periphery, as well as in Fort Worth, tens of thousands of acres, which had been purchased in 1952-53 and in 1957. For these properties, Settiniaz gives the figure of forty-eight thousand one hundred eighty-five acres, owned by five Panamanian shadow companies. The 1957 date is that of Klimrod's Nevada operation with Tudor Anghel.

As for the people who were dealing with Santana, they were members of the two largest local dynasties, and were the ones Nessim Shahadzé faced when he was conducting, in Klimrod's name, the gigantic speculative silver operation.

With Morse's assistance, Santana conducted the negotiations with his usual *brio*, following, to the letter, the instructions Klimrod had given him earlier. As for Reb, he sat in on the meetings as the Mexican's document carrier, and, with his typical sense of humor, he would jump up to light his boss's long cigars when Santana signaled him. Three planned exchanges were made: acres near Lake Cliff Park for some buildings downtown; land near the Dallas-Fort Worth Turnpike for an interest in several companies; this interest then exchanged, with or without added capital, for a majority interest in a second group of companies. It was a transaction that, though closed in July, 1964, had actually been started by Morse and Santana fourteen months earlier.

It involved, in all, about seventy-three million dollars.

"Did you really have to light that Mexican asshole's cigars?"

Diego was driving the yellow pickup. He and Reb had left Dallas about three hours earlier, at dawn, and for reasons unknown to Diego, they were headed west.

"One of the lawyers, Carlsson, facing Francisco and Morse, had seen me once before. Five years ago, in Houston. He almost recognized me. In Houston, he had been told my name was Dremmler, and this time Francisco introduced me as Fuente."

"*Madre de Dios!*" exclaimed Diego, sarcastically. "That would have been a real catastrophe. What the fuck was he doing there, anyway? El Gran Matador should have warned you that Carlsson was going to be there. You would have remembered his name."

"There was a last-minute change, and Morse forgot to mention it to Francisco. Morse won't be working with us again. Diego, I am hungry."

They had just gone through Abilene and were headed straight toward the Pecos, in the direction of El Paso. Diego still did not know why. Reb had said, "Take this road," and he had taken it. It was as simple as that. Reb had also said, as they were leaving the motel in Dallas where they had spent two nights: "Let's change our clothes," and they had changed their clothes, removing suits and ties for worn jeans, cowboy shirts that were not too new, and pointy cowboy boots that had already been worn. "All of which," Diego had complained, "are most uncomfortable for my little feet, my little pudgy backside, and my adorable little potbelly. I look like that mouse in the cartoons, Speedy Gonzales. All I'm missing is a sombrero."

"By the way," Reb had also said, "you'll need a hat. You don't walk around bareheaded in these parts."

"What next?" said Diego, with a sigh.

A kind of hut with the word FOOD in large white letters appeared on their right.

"Shall we stop?"

"No."

"I thought you were hungry."

"It will wait. We are not there yet."

"I am delighted to learn that we are going somewhere. And where is this 'there'?"

"Sweetwater."

They arrived at about eleven o'clock, on July 2. According to Diego, the place was not worth the detour, or even the stopover. It was a small place, strung out, oppressed by the sun, and as if asleep forever.

Reb selected an ordinary-looking restaurant. They ordered steaks, and, for the millionth time, without any hope, Diego explained to the waiter, who looked as if he couldn't care less, that he liked his steak rare, rare, very red, actually raw on the inside, do you see what I mean?, but with the resigned certitude that the steak would arrive overcooked. And it did. They began to eat, and then the incident occurred, while they were finishing the inevitable piece of apple pie.

A man walked in. He had large muscular arms with tattoos on them, short hair like a Marine, and was wearing a black Stetson decorated with a band of lizard or snakeskin. In his left hand he was carrying a metal garbage can, the cover of which was closed, and kept closed by a leather strap.

He placed it on the nearest stool and ordered a beer.

Diego, who knew his Reb, noticed the amused sparkle in his eyes.

He asked: "What is it?"

"The poster above his head," said Reb.

Diego looked up, but almost had to stand to read it. The key words were "Waco," which he knew to be a town in Texas, "rattlesnake roundup," and "prize money" of "three hundred dollars." A chill ran through him.

"This is what we came for?"

"Mmmmmm."

Diego knew what a roundup was. He also knew what a rattlesnake was. And he was frightened.

So frightened, he thought he might be sick.

"Ya should catch your beasts yourself," said the man with the tattooed arms, whose name was Jock Wilson. "These here are mine. But if ya want me to go with ya to find some, it's O.K. with me. Twenty bucks."

"Six," said Reb.

They agreed on twelve.

They left in the yellow pickup, driving into the burning hills, where the temperature was probably over a hundred and twenty degrees. Wilson had all the necessary equipment: sticks, at the end of which were metal pliers made of braided wire, hand mirrors, a can of gasoline, and the necessary garbage can.

They caught three right away, within the first hour: the reptiles were in the hollow of a rock, in the shade; even they couldn't bear the heat. But then two hours went by without any sign of a snake.

"There's been a lot of huntin' done in these parts," explained Wilson. "But lucky for you, Ah'm here, and Ah know this damn place like the back of ma hand. You sure are gettin' your money's worth with those fifteen bucks ya promised me."

"Twelve,' said Reb with a smile. "Plus a beer when we get back."

Using the hand mirrors to catch the rays of the sun, they systematically lighted up each crack in the rocks. At last, a swarming nest appeared. Wilson placed a small copper tube in the can and slowly began to pour the gasoline.

"Watch it, man . . ."

In the next few minutes they caught six rattlesnakes, using the sticks with pliers. One of them came close to biting the tip of Reb's boot, when he was surprised by the startling velocity of the snake's lateral movement.

"That's the rattlesnake for ya," said Wilson. "He doesn't wiggle like other fuckin' beasts; he goes right off to the fuckin' side. And he kin cover a mile and a half in one shot. Ya've gotta see it to believe it. These are racin' rattlesnakes, man. Gotta be damn careful. Ya've got one more to go, and ya'll have your ten fuckin' snakes."

Six of the snakes they caught that day were horned rattlesnakes, the longest one measuring more than two and a half feet. One was a cascabel, which was a good four and a half feet and had the usual mosaic on its back, spots united into series of stripes runing down the sides. The last three were diamondbacks, the longest of which was over six feet.

As to the danger they represented, it was evident, but with differences. The horned snakes and the diamondbacks could inject a venom that attacked the inner surface of blood vessels and destroyed the tissues. The cascabel was special; its fangs, like those of the diamondbacks, were sometimes an inch and a half long, and its venom contained neurotoxins that caused paralysis of the muscles, the heart especially.

"It depends on the guy, man," answered Wilson to a question put to him by Diego. "If ya really have to git bitten by one of these fuckin' beasts, then choose a horned or a diamondback. Those cascabels are a fuckin' pain in the ass. But, in either case, ya croak in thirty or forty minutes. Gone."

The tenth snake, a diamondback, was caught as night was falling. He was about to go after a rabbit. To keep him on the ground, then to brandish him and stuff him into the garbage pail, both Diego and Reb were needed. Wilson contented himself simply with slamming shut the cover.

"They're not ma beasts. Me, Ah'm jist the guide. Which ya shouldn't forgit. Thirteen dollars?"

"Twelve and a beer."

Diego's blood felt frozen. They climbed back into the pickup.

"Ya want to go to Waco for the tournament?"

Reb nodded. Wilson was looking at him curiously.

"Ever play with rattlesnakes before?"

"No, as a matter of fact," answered Reb.

The tournament was held in a huge barn, which had been cleared out for the event, the enormous farm equipment arranged in such a way as to serve as graduated steps and to outline a little arena. The farm was near Waco and not thirty miles from the Dallas skyscrapers.

A cage was placed in the middle of the arena. It was made of very thin wire and measured not quite ten feet by ten. There was no top; the wire mesh stopped at a height of almost four feet. The two hundred and fifty to three hundred spectators had each paid a dollar fifty to come watch.

"Do you understand what I expect from you, Diego?"

"Yes."

"Diego, if you move before my signal, I'll never forgive you for it."

"I understand, Reb."

Silence fell upon the barn. The contents of an iron box had just been spilled into the cage, and ten rattlesnakes unfolded themselves, many of them sounding their rattles. One threw himself in rage against the mesh and, opening his mouth disproportionately, twice snapped at the wire. The crowd murmured, as aficionados would have at the entrance of a handsome Miura bull into an arena.

The murmurs died down when the first team appeared. It consisted of two men. They wore jeans and shirts, Stetsons, and cowboy boots. They wore nothing on their hands. One of them carried a thick burlap bag, the kind used for grain.

They waited for the "go" signal and, immediately, began to move. One of them grabbed a rattlesnake with his long gripper, held its head pressed against the wood floor, seized it between his fingers at the strangling point right below the jaw, and then flung it into the bag, which his teammate opened only for the amount of time needed. Meanwhile, the second man swung the bag through the air to keep the other snakes at a distance.

They were not very fast. In fact, it took them over two minutes and ten seconds to put the ten rattlers into the bag.

"Not bad, but you can do much better than that," said the master of ceremonies. He reminded the crowd that the record time was one minute and nine seconds.

"Reb?"

"Not now, Diego."

Reb was standing very straight, his hands still against his body, his eyes lost in the distance.

"Reb, who will go into the cage with you to hold the bag?"

"Wilson."

There was a silence. A second team entered the cage.

"Let Wilson go fuck himself," said Diego suddenly, with somber determination. "I, and no one else, will hold the bag for you."

"No."

"All right then, Reb. In that case, you'll have to knock me out. Because I, I, will jump into that cage and I'll sit on those fucking snakes."

Diego was fighting two fears, equally terrifying to him: the real fear of the rattlers and, even worse, his terror of seeing Reb die before his very eyes without being able to do anything, even if only to die with him. At no time had he thought of trying to stop Reb from, as Wilson said, "playing with the snakes." Even if the idea had come to him, he, who followed Reb in all things, would have immediately rejected it. He saw his mission as that of someone who goes along, and, if need be, encourages and pushes, to the end of the road. Any road. To any destination.

"Reb, I am begging you." He was trembling, and his eyes were full of tears. "Don't refuse me, Reb."

"Jock," said Reb calmly to Wilson, "there has been a change in plans. Diego will hold the bag in your place. As for the rest, Jock, it's extremely simple: as long as I don't look at you, don't do anything. *Anything*. All right?"

"Man, this is crazy," said Wilson.

"I will look at you steadily for a few seconds and then, only then, and not before, you can intervene."

"All right. "If that's what ya want."

"That's what I want."

They went on fifth, right after a team of two men from a nearby town who had set a new record, and a remarkable one for the bagging of ten rattlers: fifty-nine seconds. This team stood every chance of winning the three-hundred-dollar prize, and began to celebrate their impending victory by killing the snakes and skinning them, preparatory to cooking them over coals and eating them.

The third team had been less successful. They had had to be helped from outside the cage with clawed hooks to hold down the rattlers. The snake catcher had been bitten on the leg and had been rushed off to a hospital in one of three waiting ambulances.

All went well for the first nine beasts, although their time was not the best. When the ninth snake was dropped into the bag Diego was holding, he was drenched with sweat, and almost one and a half minutes had elapsed. Reb could probably have moved faster. But each time, without the slightest sign of hesitation, his large hand would grasp the triangular head right behind the jaw and would then execute the last movement calmly, slipping the furiously undulating body into the opening of the bag without rushing. His face was blank, but twice he smiled at Diego. And Diego actually thought, for a few seconds, that Reb had decided to abandon this project.

Then came the tenth snake. It was a beautiful, lustrous diamondback, close to five feet long. As Reb approached, it adopted the combat position: the rear part of the body in a vertical *S*, the head rocking slightly back and forth, the darting forked tongue hardly moving at all . . .

. . . until it shot out with the speed of lightning when the stick in Reb's hand was less than eight inches away. In the next tenth of a second, Reb's left hand came down, grabbing the body quickly, behind the head, then closing in and blocking the body, which was whipping through the air.

"Watch it, Diego," said Reb, smiling for the third time.

He let the stick drop and very carefully changed his grip, his right hand taking the left one's place. He squeezed tighter: the jaws opened wide, unbelievably wide, with the fangs clearly visible.

"Now," said Reb.

He presented his open left hand to the snake and loosened the grip of the other. The crowd shrieked. The fangs went straight into the flesh at the base of both the thumb and the index finger.

"Diego, hold on to that bag, please," Reb said, his teeth clenched. After that, he could no longer speak.

A man leaped into the cage and grabbed the bag from Diego, who was about to drop it. Another man, Wilson, reached Reb and, in one swift move, sliced off the snake's head and disengaged the fangs from the hand. He and two others lifted Reb under his arms and knees and carried him out of the cage to a table.

Reb's whole body was trembling, and his face was chalk white. His jaw was tightly clenched, his eyes closed, his nostrils pinched; and he didn't make a sound.

Some said: "He's got to be cut."

The bitten hand was swelling, and the puffiness was extending to the wrist and forearm as the blood vessels were dying and the skin becoming necrosed.

Absolute silence settled over the barn.

"We have to wait," said Wilson. "He said to wait until he looked at me. Ask his friend."

"We have to wait," said Diego, his yellow eyes burning.

Thirty seconds.

"Watch for the ambulance," said Wilson. "Keep it cool, man."

"Forty seconds, Reb," said Diego.

"Keep it cool, man."

"Fifty," said Diego.

Reb was now shaking with spasms, and had the two men not held him down, he would have fallen to the floor.

"Keep it cool, man."

"One minute," said Diego.

Twenty-five seconds later, Reb opened his eyes, tried visibly to smile, and his clear gray eyes searched first for Diego, and only then for Wilson.

"NOW!" screamed Wilson.

They picked him up and ran with him to the ambulance, whose doors were open and waiting, the driver at the wheel, a stretcher and harness ready. A medical attendant tried to prevent Diego from climbing into the ambulance. Instead, he felt the barrel of the Argentine's Colt .45 pressing into his stomach.

"If he dies before we get there, *amigo*, we all will. *Muy pronto, por favor.*"

It was in that very ambulance that, with a knife and without any anesthetic, they cut all the necrosed flesh, along a strip extending from the fork of the thumb and the index finger, through the length of the wrist, and almost up to the elbow; about eleven and a half inches by, at the worst spot, nearly two inches. The cut was a good fifth of an inch deep and bled relatively little.

In Waco, the doctors told Diego that the wretched butchering served no purpose at all, "but those crazy people glory in it, in their scars, and your friend will have established some kind of record in that area."

In any case, of course, he didn't die from it.

9

Georges Tarras believes it would be absurd to think that in this Waco incident—and in others, which Diego Haas refused to go into—Reb Klimrod was actually seeking to die.

"He had been through hell after losing the only woman he ever loved. And it is very romantic to imagine Reb, ravaged by sorrow, running all over the world and defying at each turn this Death that had taken his Charmian.

"But that would be giving a common dimension to an uncommon man.

"He was the richest man ever to walk this earth. As of the mid-sixties, he owned and administered by himself a fortune of seven or eight billion dollars, as much and perhaps more than Ludwig and Getty put together, at that time. And he had not nearly reached his top in that area.

"No. If there was any romanticism, it was elsewhere, and at a completely different level. His confrontation with the rattlesnake is simply typical of his whole life's pattern. It's just an anecdote. All you need to remember is his first encounter with Diego Haas, in 1947, when he plunged straight into the largest, most unknown, and most dangerous jungle in the world, with very little chance of coming out alive. And building up his fortune, huge beyond comprehension, while remaining in the darkest shadows, until the very end, even that would not be enough to explain him.

"Reb Klimrod's real dimension is greater than all this. I can see it more clearly defined in his final fabulous explosion. . . . "

Francisco Santana came to New York in September of 1964. It was his first meeting with David Settiniaz, who knew him only by name. Two of his assistants had preceded him; they had come separately, didn't know each other, and each thought he was on a secret and exclusive mission. Obviously Santana was using, even with his own subordinates, the same system of airtight separation that was so dear to Reb Klimrod.

The Mexican refused to come in person to the East Fifty-eighth Street offices. He telephoned one morning, using all the agreed-upon code words to identify himself, and, in fluid, practically flawless English, politely asked Settiniaz if he would mind coming to Santana's suite at the Plaza.

Settiniaz, through a report transmitted to him by the mysterious Jethro, knew all about Santana, especially that he was climbing higher and higher in Reb's task force. The Santana team had been doing a great job and had brought to life new and impressive Klimrod expansions. Settiniaz was curious, so he readily agreed. Moreover, he didn't often have the opportunity to leave his office on business.

"I know," said Santana, "very little about you. Just what Reb has told me; that is, that I should report to you on everything, absolutely everything. May I ask you a question?"

"You can always ask a question," answered Settiniaz, who was actually amused. This was not the first time that one of Reb's emissaries, no matter what rank, hesitated to confide in him.

"Who are you?" asked Santana.

"A lawyer," said Settiniaz. "Like yourself. No more, no less."

He could guess the questions burning on the Mexican's lips: Who are you that I should account to you so precisely? Who is

Reb Klimrod? Is he someone else's agent? If yes, whose agent? Who could be above Reb, who the devil could it be? Can there exist someone in the world who can give Reb orders?

It was this last point, especially, that tortured all these men who came to see Settiniaz. In their often fanatical attachment to Klimrod, they became angry when they discovered that someone else was also privy to all his secrets, which they had harbored so jealously. And yet none of these men, not even one, had any total sense of Reb. They each held only one piece of the huge puzzle, a puzzle that could be assembled only by Settiniaz. And even he? After all, in 1964 he knew nothing about what was taking shape in South America.

Should Settiniaz have prided himself on this special position, there was, to bring his feet back to the ground, that treacherous supposition by Georges Tarras, who pointed out that perhaps somewhere in the world, even right in New York City, there could be another Settiniaz, experiencing the same feeling of pride and assembling his own huge puzzle. . . .

Settiniaz said to Santana: "My role is to keep records, and nothing else. Let's say that I am a sort of scribe."

The Mexican was scrutinizing him with his hard black eyes. Finally he seemed to relax. He asked Settiniaz if he had had the chance to look over the documents that had been brought to him by one of his assistants. Settiniaz said yes.

"It's a tremendous business," said Santana almost regretfully. "The Dallas operation alone represents more than one hundred million dollars."

"Indeed, that is tremendous," admitted Settiniaz, doing his best to look impressed. He was thinking: Right now, I am playing Reb—in a way. I who am not supposed to have a sense of humor!

"And that is not all," Santana went on. "You have to figure as much and probably more for the oil businesses in Maracaïbo and in the Caribbean. An additional one hundred and fifty million would probably be close to reality."

"That is really impressive," said Settiniaz, at the same time thinking: All in all, that must account for three or four percent of Reb's fortune. Or at least Reb's fortune as I know it. At this point, these figures lose their impact.

"Furthermore," Santana continued, "there is this desalinization plant . . ."

Settiniaz knew about that business since its inception. It had first appeared in the files in 1956, soon after the beginning of the second offensive. At first, a Panamanian company, but nonetheless one owned by Klimrod, had leased to the Mexican government, in three successive phases, nearly two hundred forty-seven thousand one hundred acres of uninhabited desert. A second company, equally anonymous, had set up an installation that could, at the same time, produce drinking water and salt. This second company was run by a man named Elias Bainish, whom Settiniaz discovered to be a cousin of Yoël who had emigrated to the United States. A third company, headquartered on the Isle of Jersey, had built low-cost housing. A fourth company had taken care of the commercialization of the plots of land, under the supervision of a Mexican trustee recommended by Santana; these plots had been resold to farmers or to Mexican companies. A fifth company, French, and one in which Paul Soubise had a large interest, had set up a port that could accommodate ships up to one hundred and fifty thousand tons.

And a sixth company, of which, by an intermediary trust agreement, Francisco Santana was the owner, had taken care of selling the salt, fifteen million tons per year.

"There are some new developments," said Santana, "and I wanted to come and tell you about them myself, if only just to meet you. There are new developments concerning the desalinization plants. We have signed contracts to have others built in Arabia, under very advantageous terms. A Lebanese banker from Beirut named Shahadzé represented us in all the meetings with the emirs, and I suggested to Reb that he reward him in some way. But this is not the main issue.

"At this moment we are negotiating for the repurchase of our plant in Mexico. The agreement is soon to be signed, for sixty million dollars, and that is a good price. The problem is elsewhere. A few years back, we made some agreements with a Japanese chemical group concerning the salt. We have just renewed them, and their lawyer, a certain Hang, is as tough as the devil. He is from Hong Kong and could make anyone crazy with his stubbornness. But that's another story. . . . I want to get to the ships. That bothers me a little. A Liberian company has been given an exclusive contract to ship salt, under conditions that, for once, do not satisfy me at all."

"What's the difference," asked Settiniaz, "since all of it will be resold to a German group?"

"This Liberian company has been making enormous profits off of us for the past three years."

"Have you discussed this with Reb?"

"Several times. He admitted that he had made an error, at the time the first agreements were signed. He would rather write it off, but he allowed me to take over the battle after I insisted. I came up against the lawyers for the Liberian company, some Greeks from New York, the Petridis brothers. Really hard-nosed. Do you know them?"

"By name," said Settiniaz. "They have a remarkable reputation."

And he was thinking: The King's Men are fighting among themselves now! I can just imagine Reb's face when Santana came to tell him he was going to strangle Nick and Tony. What a madhouse!

"Settiniaz," said the Mexican, "on certain days I have trouble understanding Reb. Most of the time, he is brilliant, really brilliant, and I am choosing my words carefully. Yet sometimes he disappears completely. I wouldn't know where to reach him if I really needed him. . . ."

"Has that ever happened? What I mean is, has it ever happened that you needed him without being able to reach him?"

"Not yet," said Santana. "But it could happen. Also, I am not speaking only of his physical absences. Sometimes he handles certain matters carelessly, like this shipping business. One could think that money does not interest him at all. I am not complaining. Quite the contrary. But I wanted to talk to someone about this. . . . Settiniaz, is there anything that I should know that I don't? I don't believe, I can't believe, that Reb could have made a mistake. You will laugh, but I think he is nearly infallible. Can you answer my question?"

"You know everything you need to know."

Settiniaz smiled. He was actually close to laughing, thinking of all these King's Men Santana had just mentioned: Hang, Shahadzé, Soubise, Ethel Court, for the Jersey company, the Petridis brothers, as well as Santana himself, and even Elias Bainish, although he was not a King's Man, but simply a man of trust to whom Reb had granted a company. These men fighting among

365

themselves, finding each other "tough and stubborn." And under Reb's mocking eye, Reb, who was committed to secrecy, as he was.

But the confusion, suddenly shown by this Mexican, who was otherwise so brilliant, was too close to that which he himself felt when dealing with Reb for him to make fun of it.

"Francisco, I have the same feeling you do when it comes to Reb. He is not an ordinary man."

Their friendship began there.

Francisco Santana had another reason to meet Settiniaz. On Reb's order, he had teamed up for the past year with Georges Tarras on a rather special mission, having to do with tax havens. At the beginning of the phenomenal fortune, it had been Tarras who, with the help of an entire task force of international experts, had taken charge of the financial organization. This had, in a way, the shape of several pyramids, one next to the other, one for each of the King's Men, in different sizes, according to the area, with no other link than Reb himself, and the knowledge Settiniaz had of its existence.

Because the essence, the existence, of this organization was secret, they had made great use of the possibilities offered during the early fifties by the legislatures of some countries, which welcomed anonymous companies whenever it was possible or useful. In his files, Settiniaz had seen a procession of businesses whose headquarters were in Panama, Monaco, Liechtenstein, Jersey, or Guernsey.

As of 1962, and until 1968, other names were added to the list, usually exotic ones, as colonial strongholds weakened and disappeared: the Bahamas, Curaçao, the Cayman Islands, the Turks and Caicos Islands, Gibraltar, Hong Kong, the Isle of Man, and even a tiny coral island lost in the middle of the Pacific called Nauru.

And, of course, Liberia.

Nearly one hundred and eighty Klimrod companies established offices in Liberia—counting those that had been dissolved.

"David," Tarras had said, "I'm getting old. The years are beginning to weigh on my poor shoulders, and flying all over the world becomes more tiring year after year. I have asked Reb to find someone who could work with me now and eventually take my place. I don't know whom Reb will choose. . . ."

It was Francisco Santana.

Settiniaz said later: "He and another man, a Dutchman I will call De Vries, did a tremendous amount of work. Their role was not to create companies (except for those Santana controlled personally), but to oversee their birth and then the security of the chosen tax havens, in the early stages. At least three of the countries—or islands, since they are so often islands—that are commonly known today as tax havens were actually "invented" by Santana and De Vries. I know this because I was in charge of a special budget, baptized by Reb 'Milton,' a transparent enough name, referring to John Milton's *Paradise Lost* and *Paradise Regained*. This budget helped to convince, let's say, the small interested governments. It was not simply a bribe. In one case, for example, the desired legal dispositions were adopted by the new state in exchange for a contract with one of our shipping companies."

Settiniaz invited Santana to dinner the following day, and the Mexican readily accepted. The two men were about the same age, a little over forty, and had similar characteristics, which, if they go without saying, are better said: they were meticulous, precise, neat in everything they did, and scrupulous. David didn't actually dislike Nick Petridis, for example, in spite of his Greek pirate's effervescent imagination, or Paul Soubise, whose language he spoke well, but whose irony annoyed him, but Santana's seriousness suited him much more.

This did not surprise Georges Tarras, who said: "El Matador has as little humor as you do, David, and you both have the same accountant's mentality. You suit each other. . . ."

Soon after Santana left New York, he had one of his assistants deliver a new file to Settiniaz. It dealt with a transaction in which the Mexican had played only a small part. He had been called in to negotiate for some property in Jamaica, without knowing what it was going to be used for. This purchase was actually part of a much larger operation, being handled by two of the King's Men, Philip Vanderbergh and Ethel Court, the purpose of which was to set up two hotel chains in the Caribbean islands. Vanderbergh and Court did not know each other and competed against one another, as arranged by Klimrod, each one in charge of one of the hotel chains.

Along with the file, Santana enclosed a letter in which he invited Settiniaz to come spend some time in Mexico, at his home in Mérida, in the province of Yucatan.

The Settiniaz brood—there were now five children—made the trip, after a few more exchanges of letters, during the spring of 1965. They spent two weeks in his rather modest home, which, because of its location, permitted a visit to some Mayan temples. Santana affirmed happily that there was some Mayan blood in his veins.

It took him ten days to come out with the question.

"David, you will probably not answer me, but there is something that is really puzzling me: what in God's name does Reb intend to do with these eight million Caribbean pine trees?"

"With *what*?" exclaimed Settiniaz, with complete surprise.

"The pine trees. Trees just like the ones you see all around us. *Pinus Carybea,* to be exact."

"What figure did you mention?"

"Eight million."

Settiniaz's surprise was sincere, and he had some difficulty in remaining outwardly expressionless. Santana naturally mistook the nature of his silence.

"Excuse me," he said, smiling pleasantly. "I should never have asked you the question. I can see that my indiscretion has put you in an embarrassing position. Let's not discuss it any further. Come and see the *cenote*. It's a kind of large natural well, very impressive, into which my ancestors used to hurl their sacrificial victims, after first covering them with jewels. Not such a bad way to die. . . ."

Eight million Caribbean pine trees, thought Settiniaz. What is he up to now?

The mystery intrigued him, and as soon as he returned to New York, feeling somewhat unscrupulous, he made a thorough review of his files. By this time, he had records of over twelve hundred companies. Strictly Klimrod companies, that is. The 1965 computer was a rudimentary one, but it was able to show that nowhere in its memory was there even the slightest mention of any transaction dealing with "Caribbean pine trees."

Settiniaz tried another entry: "trees."

He thus discovered, and was reminded, that Reb held large interests, in Norway, Sweden, and Finland, in the forestry industry. What was more, one of his Canadian companies, in as sociation with a completely unknown (to Settiniaz, at least) Argentine company, had signed enormous contracts for forest products with Nikita Khrushchev's Soviet Union, contracts that had been renewed without any apparent difficulty—with the help of Paul Soubise—the following year, 1964, after Khrushchev's departure from the scene.

Two identical files dealing with this transaction had been sent to Settiniaz, one by Soubise, the other by a Swiss Black Dog, following Reb's system of double control.

That was not all. A French-Italian forestry company had, four years earlier, sold fifty-one percent of its shares to a typical Klimrod company located in Panama.

Settiniaz, more and more intrigued, went further in his investigation.

A name suddenly appeared about which he knew nothing: Jaime Rochas. Rochas was the director of the Argentine company that had made the agreements with the Soviet Union. He was also the legal and financial counselor of the one in Panama, the one that was interested also in the forests of Africa. And it was Rochas who, in Canada, had signed at least a dozen contracts.

This showed the characteristics of a King's Man. Yet there had been no "Strictly Confidential.—To be delivered to addressee in person" report on him and no file marked SPECIAL in red.

Normally, this would mean that the person was of little importance. Here the contradiction was obvious. And, thought Settiniaz, since I can't believe that Reb could be guilty of an oversight . . .

In his deserted offices (he always waited to be alone to start doing this kind of research, which for that reason took him several weeks), he decided to look farther. He began searching for anything that had to do with Jaime Rochas. The name appeared fourteen more times, in connection with fourteen more companies. Apparently this Rochas had traveled a great deal: besides the Soviet Union, Scandinavia, and Africa, he turned up in Indonesia, Indochina, and China; and he had also taken part in important operations in South America, in Venezuela especially. Most of his activities were related in some way to agriculture, in the field of arboriculture, but on two occasions he had played a part in other businesses: an unclear one concerning kaolin, and the repurchase of an entire group of paper factories in France.

His path had often crossed those of various King's Men: Hang in China and Indochina, Soubise and Shahadzé in France and the Middle East, Santana in Venezuela, Court in Africa, Gozchiniak in Scandinavia. But the man had remained very discreet. Only Francisco Santana's chance remark about the eight million trees had permitted Settiniaz to come across his name in particular, within a system containing over thirty-five thousand names.

He felt he had stumbled onto something big.

The summer of 1965 went by without any appearance by Klimrod. The fall and winter as well. He came to New York three times, to Settiniaz's knowledge, in 1966. That year was marked by a flourishing of new companies; the number recorded by Settiniaz passed the fifteen hundred mark. Hardly a day went by without one of the Black Dogs coming to bring a new file, and this was the time when Settiniaz's capacity as an organizer was really put to the test. He was not able to go on vacation, and he had to increase his manpower. Because of a growing lack of space, in spite of the increased use of the computer, he was even considering a move. But Reb shook his head.

"That will not be necessary, David. We've just passed the crest of the wave. Things will calm down now."

Overwhelmed with work, devoting up to fifteen hours a day to it, Settiniaz no longer had time to think about Jaime Rochas. Actually, the Argentine's name had not appeared anywhere of late. Just as if he had stopped working for Klimrod, which, after all, was perhaps the answer to the mystery.

"And," he said later, "I had the usual reflex of all those who were Reb's lieutenants. I thought to myself: If he had wanted me to know about it . . . So I didn't say anything.

"Then, something happened in October of 1967."

The message received by Settiniaz set the meeting in Brooklyn Heights. The address was that of an elegant brownstone, dating from the last century, whose windows offered a splendid view of Manhattan. "Ask for Ali Dannon." The name had an Irish ring, and the first name could apply to either sex.

It was a tree-lined street, and Ali Dannan turned out to be a young woman, tall, dark, and strikingly beautiful. She was apparently a painter. When Settiniaz arrived, she greeted him with paintbrush in hand, wearing a smock spattered prettily with different colors. She received him with a lovely smile.

"He went out, but he should be back any time now," she said. "He asked you to excuse him and to wait. You wouldn't perhaps want to be the angel, would you?"

"The angel?"

She walked ahead of him, her hips swinging, to a pleasant workroom. There was a canvas on an easel, and on the canvas were circles and slashes from which emerged the outline of a child's face.

"I need an angel, right in the middle there. But you have red hair. Whoever heard of a red-haired angel?"

"I do not have red hair," said Settiniaz resentfully. "It is a reddish blond."

"That's debatable. Whatever color it is, you like good coffee, your steaks cooked medium rare, sautéed mushrooms seasoned with chopped parsley, strawberries with whipped cream, and wines from Burgundy. We ordered a few cases of Bonnes Mares; he said that was your favorite wine. Lunch will be ready in an hour and a half. But please sit down. Make yourself at home. He told me you were rather formal. If you want to use the telephone or take a shower, please do. I will finish my angel. Actually, you do have something of an angel . . ."

She was smiling at him sweetly. And it was the same story all over again: once more, David Settiniaz found himself in the presence of someone whose relationship with Reb was unclear to him. She had not mentioned him by name, but had said "he"; she also had said "we ordered . . ." which implied some sort of intimacy. And I don't even know under what name she knows him! he thought. I learned that I am expected to have lunch here, that everything has been prepared for me, even the Bonnes Mares, which is indeed one of my favorites, and which this devil of a man remembered!

"I do need to make a telephone call," he said, "to cancel another appointment."

"The study is one flight up. He said you would want to use the telephone. I prepared a full shaker of martinis for you, just as you like them!"

He went upstairs and found a white room, almost bare, which had no fewer than eight telephone lines, as well as a table, two chairs, and a few dozen books, in English, French, German, Spanish, and Italian. There were also an Isaac Bashevis Singer volume in Yiddish and some lawbooks, among them the two volumes of Sir Gerald Fitzmaurice's *The General Principles of International Law*, a few volumes of the *German Book of International Law* and the *Journal of World Trade Law*, those standards Georges Tarras had made him spend so much time on in the long-ago days at Harvard.

I see he has not given up the study of law, he thought.

Only then did he notice the green folder placed prominently on the table, near all the telephones. It had the familiar inscription: "Strictly confidential.—To be delivered to addressee in person."

And another that was less so: the initials *D.J.S.* David James Settiniaz? He reached for the green folder as he was telling his secretary that she should cancel all of his appointments until further notice.

But he didn't complete his gesture. After hanging up, he went to sit on the second chair. He picked up a book by Saul Bellow and began to read. A few minutes later, he heard the front door open and close, voices, and then, without any noise signaling his approach, Reb's tall figure appeared in the doorway.

"I'm sorry to be late, David. I wanted to walk back from Manhattan and I underestimated my speed. You should have opened the folder."

The implication was clear: Since I left it out, it was obviously intended for you. Or that I made a mistake. And who could ever imagine Reb Klimrod making mistake? Settiniaz was once again annoyed.

"David, excuse me. I sometimes put you in embarrassing situations. Please do not be angry with me."

He walked into the room and sat down, in one of his familiar positions, hands in the pockets of his jacket, his legs stretched out before him, his chin resting on his chest, and his eyes lost in a dream.

He said softly: "Would you like to look at the folder now?"

Settiniaz put down the Bellow book and went over to the table. The folder contained only one typewritten page. He read: "Settiniaz, David James, born in New York City, New York, on September 2, 1923. See preceding file. Period beginning January

372

1, 1966, and ending December 31, 1966: nothing to report. According to orders received, all surveillance will stop as of January 1, 1967, at zero hour." As the only signature, the letter J.

"Jethro," said Reb. "Diego must have told Tarras about him, who in turn must have told you. Naturally, he is the one who sends you these folders concerning some of my people. And he will continue to do so."

"For how long have I been . . . under surveillance?"

"As of January 1, 1950, at zero hour. But you must have suspected it."

"And what did he discover about me?"

"To his great despair, nothing. Nothing important. Jethro believes that any free man is a criminal who has not been found out. You and Tarras have seriously shaken his fundamental conviction."

Tarras, too, thought Settiniaz, feeling somewhat consoled.

"Tarras, too," said Reb, with his exasperating ability to read other people's minds.

"And for him, also, the surveillance has stopped?"

"Yes."

Reb raised his hands.

"David, no answer to the next question: when did I tell Jethro to stop watching Georges Tarras. Don't ask it, please. It is not important to know if I expressed my trust in Georges before I did so in you, or the other way around. Anyhow, you know how it is. Now you will ask me, now that you know I have had you watched for seventeen years, why I am stopping now. My answer: I don't know. Probably because there comes a time when you have to trust somebody totally."

"You exasperate me," said Settiniaz.

"With my way of asking the questions and then giving the answers. I know. I can't help it."

He began to laugh.

"Let's say that sometimes I can't help it." But he stopped laughing quickly. Again his eyes were lost in a dream. He looked at Settiniaz.

"Twenty-two years and one hundred and fifty-four days ago, David. Mauthausen. Do you remember?"

"Yes."

"Is your memory of it very precise?"

"Certainly less so than yours."

The gray eyes seemed darker, obsessive, almost hypnotic.

"*Mon Dieu, mon Dieu, la vie est là, simple et tranquille* . . . 'My God, my God, life is there, simple and tranquil . . .' David, do you remember the rest?"

Settiniaz felt himself weakening. Emotion was getting the better of him.

"*Cette paisible rumeur-là vient de la ville* . . . 'That peaceful murmur comes from the town . . .' "

"Yes, David."

"*Dis, qu'as-tu fait, toi que voilà, pleurant sans cesse,/Dis, qu'as-tu fait, toi que voilà, de ta jeunesse* . . . 'Oh, you, what have you done, weeping endlessly,/Oh, you, what have you done, with your youth . . .'"

Silence. Reb nodded. He was smiling, looking extremely warm and friendly.

"I am not trying to . . . use emotional blackmail, by stirring up all these memories. . . ."

He moved his legs and his hands, which, coming out of his pockets, unfolded, revealing the long scar where the thumb and index finger met.

"I was really thinking about that day in May of 1945 before, while I was walking. 'I will never forget that I saved your life.' It was also a Frenchman who wrote that. And it is true that you owe me something. I would have died had it not been for you. I have not forgotten that."

"You never forget anything."

"That's not always an advantage."

His words expressed anguish—and it seemed inconceivable.

A new wave of emotion swept over Settiniaz, who was thinking: And that woman downstairs looks like Charmian. . . . There was another silence.

After a while Reb stood up and began pacing.

"Jaime Rochas," he said. "I was wondering how long it would take you to find his name. It took you less time than I had expected. And ever since I realized you knew, I have purposely avoided you. I was not ready. What gave you the clue? Francisco Santana?"

"Yes."

"I noticed his surprise when I spoke of those eight million

trees in front of him. And you went to visit him in Mérida. It was logical that he would mention them to you. David, there are two men who have almost identical names: Jaime Rochas and Ubaldo Rocha. The second one is a Brazilian. You should not confuse them. And there are other names you will soon learn: Emerson Coëlho and Jorge Socrates, also Brazilians. Enrique Escalante, Jim MacKenzie, Jean Coltzesco, Trajano da Silva, Ung Seng, Uwe Sobieski, Del Hathaway, Elias and Ethel Weizmann, Maurice Everett, Marnie Oakes are less important, even though they are extremely important to me. They don't appear in any of your files. But they are the reason we are meeting today."

He sat down again. The sun was shining brightly over the East River and Manhattan, and gave a human feeling to the mass of concrete buildings.

"David, for the last few years, I have been operating a certain number of businesses simultaneously. You and I are the only ones to know how many and how complex they are sometimes. You probably know better than I what I am worth, in terms of money. In that area I never really had the taste for addition. It doesn't matter to me."

He smiled. "And you know it is not affected on my part."

"I can give you the figures," said Settiniaz. "If you give me a little time. Four, maybe five weeks. With a two percent margin of error."

"I don't give a damn, David."

"You are the richest man in the world, by far."

"That's nice," said Reb, with a slightly amused irony, but with no discourtesy.

He stretched out his large, thin hands, which were tanned except where the scar was. At that time, Settiniaz didn't know where it came from. Reb was not wearing a watch or a ring.

"David, for the past few years I have been working on something quite important, which means a great deal to me, more so than anything else I have ever done. I have not spoken of it to you and did not intend to until next year. It is a very long-range endeavor, David. In two years, if you agree, I would like to take you there, to see exactly what it involves. . . ."

He is still hesitating to tell me about it, thought Settiniaz, who knew Reb's ways well enough to see, in all these sentences put back to back, a delaying tactic.

"It's true," said Reb. "I am still hesitating to tell you about it."

"In that case, don't say anything."

The large hands came together for the first time.

"David, I am creating a country."

And he had already invested eight hundred million dollars, he said. But that was just the beginning. He figured he would need at least four billion dollars. Maybe more. Probably more. There were quite a few problems to be worked out. He said "quite a few" in the same tone he had used a few minutes earlier when he said that all the businesses he had created were "many" and "complex."

The young woman painter came to announce that lunch was ready, and during the meal they discussed painting and books and films, with Reb furiously defending a Nicolas de Staël whom Ali was attacking.

But as soon as they had finished, they went back upstairs to the white office and locked themselves in.

The King said that he had more or less always had this idea in mind, "ever since 1949 or 1950. Not before, not really." Perhaps not as clearly. He had not for a long time thought the whole thing through. But now he had come to the end, or almost; one never really knew.

"I mean to the end of my dream, David. As to its realization, I am still far from it. There are serious problems to overcome and much opposition to counter. . . . And yet I am right. A free man who could not reach the border of his legitimate dream, because of these obstacles, because of the intervention of states, or of one single state, that man would live a second-rate existence, subject to the first despotism to come along, in an era of the most profound savagery. You know me a little, David. . . . Could I ever accept that?"

Suddenly inexhaustible, he went on for hours and hours, sitting across from David Settiniaz, who was overcome by stupor, as he alternated between believing in the project—he, also—and measuring the impossible folly of it. He did not utter one word while the calm voice was enumerating the plans that had already been achieved, those that were currently being undertaken, and those to come.

But at last he did ask: "Have you told Georges Tarras about this?"

A smile.

"Yes."

"Who else knows about it?"

Silence. The pale gaze suddenly became terribly sharp, almost ferocious for a few seconds.

"Besides Georges and you, David, no one in this part of the world. No one besides the people down there."

"And Diego Haas?" Settiniaz could not help asking.

Again there was silence. Night was falling.

"I am finished for the moment, David," said Reb. "Remember: not next year, but the year after, I would like to show you something that is sufficiently established. And I would very much like to have you come and visit. Whenever you wish, as of, let's say, the end of April. Call Diego in Rio and simply tell him that you want to come spend a few days at his home in Ipanema. Come alone, please. . . . One more thing, David: I will be relying on you more than ever now. If you accept. And if you accept, you will have all the necessary power. I expect to be rather busy in the next few years. . . ."

Settiniaz purposely made the trip to Maine.

He was familiar with the amusing little house and its red rooms, many reds, actually, which belonged to the Tarrases. He had gone there during the years immediately following the war, when he was once again a student at Harvard, and Georges Tarras again his professor.

The house had not changed, but two rooms had been added.

"To store . . . well, store! To pile up all these books. I really no longer know what to do with them."

"Change houses."

Settiniaz had no idea how much money Tarras earned yearly, but knowing Reb's generosity, he imagined it must be quite a lot. Enough, certainly, to permit the former professor to buy three or four houses.

"Don't be silly, Master Settiniaz. Where the devil would I be happier than here? And, what's more, I like the scenery."

Through his glasses, he looked at his visitor sharply.

"What is troubling you, David?"

377

"He has told me about his project."

"Ah!" said Tarras simply.

After a pause he went on, quite naturally: "It is my teatime. Would you like a cup?"

Only then did Settiniaz, confused, realize that his friend was alone in the house.

"How is Shirley?"

"She is away for a little while," answered Tarras.

But the way he answered caught Settiniaz's attention:

"Is everything all right?"

"A few little problems. The poor thing is not so young anymore, in spite of what she may think. But nothing serious. Let's talk about you."

He smiled with the same happy sarcasm as Diego Haas did.

"About you, but not about Reb. David, as far as Reb is concerned, I am unwavering. You are, too, although you resist, with your usual valor. I will not discuss what he does. For me, everything is simple: I will have had the luck in my lifetime to meet a genius. A mad genius, or a genial madman, however you like; it all comes to the same thing. But a genius. With a destiny. And I have all the affection in the world for him. What he does he does well, whatever it is. Whether I understand it or not is of no importance. So let's not go on about it. What's bothering you so much? The new responsibilities Reb will give you?"

"That alone would be enough to keep me up nights," said David.

"You have surrounded yourself with the best possible team of lawyers and specialists. You have a fantastic sense of organization. I always suspected it, but Reb could see it; he gambled on you, and he is winning. For the past fifteen years . . ."

"Seventeen."

"For the past seventeen years, you have been collecting the most infinitesimal information on the largest empire ever created by one man. You are probably the only one who can make any sense of it. Even Reb, as phenomenal as his memory can be, would probably be incapable . . . Still no milk?"

"Still none. Thank you."

". . . Incapable of listing all his achievements. He *is* human, although I somethings think of him as extraterrestrial. . . . The sugar is in the jar marked 'Laurel.' No, not for me, thank you;

I am no longer allowed any. And, what's more . . . Let's go back to my study. I love to have my tea and muffins near the fireplace."

They left the red kitchen for the scarlet study, passing on the way a carmine dining room, a lees-of-wine hall, and a geranium living room. David knew there were also a rosy laundry room, a ruby-colored library, and a second one, in garnet, a tomato garage, a cherry pantry, and a cyclamen television room. "That one," Tarras had explained, "was a whim of Shirley's. Cyclamen! Can you believe it?"

They sat down in front of the fireplace.

"And what is more, my dear David, why the devil do you think that, ever since the early days when you were my student, I preferred you to the others? Was I in love with you? I am teasing you. Reb thinks of you what I think of you. We have discussed it, he and I, if you want to know everything. Yes, of course, he consults me sometimes, or he thinks out loud in front of me. He does not expect you to multiply his fortune many times over for him; it doesn't need it, and it will develop on its own and reach Himalayan proportions, even if you do nothing more than sit on it. I am not an enemy of scruples, but I don't go overboard. . . . Why don't you try one of these muffins . . . ? Would you believe that Reb had an entire family brought over from Ireland, and set them up here, simply because Mrs. Cavanaugh, who is the brains in the family, makes the best muffins in the world? It's true. Don't tell me he's crazy, or that his project is crazy, and that I am crazy to believe in it."

Georges sat back in the large burgundy armchair.

"David, my boy, I don't know when he will launch it, but even if I know the end result beforehand, it's going to be a fucking good battle. Let's drink a toast to folly and to dreams, because they are, David, the only reasonable things."

A Turtle with a Wooden Leg

1

Ubaldo Rocha cut the boat's outboard motor, and silence settled over them instantly. The brownish river seemed stagnant; if not for the unexpected swirls and gurgling sounds, one would have thought the waters were dead. As always at the beginning of the dawn, the humidity, which had condensed high on the green walls of vegetation, fell like rain. Large slippery drops dripped from the leaves, and every so often made a clapping noise. But that was the only noise; even the toucans were silent.

MacKenzie and Coltzesco were already awake, and so of course were Jaua and his three men. One of them decided to move. Climbing over the rail his naked body slipped into the water, which reached to his waist. He was able to guide the stern of the boat into a channel that would have been invisible to anyone else. In some places, the boat passed under vaults of greenery, low and dark, and the men in the boat were forced to lie flat.

"*Aroami*," said the Indian.

"Watch out for the snakes," translated Rocha for his two white companions.

They went about sixty yards, using the lower branches to haul themselves along. All of a sudden, light and dawn returned, at the end of the vegetal tunnel. They came out onto what seemed like a little pond totally enclosed by the jungle. A gray mist hung over the surface of the water. It carried a slight smell of smoke, which Rocha's sharp nostrils recognized. The Yanomami did, too, apparently. Jaua reacted with an almost imperceptible movement of his eyelids.

They beached on a small low bank. Materializing with an almost magical instantaneousness, the escort appeared: thirty men in all, the tops of their heads shaved, completely naked, the penis held straight up against the body by a thin belt of braided liana tied below the foreskin. They carried large war bows made of black wood. Not one word was exchanged. The boat was pulled out of the water, the motor lifted off and covered, and everything was then tucked away under foliage. They even erased the traces left on the spongy ground by the boat's keel.

The forest swallowed the whole group, which advanced in the usual formation: a parallel file on either side of the path—if you could call it a path; even Rocha, with his twenty years of experience in the forest, could not have made it out. At one point, they heard a snapping sound, exactly like that of a suddenly released cord hitting the shaft of a bow.

The guides stopped in their tracks, alert. Some of them went ahead while the rest of the group waited. But they returned quickly, laughing silently and holding up spider webs they had had to cut down to free a passage, proof that the surroundings held no enemies waiting in ambush. Rocha was no fool: something was brewing. For over two years now, he had not heard of a single bloody encounter. But one could never be sure with the Yanomami. A simple incident over a woman or a hunt could escalate rapidly, and he had often seen these furtive clashes, swift as lightning, during which arrows measuring nearly five feet would suddenly, without any warning at all, fly from behind a jungle wall that had seemed devoid of any human presence.

They went forward for several hours. Every so often, groups of screeching monkeys would swing through the green vault above their heads, too high to be intercepted by arrows. The march did, however, turn into a hunting expedition. First, they came upon fresh traces of a herd of wild pigs, and three or four men left the group, having covered their chests and shoulders with an odorous brown substance. To hunt pigs, one had to be perfumed and ready; and one was never supposed to utter the name of the prey, or it would vanish instantly. The first guide to spot the little pile of leaves kicked up by a boar digging in the earth would simply say, in a special tone of voice: "I saw some birds," and the others would understand. During the next few hours, two other patrols left like the first one, following the burrowing marks left by dogs, or stopping to search through the dwelling place of an entire family of armadillos. Rocha had the good fortune to come nose to nose with a bright green phosphorescent snake, in the bleak shadow, and immediately bludgeoned it with the flat part of a machete. He offered it to Jaua, who pulled out its venemous fangs by planting them in a tree trunk, decapitated it, and tied the butchered body to stop the bleeding. The Shamatari laughed.

"If the hunters come back empty-handed, we will still have something to eat tonight."

But the signs were favorable: they had not come across any *orihiyé*—animals who had died of natural causes; they had not heard any *kôbari* bird calls. The hunters had been careful to "close the path" by leaving broken branches behind them and across their path to hold back the game, and they had not defecated near any of the armadillo burrowing places.

When the hunters rejoined the group a few hours later, they had with them two peccaries and other small creatures.

The evening stop was organized around a fire, where they began to smoke the meat, while the younger men hung the hammocks. As night fell, they found some bees in the hollow of a tree. They diluted the honey in water and drank it. None of the meat killed that day was eaten; it would have brought bad luck. Instead, the meal consisted of boiled macaws and aras, which had been speared, but mainly of roasted bananas, nuts, caterpillars, and giant termite heads. MacKenzie abstained from the last two. The botanist, who specialized in tropical fruit arboriculture, had lived in New Guinea and in Africa, but he retained some reservations when it came to food. Jean Coltzesco, on the other hand, devoured the termites. As a geologist, he had spent years in the Andes and in Central America, and he made do with most things more easily than the Scot did.

They left in the early hours of the following morning, after Jaua kindled the embers they were leaving behind, reciting the ritual formula: "Ghost, ghost, you will remain to put out the fire. . . ." Had they not done this they would have faced the danger of being attacked by the souls of the dead, who roamed through the forest, unable to make fires; some were harmless, but others were capable of breaking a hunter's ribs by grabbing him from behind or, worse yet, seizing his "vital center."

By the end of the following afternoon, they reached the *shabono* where Reb was.

The camp, which was a temporary one, was at the top of a hill and contained nearly two hundred and fifty people. The triangular huts formed a circle around a clearing, surrounded by a hedge of thorny branches, which were meant to prevent an attack or an infiltration of ghosts or other *shawaras*, demons who were carriers of epidemics and diseases. The roofs of the huts were made of large leaves, with thorn-covered leafstalks, the *miyoma*, which were more resistant than the *ketiba* leaves used for overnight stops.

Even before daybreak, Reb was getting himself ready, under Coltzesco's curious gaze. Entirely naked, his hair nearly reaching his shoulders, he wore an exceptionally shiny green snakeskin band around his forehead. He smiled at the geologist.

"You, too, should wear a belt. You never can tell."

He pointed to the large bands of bark the mothers placed around the waists of their children to protect them from emanations.

Coltzesco was hesitating. "Is he kidding or not?"

"Do it," said somber Ubaldo Rocha.

He said a few words in Yanomami. A woman came over, giggling, her face in her hands. She placed the bark over the leather belt the geologist was wearing.

In the meantime, Reb had taken from the roof of his hut a package wrapped in leaves. He took from it scrapings of bark and liana and pieces of several plants, held together by a liquid resembling latex. He carefully poured this mixture into a banana leaf. Then he took some of the fibers of an old hammock, placed them in a circle around the leaf, and set them on fire. It burned for a short time, but the night's humidity soon put it out. Reb repeated the procedure, with other fibers, patiently, until the mixture was dry enough to burn away completely. From time to time, he stirred the little pile, never touching it with his fingers, but always using a stick.

He finished by pulverizing the ashes with a stone. Having transferred them to another leaf, he folded it and sweezed it hard between his hands and his thighs, rocking back and forth, chanting an incantation in Yanomami.

With more leaves, he made a cone, into which he poured the ashes, which were now an ocher color. While he was doing this, a fire had been lit next to him; a terra-cotta calabash was placed

386

there. The water in the calabash began to boil. Reb placed the cone above a second calabash, which was empty, and, exactly the way one makes coffee, slowly poured, almost drop by drop, the boiling water over the ashes. An amber liquid, which became darker and darker, began to drip through the bottom of the cone.

"Curare," said MacKenzie, who was leaning forward, fascinated. "The Yanomami are the only ones who make curare by percolation. All the other Amazonian Indians obtain it by boiling. The plants are of the strychnos type, and their mixture gives an indoleacetic alkaloid when it reacts to ceric acid. . . ."

"Silence, please," said Rocha. "This is a ceremony."

The warrior-hunters had approached, quiet and serious in the growing light of dawn. Each of them carried a little terra-cotta bowl, in which they were given their share of curare. They dispersed and with the same quasi-religious slowness began to coat the tips of their arrows, using weeds and drying them immediately over flameless fires.

Reb, his entire body uniformly tanned, was now standing perfectly still, staring at Coltzesco and only at him, with eyes that seemed lighter than usual, as if to dare him to discern whether in all of this there existed the smallest place for a skeptical smile.

In the following instant, as the sun's light finally shone over the endless green sea of trees, a helicopter appeared, anachronistic enough to seem a hallucination. It was a large Sikorsky equipped with antennas that put it in direct touch with the rest of the world.

The apparatus landed in the very middle of this Stone Age encampment.

"Sixteen new kinds of trees recorded," said MacKenzie in his slightly raspy voice, his Scottish accent strong. "Which brings to two hundred and forty-eight the total number of known species in the territory. But none of them specifically fit the established criteria. The diversity of fibers and resins is too great, the cellulose we could get from them would be of an inferior quality, and we would again be faced with the problem of reconstitution. In the best of cases, forty years. More likely, fifty or sixty . . ."

The cabin of the helicopter was large enough to have been divided into an apartment at one end and a garage holding a

Land-Rover and a Jeep at the other. The apartment itself was divided into four rooms: two bedrooms, one for the King, the other with enough bunk beds for six men, a bathroom, and a conference room, where the radio and telephone systems were set up.

Reb was talking to New York. He said, in English: "I would like to have those figures, Tony, please. And then, let me talk to Nick."

Looking at MacKenzie: "The approaches?"

"We will have to open a road over approximately one hundred miles. Three bridges will have to be built. Da Silva will give us a more detailed report."

Reb nodded. He said: "I'm listening, Tony." For the next two minutes, the distant voice read him figures. "Tony, the prices quoted by Kushida are still inconsistent. Get in touch with him and find out the reason for these changes. I'll call you back in two hours. Now let me speak to Nick, please. . . Yes, hello, Nick. I'd like to know why that cargo remained at the Cape for four days longer than planned. And also, why is this insurance company taking so long to settle our claim? Call Lance Lovett in Chicago; let him take care of it. Another thing: find Paul and tell him I will be calling him in fifty minutes. Yes, I know he's in Vancouver and that it is one o'clock in the morning there, but I need to speak with him. Thank you, Nick."

He hung up.

"Why one hundred miles of new road? We could use the K17 section."

"That would mean a connecting road and even more construction. But I can ask Da Silva."

"I will ask him myself, Jim. Jean?"

"Kaolin," answered Coltzesco immediately. "The studies conducted for the past nine months have been confirmed. The quality of the deposit is one of the best, and the deposit is literally just below the surface. If you scratch it with the heel of your foot, you can see it."

"Have you made an estimation?"

"Roughly, I would say between thirty and fifty million tons, at least. I left a team there, as planned. I'll have more precise figures in six weeks."

"That would rank us what, worldwide? Second?"

"Third. But we can keep hoping."

"Hong Kong on the line," said the voice over the speakerphone. Reb picked up the receiver.

"Yes, Hang. Tell me about this Singapore business, please. And then about the Wellington deal. I'm listening."

Twenty-nine hundred feet beneath the helicopter, a clearing that looked natural suddenly came into sight. But a runway over two miles long had nevertheless been carefully laid out there between a double row of trees. Through the rectangular window, Coltzesco saw several green-and-white buildings. He tried to relax. Spending two months in the heart of the jungle, as he had just done, did not impress him much; and he had actually enjoyed it, despite the innumerable discomforts and obvious risks.

But he was terrified of the helicopter.

And he wanted a woman. Dressed, preferably. He had started dreaming about brassieres and garter belts.

The landing strip in the heart of the jungle was not quite two hundred and fifty miles from Manaus, to the northwest of the former rubber capital.

In 1969, the number of buildings it serviced was not above sixty, if you didn't count the hangars, which housed twelve helicopters of all sizes and seven planes, among them a Boeing 707, two DC-3s, and a Caravelle, and the enormous garage, which was also invisible beneath the vegetation and which held one hundred different kinds of vehicles, as well as construction equipment.

The nuclear power plant was even less visible; it was almost completely buried. An observer flying at low altitude would never have suspected the importance of this plant. He would have seen some construction, certainly, but what he saw would have been far smaller and far less extensive than what was actually there, and he would have thought it to be a larger-than-average *fadenza*, but that was all.

This perfect camouflage was a source of great pride to Trajana da Silva. At regular intervals, as work was progressing during the last five years, he would fly over the area himself. He had taken countless aerial photographs and studied them with a magnifying glass, as a spy might have. On several occasions he had modified the plans drawn up by his task force of eight architects and engineers (he was both), going as far as adding trees and closely watching the colors of their foliage, so that there would never be any hiatus in the green ocean.

Only the landing strip had presented a problem, which remained unsolved for a long time: how could an opening over two miles long, and perfectly straight, not be visible from the sky? Reb was adamant about this; and he wanted to be able to land even the largest plane at any time of the day or night.

Da Silva had done his best, breaking up the geometric pattern as much as possible by placing what appeared to be burned-out forest patches on the sides of the runway, and by using decoys, such as false trees painted directly on the rotation area, a false river crossing the runway (the pilots had been insensed by this), a false swamp, which glimmered in the sun just as a real one would have. This was the idea of Herb Tolliver, who, in Libya during the Second World War, had joyfully tricked Rommel's Germans with countless tanks made of wood and cardboard.

All of this was completed by a handy job of painting on the runway paving. The result, all things considered, had been quite satisfactory, though not to the pilots, who still claimed not to know where to set their wheels down. They had had to install multicolored and blinking ramps that would function even in broad daylight, and man the control tower, which was perched among the trees of a nearby escarpment (false, of course), with specialists in zero-visibility landing procedures.

But it was all there. Unless one pressed one's nose to the ground and walked around among the buildings, one would never suspect that, depending on the time of year, more than fourteen hundred people lived and worked there.

Da Silva slid the previous map away and another one appeared, to the two-millionth degree.

"This is the Serra de Curupira," he said. "The Rio Catrimani is to the south, and here is the Mucajaï. To the right, the waters of the Apiaú. Jean Coltzesco has worked in this area." He traced a circle with a grease pencil on the thermoplastic surface. "I thought of using K17, which is never more than forty-three and a half miles away. But the construction work would be enormously difficult. The area is very uneven to begin with; it's in the foothills of the Parima, where there are peaks of forty-five to forty-nine thousand feet . . ."

He kept talking, with Reb's eyes on him. As always, he had the annoying feeling that Reb knew what he was about to say even before he said it. A Brazilian, Trajano da Silva had been recruited in 1953, sixteen years earlier, by Jorge Socrates, a lawyer from Rio. At that time, he was quite satisfied with his recent degree in geometry. Things had happened quickly. He had been sent to Switzerland, to the Polytechnicum in Zürich, where Einstein himself had taught, all expenses paid and then some. After that, now with a salary, he had spent two years in Marseilles, training at one of the most renowned public-works firms, this through the intervention of a certain Soubise. He had then worked in Cuba, on the Hong Kong airport, and in the United States. Only after that did he enter the King's service.

And for him, whom he called "Reb," as everyone did, he felt a respect that bordered on devotion, an endless admiration, a slightly timid but unwavering friendship.

"Very well," said Reb. "Lay out this track however you think best. Get together with Jean. He's done a great deal of research that can complement yours. Now, Trajano, the port, please. How far along are you?"

Reb was speaking Portuguese, mixing in every so often a few words of Spanish, English, or French, depending on whom he was addressing and the language or languages they understood.

Da Silva brought out other maps, all of which had been drawn up by teams recruited from top specialists of companies like Rand McNally, Teikoku Shoin, L'Esselte, and the Department of Geography of the University of São Paulo.

The port that was beginning to take shape was on the Rio Negro, eighteen and a half miles to the northwest of the mouth of the Rio Araçá. This was the third general project. Two other harbor installations were, if not projected, at least largely outlined: one also on the Rio Negro, sixty-two miles south of Moura— where Ubaldo Rocha was born—and the other on the Amazon itself, downstream from Manaus, near Itapiranga. Da Silva gave his report as precisely, as briefly, and as rapidly as he could.

He was about to add a few details about the base at Caracaraí, the most northern one, on the Branco . . .

Reb shook his head, smiling.

"Thank you, Trajano. I was there just recently. When will you be going to Rio?"

"There is no hurry," answered Da Silva, returning his smile.

Six months earlier, his wife had come from Niterói with their two children, who were now attending the school built the preceding year. And he didn't miss Rio, involved as he was with his work.

It was about eight o'clock in the morning. For the next two hours, Reb heard the reports of the two agronomists, Enrique Escalante and Ung Seng, who shared the task, the Venezuelan taking charge of the cultivation of fruit, cocoa, heveas, and paránuts, while the French-Cambodian watched over the rice plantations and the raising of stock.

Born in Kompong Cham, the Khmer had, like Trajano da Silva, been trained, as an engineer, thanks to a system of scholarships offered by a foundation whose president was a certain Georges Tarras. He and Escalante had worked together in Malaysia and in the Philippines, for three companies operated by Hang. From the Philippines, he had brought back a variety of long-grain rice, the IR 22 which, in his opinion, would easily adapt itself to the Amazonian soil.

He said, in his sharp voice: "I foresee two crops a year, in August and January, with a yield of about five tons per hectare."

"The average for Brazil?"

"One and a half tons per hectare. Besides the Philippine rice, we will use the *apani* kind from Surinam. The tests we conducted showed very favorable results."

"Talk to Uwe about the silos."

"It's already been taken care of. He will tell you about it in the plane."

Uwe Sobieski's passport showed West German nationality, but he actually came from eastern Prussia and had crossed through the Iron Curtain in a truck carrying his entire family, a truck he had converted himself. For the Amazon task force, he was in charge of everything concerning technical installations, factories, dams, and plants. Under him were fifty engineers, in different fields and of different nationalities.

Unlike Escalante, Da Silva, and Ung Seng, who, that day, remained where they were, he climbed aboard the 707, along with Del Hathaway, the North American in charge of underground resource exploitation who worked with Coltzesco, who was more specifically involved in prospecting, and another man, a geographer, also North American, named Maurice Everett, who had been co-ordinating all the work done by the cartographers for the past nine years and maintaining the separation between the various teams, so that no one would have any conception of the total plan.

Also on board the plane was Marnie Oakes, a forty-five-year-old woman, blonde and calm, not pretty but exceptionally efficient, who had the final word on logistics, transportation, all trips taken by everyone, including Reb, at least within the Amazonian borders. Her group also controlled communications. It was she who had dispatched the Sikorsky to an unknown clearing in the heart of the jungle at the required hour.

The 707 took off in midmorning. It landed in Rio at three o'clock in the afternoon. The plane was registered in Panama and had been officially chartered by a travel organization run by Ethel Court, a London millionairess.

Waiting in Rio was Diego Haas.

Not alone.

Jorge Socrates was also there, but, as usual, Reb Klimrod's welcome was anonymous. He had always been definite about that, never permitting any welcoming parties or other group meetings in any airport or other public place. As they got off the plane, the members of his task force discreetly dispersed, rather than walk along with him.

"As if they didn't even know you," kidded Diego.

He took Reb to the car, in which Socrates was waiting, his briefcase, full of documents, resting on his lap. Jorge was a true Carioca, born at the foot of the Corcovado. A little taller than Reb, he resembled Santana in his nonchalent precision and his elegance. He had been working for Reb since 1952. His family fortune had already been considerable before he met the King, and it had since increased tenfold. He spoke four languages besides Portuguese: English, French, Spanish, and Italian. Diego thought he was as intellegent as Paul Soubise and almost as intelligent as Georges Tarras, Tarras representing for Diego the quintessence of human intelligence, not counting Reb, of course.

"There are big problems with Andrade," said Socrates as soon as the car pulled away. "He came back to the charge, just as you predicted he would. He wants five hundred thousand dollars, to be paid in Switzerland."

393

Leaving the airport, Diego had turned left. He drove the old Chevrolet past the Museum of Modern Art, where a Miró exhibit was being held, and down along the beach by Flamengo Bay. Behind him, Reb was reading through the files Socrates had given him.

"What do you think?" asked Reb.

"I would not pay it, of course," said Socrates. "He is not worth it, and the principle itself is unacceptable. May I ask a question?"

"Yes."

"Do you have the means to dispose of him?"

Reb smiled as he continued reading.

"Yes. What is he threatening to do?"

"One of his uncles is a big shot in the Indian Protection Service. Andrade thinks he can mobilize the entire SPI against you, or, since he does not know of your existence, against those representatives of yours that he does know as official owners. He is threatening to stir up the worst kind of trouble, using as a motive cruelty and planned genocide.

The gray eyes slowly left the documents and came to rest on Socrates, who immediately raised his hands, in a gesture of appeasement.

"Take it easy, Reb. I know how much this means to you. I am just telling you what is going on. Don't take it out on me."

As they came in sight of Sugar Loaf, Diego left the oceanfront and began the climb toward Laranjeiras and Cosme Velho. Corcovado would appear from time to time between the buildings, projecting into the blue sky its monumental white Christ.

Reb asked: "The name of the uncle?"

"João Gomes do Oliveira."

Reb had interrupted his reading and seemed to be interested in what was passing along Laranjeiras Street, the neighborhood where the coffee barons had established luxurious houses. At that moment, Diego's eyes crossed those of Reb in the mirror and did not mistake the expression in them: He is absolutely furious.

"This same uncle has among others a property, a little *pied-à-terre*, around here, as it happens. That one, over there, with the hibiscus and the large terrace. He also has some property near São Paulo, I believe. I can find out more, if you want me to."

"No, thank you, Jorge," said Reb with the greatest calm, "that will not be necessary. I will take care of it. Anything else?"

"A billion things."

Diego was driving on the side of Corcovado, not far from the cog railway. He turned into the superb ancestral grounds of the Socrates family (whose real name was actually much longer than that), into a tropical garden inhabited by monkeys and giant butterflies, blue and black ones. He stopped the car in front of the white porch, and let the two men out. After turning the car over to one of the servants, he went to the screening room. He watched *The River of No Return* and *Some Like It Hot*, and was halfway through *Niagara*—he was in his Marilyn period—when Reb reappeared.

This time, Reb sat in the front seat of the Chevrolet.

"Home?" asked Diego.

"Home."

They went down onto Botafogo. Night had fallen on Rio, Diego's favorite city, making it sparkle.

"Tired?"

"Yes" said Reb.

But he has not digested his rage. On the contrary; it's rising. The volcano is about to erupt, thought Diego. He hoped, without counting on it too much, to be around to witness the soon-to-be-held execution of Andrade and his uncle.

He said: "I really hesitated over tonight: Gina, Sandra, or Melissa?"

"You chose Melissa."

"Shit, you could at least pretend to be surprised."

They passed through the Tunel Novo, came out onto Copacabana. Diego's house was on the next beach, Ipanema, an area where houses were not large, but which was beginning to supercede Copacabana. The house was on a quiet street, a villa of a dozen rooms, with a view of Rodrigo de Freitas Lagoon, and the green mass of Corcovado filling the bay windows.

Three beautiful and playful mulatto girls ran the house to a samba beat. Diego led his normal existence, without neglecting the extras.

He and Reb spent a peaceful night. Melissa, one of the mulattoes, was a singer. She waited in bed for a long time, though she was used to it, while in the soundproofed study on the ground floor, Reb was making another barrage of telephone calls.

The following morning, the two men left together for the airport.

Reb wanted to greet David Settiniaz personally on his first visit to Brazil.

2

"I am Jethro," said the man to David Settiniaz. "I suppose you know at least my name."

"Not 'at least,' " answered Settiniaz. "At most."

He was staring at the man without even trying to mask his curiosity. So this was the one who, for over fifteen years, had followed him day and night, without ever letting him feel the weight of his shadow. In a way, Settiniaz was disappointed. He had expected a special kind of physical appearance, and Jethro's main characteristic was that there was nothing special about him. Even his clothing was unremarkable.

"There is a question I would like to ask you," said Settiniaz.

The brown eyes behind the glasses became even more inexpressive than before.

"What is it?"

"Two years ago, I learned from Reb that you had stopped watching me . . ."

He deliberately left the question unasked, but the little trick, so naïve, was a total failure. Jethro continued looking at him with the air of a maître d' waiting for a guest to make his selection from the menu. Settiniaz had to go on.

"Reb . . . Mr. Klimrod told me you had not found out much about me. He said: 'Nothing important.' Which means that you did find something."

Jethro smiled pleasantly.

"Mr. Klimrod . . . Reb warned me that you might ask this question and has authorized me to answer it. I will answer you with a double name: Elizabeth-Mary. And a date: July 28, 1941."

Puzzled, Settiniaz searched his memory and, suddenly, the incident returned. It was Boston; he was eighteen years old. The policeman's flashlight had lit up the inside of the car where he was fooling around, and fumbling pretty badly. With Elizabeth-Mary . . . Good God, I don't even remember her name! he thought. In a panic, he had come up with nothing more intelligent to do than give a swift kick through the open window (his position made it easy for him to do this), which, in turn, sent the flashlight flying, as well as the policeman at the other end of it. This poor man had, naturally, recorded his license-plate number. Two hours later, David's mother was pulled from her bed; she had in turn called Uncle Arnold (he was a senator), who had arranged things, so there was no official record.

More than a quarter of a century later, the so scrupulous Settiniaz could still feel prickles up his back as he remembered that night. Nevertheless, he asked: "And that was all?"

"Nothing else," said Jethro. "You are a man surprisingly without mystery, Mr. Settiniaz."

"I have perhaps done something worse you did not find out about."

"I do not think so," answered Jethro politely. "I really do not think so."

Reb's padded door opened and Reb himself appeared.

"David, a thousand pardons. I need just a few more minutes."

Jethro got up, walked in, and the door closed behind him. A mulatto girl appeared and asked Settiniaz what he would like to drink. They came to an agreement, using sign language, on a lime soda. The girl left, barefoot on the tile floor, with a dancing and incredibly voluptuous gait. It was the middle of the afternoon. Settiniaz had been in Rio for a little over four hours, and in April, the Brazilian fall had turned out to be very humid and very warm, not far from ninety-five degrees Fahrenheit.

At Copacabana, where they had had lunch, Reb, Diego Haas and he, Settiniaz, already stimulated, had seen numerous extremely appealing girls on the beach wearing little black bathing suits that revealed their entire hips, up to the waist. He had also noticed, with less emotion though, some marvelous soccer players, playing barefoot in the sand, and had been reminded of his childhood in France, when he himself would kick the ball with his fellow students at Janson-de-Sailly. There was a small difference though: between these amazing artists and himself, there existed the same difference as between Pavlova and a stripper.

He walked out onto the terrace, from which you could see a

lagoon and a green cone, on the top of which stood a gigantic Christ.

Settiniaz, he said to himself, you didn't have enough martinis at lunch at Copacabana. . . .

He felt nervous, almost anxious. A year and a half before, in the brownstone in Brooklyn Heights, the home of the woman painter who resembled Charmian, Reb had started to tell him the untellable, to picture the fabulous project he envisioned. During the following eighteen months, Reb had been almost invisible. Settiniaz had seen him two or three times, but each time for no more than a few hours. The Black Dogs' activities, which had been so numerous, especially in 1966, had lessened.

At the end of 1969, David Settiniaz conducted the same kind of evaluation of the King's fortune and activities that, fourteen years earlier, had led him to estimate his worth at around one billion dollars. These were his notes, his secret estimation, which, in the end, he did not use when he came to list the gigantic final state of the Klimrod empire:

> One thousand six hundred companies
> Jaua Food (excluding subsidiaries). Value: one and a half billion dollars
> Communications, Publications, Radio, Television (Roger Dunn): one billion
> Casinos (Nevada, Bahamas, Puerto Rico, Atlantic City). Director: Henry C. [The strangely peaceful cohabitation of Chance (therefore Klimrod) and such men as Meyer Lansky, Lou Chester, Mike Coppola, and Wallace Groves shocked Settiniaz. It had been maintained for a long time through the good services of Abie Levin, partially helped at that time by several "financiers," about whom the FBI and the CIA had much to say.]
> Hotel chains: three; motel chains: six
> Railway and airline companies
> Fleet: six and a half million tons
> Naval construction: interests in nine countries + freight companies
> Oil refineries (Scotland, Venezuela): interests in companies in California and the Gulf of Mexico
> Near and Middle East concerns (Nessim Shahadzé)
> Banking and financial sections
> Insurance companies (Philip Vanderbergh)
> Real estate (U.S.A., Europe, South Africa)

Mines (South Africa)
Coal (Australia, Canada, Argentina, Bolivia)
Gold mines, silver mines (the Rockies)

Settiniaz was in charge of all this—inasmuch as it was necessary to run any part of it. The strength of the organization was such that a simple control was all that was necessary.

Settiniaz estimates the King's fortune at the end of 1969 at around ten or eleven billion dollars.

The machine was far from its optimal output. Had Reb Klimrod continued to give it his powerful impulses instead of starting to live on its profit, some phenomenal sums could have been reached: twenty, twenty-five, perhaps thirty billion dollars.

Each one of these one thousand six hundred companies, even the least spectacular and most prudent of all the King's businesses, would have been enough to make an ordinary man's fortune, and to have him be considered a rich man by his neighbors on Park Avenue or in Palm Beach or Scottsdale.

All of the King's Men, individually, were well-known multimillionaires, whose faces and movements were constantly showing up in the newspapers.

"David? I can understand how one can become fascinated by Corovado, but I am ready for you now."

Reb's quiet voice sounded amused. Settiniaz pulled himself away from his calculations and turned around. Reb was at the door, wearing a bathing suit and carrying a towel.

Jethro had disappeared, like a shadow. Settiniaz never saw him again.

"Excuse me, I was dreaming," Settiniaz said flatly.

"How about a dip in the Atlantic, to see if the waves will knock us over. And don't take anything of value to the beach, or it will be stolen."

"Are we going to walk through the streets in bathing suits?"

"We're in Rio," said Reb, smiling. "Without a bathing suit, they might stop us. And you don't need to wear a tie with your bathing suit."

One hour later, he spread a map out on the table. It was a surprising mosaic; the previous outlines of rivers, international and state borders, towns, villages, smaller agglomerations, and official roads had been almost erased, or had faded.

Instead, plastic strips of red, blue, purple, yellow, and green were juxtaposed like pieces of a puzzle. In all, perhaps four hundred pieces.

"This map is at what scale?" asked Settiniaz.

"Fifteen hundred-thousandth. But I have more detailed ones, of course."

"Are these maps commercially available?"

"Officially, they do not exist, David. Even this country's government does not know of their existence. Can I go on?"

The large tanned hand moved.

"Here, Peru. . . . Right here there is a large village called Benjamin Constant. Here are three countries' borders: Peru, Colombia, Brazil. And if you go to the north, Venezuela. This is the Rio Negro, and here the Branco. . . . The Equator is this gray line. To the northeast the Republic of Guyana, formerly British, and independent since last year. . . . Then through the Tumuc-Humac Mountains. We will fly over them; they are really something. I went through them on foot. . . . Surinam, a former Dutch colony, which is currently under autonomous internal status, and should sooner or later become independent. . . . And, finally, French Guiana where, it seems, your French cousins are going to establish a rocket-firing base, next year probably, in Kourou. . . .

"David, it is extremely simple. Everything that is in green means that the title deeds have been obtained and are not in dispute. The yellow means that the acquisition has been made but that it cannot yet be considered completely definitive because of various problems. Purple represents acquisitions currently in progress that should not present any problems. The blue are also acquisitions in progress, but these might be more difficult and involve more time and money. Finally, the red represents territories that are, in principle, unattainable, unbuyable, if you prefer, again for various reasons. Which does not mean that we have completely ruled out the possibility of purchasing them."

The exact words from eighteen months earlier were still in Settiniaz's memory. In the small white study that faced the East River and Manhattan, Reb had said: "I have bought some land, down there."

400

Some land!

"Reb, do you really mean to say that you have bought all this?"

"Yes."

The gray eyes were impenetrable. There wasn't the slightest trace of irony, or even the glimmer of a smile.

"Bought all this in your usual fashion, using figureheads?"

"Yes."

"And no one, besides those in your confidence, knows that only one man is behind all of these purchases?"

"No one."

"Not even the governments involved."

"Not even them."

"Did you use secondary trustees?"

"One hundred and eleven of them."

"Who in turn are controlled by primary trustees?"

"There are three of them, or there were: Emerson Coëlho, Jorge Socrates, both Brazilian, and Jaime Rochas, Argentine. Emerson died recently, and his son replaced him. Jorge is the most important of the three, and it is he who is in charge of all the operations."

The King's Man here, then, is Jorge Socrates, thought Settiniaz, except that I don't have a file on him.

"You will soon receive—in fact, he will be there when you return to New York—a visit from one of Jethro's messengers, who will give you a folder on each of these men, Jorge in particular. These files are practically empty, almost as empty as yours."

The tone was as always quiet and courteous, but there was no doubt: there was no longer in Reb the sort of restraint, of almost mocking detachment, with which, since 1950, he had conducted his businesses and announced his new developments.

This discovery alone would have been enough to fascinate Settiniaz, in light of what he knew—more than anyone did except Georges Tarras and Diego Haas—about this man facing him. But there was something else: this bizarre assemblage of colored pieces, where green was clearly predominant, appearing more frequently than all the other colors put together.

Of course, Settiniaz asked: "Reb, what size area are we talking about?"

"The whole thing?"

Settiniaz shook his head.

"I am getting lost in all these colors. . . ."

"Green," said Reb, "only the green: forty-seven thousand square kilometers. To which you have to add the yellow: twenty-seven thousand. For the purple, figuring a forty percent chance of success, which is not likely: fourteen thousand square kilometers. Seven thousand five hundred more are probable in the blue area, And because I believe in the impossible, David, I will add two to three thousand more in the red zone. For a total of ninety-eight thousand square kilometers."

Unaccustomed then to these measurements, Settiniaz tried to convert them into square miles, then, hopelessly, into acres.

Red smiled.

"David, perhaps you need some basis for comparison. Rather than delve into calculations, as you are probably doing at this very moment, let me tell you that this territory is roughly equal, in its surface area, to the states of Massachusetts, Vermont, New Hampshire, Rhode Island, and New Jersey put together. And, with a little luck, I will be able to add to it the equivalent of Delaware, and perhaps Hawaii. On a European or world scale, it would be larger than Portugal or Austria, comparable to Tunisia. Or, for one last comparison, it would be the equivalent of, and probably within two years larger than, Switzerland and the Low Countries together.

3

During the conversation he overheard between Reb and Jorge Socrates, Diego Haas had heard the names of Andrade and his uncle, Gomes do Oliveira. Diego had wanted to witness what he called the "execution" of the two men, using the word in a figurative sense. In fact, things took place in such a way that he knew almost nothing about it, and, besides Socrates, the main witness turned out to be David Settiniaz.

There were, to begin with, some photographs David saw on Reb's desk four days after his arrival in Rio. That he should have left them on his desk was already an indication, but he added: "Look at them, please, David."

There were at least sixty, measuring eleven by fifteen inches, all showing Indians—men, women, and children—dead or horribly mutilated, with such unbelievable savagery and refined cruelty that the New Yorker blanched.

"This is horrible."

"There are more. I know, David, this is not pleasant, but I would like you to have a look at them."

The following photographs were, in comparison, less unbearable, in a way. Several shots showed ossuaries, different ones, where dozens of corpses were piled, and there again, men, women, and children were united in death. That was not the worst of it, though. Other shots showed the same ossuaries but in these they were surrounded by several men, some of them in a festive mood, pouring gasoline from cans . . .

. . . and then throwing torches, while posing for the photographs.

"And the third group," said Reb. "In the metal cabinet, on the right shelf. David, please, I am not showing you this without a good reason. . . ."

The third group showed Indians hideously disfigured by leprosy.

"David? Does this remind you of anything?"

"Mauthausen."

"Except for the leprosy, yes. David, this is what is called, since 1906, the Indian Protection Service. I don't mean to imply that all the men and women who have worked and are currently working for the SPI are bastards and torturers, as those who committed the acts you just saw were. I am simply saying that within the SPI there are an abnormally high number of bastards and torturers, a number way above the average that one usually finds within any human collectivity, whatever the color of its skin, the language it speaks, the religion it does or does not adhere to, the political system it follows or is subjected to. I use the words 'bastards' and 'torturers' because I am incapable, in spite of the many languages I speak, of finding any other words that would better express my anger. . . ."

403

His eyes had that lost look.

"I don't like to talk, David. Except when it comes to concrete things, such as when I have to tell someone what he should buy from me or sell to me. No, really, I do not like to talk. . . . "

He stopped.

"Forgive me, I do not want to hurt your feelings. You are abnormally normal. Even Jethro has finally come to accept this. I entrusted you with a task and I have not regretted it for one minute. You have done an outstanding job, and for the past year, by taking over the financial management of almost all of my companies, you have increased even more the gratitude I feel toward you. But I am making use of you in still another way, David. I am using you . . . your normality as a sounding board, to gauge my dreams, or my folly."

"I am not philosophizing. One of two men involved is named Andrade. He has tried, very naïvely, to blackmail us. I would normally have disposed of him as I have others. But he used the one argument that could really infuriate me. He threatened Jorge Socrates with interference by one of his uncles, who is the second man, and whose name is Gomes do Oliveira. Gomes is a high-ranking member of the Indian Protection Service. I asked for some information concerning him and I have just received it."

"From Jethro."

"In a way. This information is partly in front of you, David. These men who were burning the corpses are *garimpeiros*, gold and diamond seekers. I had trouble with them some years ago, but I did not seek vengeance at the the time: they were poor devils. This time I am not personally involved. But nevertheless I am furious, very furious, David. . . . "

There was strong contrast between the words and the softness of the voice and the smile . . .

"We have identified the men in the photographs. We know their names, ages, hometowns, and mostly who supplied their equipment, who financed their trip from Belém to the Rio Ta-pajós. We have even obtained receipts. They were found by a man who works for a company in Rio. And one of the main shareholders of this company is João Gomes do Oliveira, a high-ranking member of the Indian Protection Service, who, eight months ago, transferred eight hundred and seventy-five thousand dollars to a Nassau bank account, of which we have the number.

Just as we know everything about Senhor Gomes do Oliveira. And he is quite far from being as transparent as you, David. Quite far."

"What will you do to him?"

"The Indian Protection Service was founded at the beginning of the century by a man named Mariano da Silva Rondon, who was a pure and generous idealist. He does have some heirs today, some of whom are admirable, in this same service. But I am not an idealist. At least not in that sense. There were thirty-eight *garimpeiros*, organized in an infernal column. They started their killing by distributing poisoned flour and sugar. Then a medical team—medical, David; there were two doctors among them—proceeded to inoculate nine hundred Indians with leprosy through vaccinations. The survivors were massacred by machine gun, napalm, and gas. I am not making any of this up; I have proof of everything, and you can check it. In fact, I would like you to check it. I told you that you are a gauge for my own feelings."

"Don't make me the judge in this matter."

"That is not what I asked you to do: I am only asking you to watch what will take place, as an impartial witness."

Jorge Socrates describes it as a dance of death.

David Settiniaz followed all its different phases. His first trip to Brazil, in April of 1969, was followed by several others, up to four or five trips a year, during the following years.

Actually, until the end. For more than sixteen years, he had been a kind of "registering machine," filing away all the information he received. Seeing Reb only for short periods of time. Remaining sometimes for weeks without any sign of him, to the point where he had, on several occasions, actually thought that Reb might have disappeared for good, either by choice or because he was dead.

No newspaper or radio or television station would have been interested in reporting the death of an unknown person named Klimrod. And besides, who would have notified them in the first place? Haas? He would have had to survive Reb, something that was not likely to happen. And, had the King not given him specific instructions as to this possibility, Haas would not have told anyone.

Many of the King's Men shared this fear. Passing through New York one day, Nessim Shahadzé told Settiniaz of his concern. He had not seen Reb for five months. Settiniaz reassured him by telling him that he had seen him the previous week. This was not true: his last meeting with Reb went back several weeks. . . .

The only one who did not worry about these things was Georges Tarras. He laughed at Settiniaz's apprehensions. For him, the King was immortal. . .

As of 1967, things changed.

Settiniaz's function had been modified. From "scribe," he became a plenipotentiary administrator. He was in charge of management and had to make decisions. This required closer and more regular contact with Reb. A new procedure was established, by-passing the "obligatory passage point," the filter that was Diego Haas.

Strangely enough, their personal relationship during the course of this period was not as good as it had been before. Perhaps because of the indelible scar of Mauthausen, because of the cold, almost hateful callousness that had grown in him. What's more, Reb vowed endless love for the Indians. It was among them that he had sought refuge after Bogotá. "He would have remained a solitary man," said Tarras, "even if Charmian were still alive." Reb's only real moments of peace were those he spent with the Shamatari, when he himself became one of them. He returned to them each time he felt the need to "touch ground."

Settiniaz still feels a certain amount of hurt. "This was the only point on which we could not agree: the Indians. And his attitude toward them. Like hundreds of others, I had been fascinated, seduced, and dominated by the King; he often exasperated me; sometimes, though rarely, I came close to hating him. He aroused these extreme feelings in people for the very reason that he himself was out of proportion. The truth is that from the beginning there was a tragic contradiction between what he wanted to do for the Indians and what he actually did for them. Even, and especially, if you don't question his love for them; and that explains his unrelenting cruelty toward Gomes do Oliveira. Not that I feel any sorrow for what happened to him: the man was the scum of the earth, no doubt about that. . . . But still . . . "

4

The man in charge, according to Socrates and Settiniaz, who in their respective accounts agree on this point, was a certain Prosser; this was not necessarily his real name. Settiniaz considered Prosser to be the head of a kind of "action team," which complemented Jethro's research team. Settiniaz firmly believes in the existence of such an organization. It would explain the fact that an exceptionally small number of primary or secondary trustees ever tried to abuse the situation.

The stockbroker's name was Maceio. He was contacted, and bought—there is not other word for it—by Prosser during the first few days of May 1969. He had been João Gomes do Oliveira's investment adviser for fifteen years. Jethro's research established that he operated in the international financial markets in collaboration with one firm in New York, another in London, and a brokerage house in Zurich.

This same investigation, as precise as an X-ray, permitted a glimpse of Gomes do Oliveira's fortune. His main income came from his activity as a diamond broker; he also owned some real estate, which he had inherited: a *palacete*, in the Laranjeiras neighborhood of Rio, a country home near the Tijuca forest, a *fadenza* that produced tea on twelve hundred acres in the state of São Paulo, and two large apartments, which were rented, in a new building facing the beach at Copacabana. These were his official possessions, those that were in his name. Besides these, there was close to a million dollars in a numbered account in a Nassau bank, and two small buildings in the United States, under the cover of a Bahamian company.

The first phase was the setting up of the bait. Maceio, the stockbroker, got in touch with Gomes and told him that, through some confidential information he had just received, he had learned of a very interesting speculative operation which could be carried out on the stock market.

"It is called International Electric. I am sure you have heard of it. I have forwarded to you the usual background information. The company is in good shape, and well managed. It presents all the guarantees. My sources tell me that there is going to be a public offering, very shortly. The stock will therefore be going up. I will be investing in it myself. I am giving you the chance to take advantage of a good tip: a short-term operation, three months . . . ."

Gomes accepted. And was glad he did. Even though the announced public offering did not take place, the stock, which was not "blue chip," had, in the past few weeks, risen spectacularly, under the influence of powerful financial groups that were buying and buying.

The second phase was getting the commitment.

"Listen," said Maceio, as ordered by Prosser, "you have already made nearly one hundred and fifty thousand dollars. You can stop there. I wouldn't if I were you. Personally, I am going in again. All my sources in New York, London, and Zürich are assuring me that it's not over, that it will keep going up, that these financial groups are not finished yet. And I believe the time has come to make a big move. Do you want my opinion? You can pick up two, maybe three million dollars in six months. Yes, six months. The only condition being that you agree to buy a large quantity of International Electric stock in six months, and to pay for it at the time."

"The risks?"

"The risks are classic," commented Maceio. "They are those of margin calls, and since they take place at the end of the road, you can believe me, there is no danger here. I have already explained to you what a margin call is: when you place an advance order for, let's say, ten million dollars, in order for the broker to take your order you must give him a deposit. In your case, I could probably arrange for your deposit to be just ten percent of the actual amount of the transaction. You would then only have to put out one million dollars, with which you would have the right to buy, six months later, for ten million dollars, what will then in reality be worth twelve or thirteen, perhaps even fourteen million dollars And in six months, a little paper shuffling will permit you, practically on the same day, to sell for twelve, thirteen, or perhaps even fourteen million these shares you will have bought. And you can pay for your purchase with the proceeds from your sale. All in all, a profit of two, three, perhaps even four million dollars. It's very simple."

"But what about the margin calls?"

"The possibility always exists," said Maceio in his reassuring voice. "Theoretically. If market fluctuations were such that, in a six-week interval, the risks exceed the amount of your deposit, the broker might ask you for an adjustment. But, quite frankly, João, I don't see a chance of that happening. This is one of those opportunities that come along once every twenty years. I know this Nessim Shahadzé personally, the one who, with Vanderbergh, an American, and our fellow countryman Socrates, will make this public offering of International Electric. He is Lebanese and a topnotch financial expert, capable of lining up five or six billion dollars like that; he has all the oil emirs behind him. You can do whatever you like, but I am going to jump on this occasion."

"I don't have a million dollars."

"That's too bad. As you can see, I have staked everything I have on this. I even took a mortgage on my house in Niterói. Why don't you do the same? You own that tea plantation. And your apartments. Without counting what you must have squirreled away, you rascal. João, time is of the essence. Do you want to find a bank that will help you? Each day counts; it's first come first served."

The bank that took the mortgage was headquartered in São Paulo. It was represented during this transaction by one of the city's largest firms, that of the late Emerson Coëlho.

Urged by Maceio, Gomes do Oliveira placed an order of one million sixty thousand dollars with a New York brokerage firm, which, apparently, had nothing to do with Reb Klimrod.

The third phase took place in a completely different area. David Settiniaz and Jorge Socrates cannot say in what measure the King played a role in it, if at all. The Brazilian, although Brazilian, leans toward the affirmative, without, however, offering any proof: "For more than ten years, ethnologists and scientists of all kinds, as well as religious leaders, had been calling attention to the actions of the Indian Protection Service. Until then, no protest had ever reached the ears of the government. It was an established fact that the government in Brasília was in the process of forming an investigating committee, which would eventually lead to the dissolution committee, which would eventually lead to the dissolution of the SPI and to its replacement by the National Indian Foundation, the FUNAI."

An established fact also, that in the lower ranks, one hundred officials were dismissed and tried, while hundreds of others were demoted or transferred.

João Gomes do Oliveira, without waiting for the SPI to be dissolved, resigned. He felt he needed to justify his resignation by holding a press conference, at which he spoke of his "indignation, anger, and shame at having my name—a respectable one, belonging to a family which has always distinguished itself in the history of this country—tarnished, even involuntarily, by these ignoble acts, of which, of course, I had no knowledge. If I had, I would have taken immediate action. . . . "

Settiniaz, in the meantime, had returned to New York. That summer he received, without any added memos, translations and photocopies of newspaper clippings showing Gomes do Oliveira's virtuous indignation. He remembers being surprised: everything seemed to indicate that Gomes was going to be able to pull out of this with dignity.

For the fourth phase, the stage was set in London. It is in London that the Central Selling Organisation, the commercial section of the De Beers Company, holds its sales of rough diamonds. When it comes to putting these into circulation, the CSO controls seventy percent of the world market. The rough diamonds they sell come mostly from South Africa, or from the Soviet Union and central Africa. Their annual figure, at that time, was over two hundred million dollars. The sales ritual is unchanging and solemn. The brokers come from all over the world; they are few and are selected by the CSO itself, which alone is in charge of admission; their reputation must be spotless. They are seated before a turning table, and the rough diamonds are presented to them in lots of one or two hundred thousand dollars' worth. No discussion is possible, and only the choice of lots is open. Each broker is expected to buy at least one lot.

Gomes do Oliveira was one of these brokers.

The file was delivered to six different places, each time by an anonymous messenger. They all bore the words Settiniaz knew so well: "Strictly confidential. To be delivered to addressee in person." They all contained the same thing: three photographs chosen from those Klimrod had shown to Settiniaz, plus three more, which showed the leader of the *garimpeiros* with Gomes do Oliveira. A number of the photocopies of documents established the fact that this *garimpeiro* had been working for Gomes for fourteen years; that the two doctors who had performed the "vaccinations" had been paid by him; that he had personally accompanied them to the plane for La Paz when the task was completed; that the plane tickets had been issued by an agency in Belém and charged to Gomes's account; that this same *garimpeiro* was employed full time as a foreman at the *fadenza* in São Paulo, although he had never been seen there, and although he received the rather exorbitant equivalent salary of twelve thousand dollars per year; that this same Gomes do Oliveira had flown at length on two separate occasions, in a small plane, above the sites of the massacres, asking his right-hand man many questions about what he called "the operation" ("enclosed also is the testimony of the pilot as received by a Belém judge"); that there had been written exchanges between Gomes do Oiveira and a European company headquartered in Switzerland, and that in one of the letters, dated four days after the massacre, the Brazilian announced: "the path is clear now."

The first margin call was the fifth phase. This margin call was in the amount of two hundred and fifty thousand dollars, payable immediately to the New York brokerage firm. Already crushed by his glacial exclusion from the very select club of diamond brokers accepted by the De Beers CSO, Gomes do Oliveira accepted this new blow dealt him by fate with a feeling of doom. It took a great deal of insistence on Maceio's part to convince his client to sell off, in a few hours, part of his inherited real-estate holdings, in order to get the money together.

The first margin call had come on November 14, 1969. The second—for ten percent or one hundred thousand dollars—came on the twenty-fourth of the same month. The third came on Christmas Eve; the fourth—again for twenty-five percent—on January 19, 1970. All the money deposited in the Bahamas went to pay these, with Maceio saying: "João, either you pay or you go bankrupt, losing everything you have invested so far. You must have slipped up somewhere, or how else can you explain the fact that those New York brokers knew about your real-estate holdings in the United States? In any case, I am not much better off than you. If not for my uncle in Manaus, who has agreed to help me, I would have gone broke a long time ago. But I am beginning to see the light at the end of the tunnel. We will pull out of this. This Nessim Shahadzé is the devil; he is forcing the market prices down so that he can buy up everything later. We have to hang on, and we will come out ahead. . . . "

In the meantime, a financial establishment in Hong Kong, represented by a man named Hang, sold off every share it owned of International Electric. A European group headed by a Frenchman by the name of Soubise did the same. Followed thereafter by large Mexican shareholders brought together by a certain Francisco Santana . . .

"João, we have to wait. Look: this American group is buying, the Vanderbergh group. They are buying at a low price, but they are buying. That means they, too, feel confident about International Electric. It is just a question of time. . . . "

The fifth margin call came on January 30, and was for thirty percent.

The newspapers took over for the sixth phase. They published with glee on the very same page and side by side the virtuous declarations made by Gomes do Oliveira at the time of his resignation from the SPI and "the results of investigations conducted by our reporters." Almost without exception, the Brazilian papers—for the press world-wide got hold of the story—published the same documents as those that were sent to De Beers and its commercial section.

International law offered help for the seventh phase. Owing to certain circumstances, all the Indians rescued from the massacre were taken in hand by an American humanitarian organization run by a former Harvard professor by the name of Georges Tarras. In spite of the care given these unfortunate people, a great number of them died of their terrible wounds. The medical planes that had picked them up took them, not only to other areas of Brazil, but also to other countries, the United States especially. Their deaths, which were registered outside Brazil, following brutal treatment that had occurred on Brazilian soil, made of João Gomes do Oliveira a guilty criminal according to international laws, guilty of "crimes against humanity." His passport was revoked, pending a trial.

It wasn't necessary. He had acquired overnight the notoriety worthy of someone like Mengele. Had he still had enough money to pay him, even a taxi driver would have refused to pick him up.

The eighth and final phase was the one that most horrified David Settiniaz, because of its relentless and glacial ferocity.

The first Indians appeared in April 1970. There were no more than twenty of them, doing nothing but standing, in absolute silence, in front of the house where Gomes do Oliveira had found refuge: the one that belonged to his nephew, Andrade, who had also lost all his money, which he had loaned his uncle for his unfortunate speculation. Night and day, they stood there, in relays, to assure a kind of hallucinatory guard.

Then their number began to increase, little by little. Soon, there were one hundred of them, and the two times the police came to force them to move, they peacefully let themselves be taken away. But others immediately came to take their place. And each time Gomes tried to escape them, finally ending up in a village in the south, Curitiba, six hundred and twenty miles from Rio, they followed him, obviously having all the money they needed.

Gomes do Oliveira killed himself with a bullet in the mouth. Only then did the Indians leave.

5

Nineteen-sixty-nine was a determining year for several reasons.

First, it was the year Reb Klimrod bought a business in his own name.

The news more than surprised Settiniaz, who, when he learned of it, was dumbfounded.

"I don't believe my eyes or my ears," he said. "You mean to say that, for the first time in your life, you are the official owner of something?"

"In a way," said Reb.

He and Settiniaz had had lunch in a *charruscaria*, a kind of grill, and had eaten a rib steak "badly over," to use the Brazilian expression, meaning very rare. The surprise had been the dessert.

Reb said: "We will have dessert and some *cafezinho* somewhere else, if you don't mind."

He had taken the New Yorker two blocks away, in Hilario Gouveia, and Settinaiz's heart stopped when he read the sign above the pastry shop, written in ten languages: REB'S VIENNESE AND TYROLEAN PASTRIES.

The tearoom was packed, but one table had apparently been reserved. Reb casually picked up a menu but did not bother looking at it. "Now, let's see: *Apfelstrudel? Milchrahmstrudel?* That's a turnover stuffed with sweet curds, in other words, with curdled milk, cream and currants. *Sacher torte?* That's a chocolate cake with apricot jam and chocolate icing. *Quetschen-Knödeln?* Those are little pastries stuffed with sugar candy and slivered almonds. Excellent. Or what about a Drunk Capuchin? Which is a little roll made of almond paste with raisins cooked in wine. Unless you prefer, and they recommend it here, the *Ischler Törtchen*, the famous little Ischl pies, which are, as everyone knows, the best cakes in the world?"

He looked at Settiniaz with the polite stare of a waiter; but an amused glimmer shone in his light eyes.

And then a sort of Trapp family, with at least six girls with blond braids and dazzling smiles, appeared at the table where the two men were sitting. The youngest ones kissed Klimrod on the cheeks and, while they were at it, also kissed Settiniaz.

"My associates," said Reb. "We are thinking of expanding. We already have a branch in Ipanema and another one in the city center. We are thinking of São Paulo and of Petrópolis, which is a tourist resort north of Rio. And Teresópolis is also being considered; that's a mountain-climbing area; it's the perfect setting. Zita, Maria, Regina, and two or three others are thinking of creating a chain. But I am hesitating. I am not a major shareholder; I own only forty percent of the shares, and the financial risks would be considerable. It might perhaps be wiser to borrow from a bank. What do you think, David? You are a businessman."

Clearly the King was having a good time.

And this was, to Settiniaz's knowledge, the first sign that the formidable thrust, which had started nineteen years earlier, when he arrived in New York, was now marking a pause.

It was also the time when Reb began to speak of his past. To speak of it in no chronological order, but by sudden and unexpected backward leaps. This would happen at any time, usually in a plane, during a night flight. He would suddenly start speaking, bringing up a scene that had taken place twenty or twenty-five years earlier, during his youth, or what replaced it, without ever saying what took place before or after. He really had only two confidants: Georges Tarras and David Settiniaz. And it took many years for them to break the pattern of discretion instilled in them by the King, and to decide to share their experiences with each other. By piecing together all the stories Reb had told each of them, as well as those of other witnesses, they were able to reconstruct his life.

This was also the year when, flying in the huge Sikorsky helicopter, Settiniaz flew over Amazonia for three days, going as far as the llano of Colombia and Venezuela, following at a low altitude the flow of the Guaviare and the Orinoco, to the small town of San Fernando de Atabapo. And there, Reb, in his slow voice, disclosed, with apparent indifference, a few memories of his wild romp of 1947–48, of his trip up the Orinoco, of his crossing of the Serra Parima, and of his encounter with the Guaharibos.

The Bogotá incident, when Reb killed two men, was told to Tarras by Diego.

But 1969 remains, above all, the year Settiniaz finally became aware of what Reb was creating in Amazonia. He had already had some trouble recovering from the stupefaction he felt when he heard of the magnitude of what was no longer a project. Stupefaction that was increased by the fact that Reb had undertaken and accomplished all of that while he, Settiniaz, who knew almost everything about the King's businesses, didn't suspect a thing.

Reb, alone, had acquired this property, and without awakening suspicion in anyone, without any of the governments involved raising any questions. Settiniaz was not naïve: he fully realized that a breach of trust must have played a part in all of this. But that was not enough of an explanation. "I am creating a country,"

415

Reb had said. Jorge Socrates had started buying land for Klimrod in 1954 and, according to him, Emerson Coëlho had been doing so even before that. At that time, the territory was already one million seven hundred thirty thousand acres.

The deeds in Settiniaz's possession prove that the first purchases of land were made in 1950; in other words, at the time Reb emerged from the forest to come to the United States. The first operations were handled by Ubaldo Rocha, and the money used came from the sale of diamonds. Rocha refuses to talk about it. If discretion was always a common trait among the King's Men, Rocha, the half-breed from Moura, was certainly the holder of an unbeatable record in that trait.

But in 1950, Klimrod was not dreaming about a kingdom. The purpose of his early acquisitions was probably to assure for himself and the other Shamatari the official and indisputable ownership of a part of the territory where they lived.

Emerson Coëlho served as agent in the second round of purchases. At the basis of this one was an almost legendary figure, a colonel of the Brazilian Guard, a former rubber worker, who had become a senator: José Julio de Oliveira, no relation to Gomes. The colonel, "Zé Julio," between the end of the nineteenth century and the first thirty years of the twentieth, had carved for himself, with much energy, and undeniable physical courage, and by the use of violence and corruption, a small empire on the north bank of the Amazon. He had contracted leprosy, and in 1948 had sold everything to a consortium of Brazilian and Portuguese businessmen. From them, Coëlho, who died in 1966, had purchased, for two million two hundred thousand dollars, an area estimated to be seven million four hundred thirteen acres. If this acquisition, which was spread out over time (which explains why Socrates, when he became involved, knew only about the one million seven hundred thirty thousand acres), was the most important one, it was not the only one: the São Paulo lawyer had made similar purchases for other companies—there were thirty-eight in all—of properties and *fadenzas* throughout the immense area of northern Brazil.

Jaime Rochas, the Argentine from Buenos Aires, was conducting similar operations, starting in 1956, in the two Spanish-speaking neighboring countries: Colombia and Venezuela. He can be credited with the acquisition, in several stages, of almost four million four hundred and fifty thousand acres.

Thus, begun in 1950, the scheme as it stood in 1969 was almost completed. It was, at most, a matter of two more years, which would finish a patient conquest spread out over twenty-one years. The transactions were still being handled by the firms of Socrates and Rochas, and, to a lesser extent, by the São Paulo team, which was somewhat weakened by the death of its top man.

One hundred and eleven companies, at least two-thirds of which were Brazilian (or seemed to be) had been used, employing all the resources of Brazilian, Venezuelan, Colombian, and even international law. With the expected result that in the eyes of a stranger—in other words, everyone—all of this was not the property of one company, but of one hundred and eleven different companies, with no connection between them. Except for the fact that all of the areas involved were in great proximity to each other. . . .

There was really a perfect understanding among all these landowners. But there was no law prohibiting this.

In 1969, and for some time after that, Settiniaz sincerely believed that Reb Klimrod, just as Colonel Zé Julio before him, had no other purpose than to carve out for himself a personal kingdom. All the outward signs confirmed this, as well as all the remarks made by Reb himself.

6

The Sikorsky landed in an area Settiniaz thought, at first, was covered with grass. Even from a height of fifty feet it looked like an ordinary clearing in the forest. But that was just a reminder of the time when the largest concern was trying—successfully—to camouflage everything in the jungle. That time was over. It was now 1974, and this was Settiniaz's fifth visit to the Kingdom. And, from all the buildings that were visible, it was clear that they were now working in the open.

This time, there was even a paved road, which had not been

there during his last visit. And there were many cars, from which a group of people began walking toward Reb to welcome him. Settiniaz recognized most of them. He saw Escalante, Sobieski, Trajano da Silva, and, of course, Marnie Oakes, with her ever-present clipboard.

Two people approached him.

"I hope you remember us," said the woman.

"Ethel and Elias Weizmann. I certainly do remember you."

He had met them five years earlier, when he had first learned of the project. Neither of them was very tall or very young. They were probably between fifty-five and sixty. Between them, they spoke at least twenty languages. For many years, starting in 1946, they had worked for the International Children's Fund, then for UNICEF, before going to the Center of International Affairs at the United Nations in New York.

"How nice that you have not forgotten us," said Ethel. "You know, we are very important people: we are, in a way, the ministers to Reb's population."

She smiled, with her shy little bird air, which was so deceptive. This woman, who weighed no more than ninety pounds, possessed energy and dynamism that were positively phenomenal—as well as exceptional physical and moral endurance. She had survived Bergen-Belsen and three other camps. Elias, who was American, had met her after the war. Until her death, in 1980, he had never known her not to be cheerful and capable of working twenty straight hours or of running to the ends of the Serra de Pacaralïma.

She said: "Reb has asked us to take care of you. Is it the word 'minister' that surprised you?"

"A little," said Settiniaz. "I didn't realize that things had gone that far. Of what population are you speaking?"

"The Indians and the *caboclos*, of course. The *caboclos* are the half-breeds who work in the jungle, usually as farmers. But they are not the only ones. We also take care of immigration."

She had a sharp but perfectly charming laugh.

"It seems you are going from one surprise to another, David. Of course, we will call you David, and you call us Elias and Ethel. Elias doesn't speak much. It's true that I don't give him much opportunity, but he does speak, every so often, when I am not around. Do you know that he speaks thirteen languages?

Right now, he is learning Vietnamese. And Yanomami, of course. His Yanomami is almost fluent, better than mine. . . ."

She drove, looking like she was at the wheel of a large ship. Reb and the rest of the group were already headed toward the town. Ilha Dourada, the unofficial capital of the Kingdom, had, during the last five years, grown spectacularly. Settiniaz had not been there for three years and could hardly recognize any part of it: he could see hundreds of buildings, none over four stories high. But he knew that each had at least two or three underground levels.

"How many people live here now?"

"In Ilha Dourade proper? Counting men, women, and children, about seven thousand eight hundred. Do you want the exact figure?"

"No, thank you. And in the other areas?"

"Six thousand nine hundred in Verdinho, five thousand six hundred and fifty in San João de Beirasal, eighteen hundred in Diamantina. Plus a few outposts and development areas here and there. Plus, of course, the *silvivilas*, the forest villages. We have an average of two thousand inhabitants per village, and one village for each fifty thousand acres of forest. We have sixty villages planned, twenty-four of which have been completed and nineteen of which are almost finished. Have you ever visited any of them?"

"Once."

That had been in 1971. The helicopter had landed on a soccer field. Settiniaz had discovered an agglomeration of individual houses in parallel rows and three communal housing buildings. All of concrete. Nothing very inspiring. It was clear, functional, but rather depressing. Ethel Weizmann smiled.

"That was one of the reasons that made us accept Reb's proposal, David. These engineers and architects are sometimes too systematic; they go for whatever is fast and inexpensive. For thirty years, Elias and I have been traveling all over the world trying to stem the tide of misery. At least here, our efforts are rapidly visible; we can see the results, so it's less heartbreaking. And it is hard to resist Reb when he tries to be seductive. I am not speaking of money, of course. . . ."

Settiniaz was trying to calculate.

Elias Weizmann must have sensed it, for he said, managing to slip in a sentence: "Don't bother, David: sixty-nine thousand six

419

hundred and twenty-four as of today. Plus Jean Coltzesco's prospecting teams, and those of Trajano da Silva and Uwe Sobieski
and other teams. In all, seventy-four thousand three hundred
people."

"Don't listen to him," said Ethel. "He was always terrible at
arithmetic. The exact figure, at this moment, is seventy-five
thousand one hundred and eighteen. Within a year, with the
planned developments in San João and especially in Diamantina,
we will soon number more than one hundred thousand. The
General Plan foresees two hundred and seventy-five thousand
inhabitants in five years. Personally, I think we will go beyond
that figure, easily."

Settiniaz was staring at her, dumbfounded. She took him by
the arm.

"Come, I'll make you some coffee. You look like you could
use some."

The General Plan—and it was followed to the letter, confirm-
ing Ethel Weizmann's prognosis, since in 1980 three hundred
and sixteen thousand people were living in the Kingdom, without
counting the Indians and the two or three thousand indomitable
caboclos who had refused to integrate—estimated a total expend-
iture of four billion four hundred million dollars.

A figure that was exceeded, of course, and by a great margin.

In May of 1980, life in the Kingdom was as follows.

The towns were all created on virgin land, never lived on since
the beginning of time. There were six of them. None had over
twelve thousand inhabitants, in order to avoid excessive, inhuman
urbanization. The most important of these towns, because it was
the first to be founded, was Ilha Dourada, on the banks of the
Rio Negro. The five others were: San João de Beirasal, Verdinho,
Diamantina, Monte Grasso, and Quarenta (from the name for
the milestones planted every ten miles by the road-building teams
headed by Trajano da Silva).

Each town had a thermoelectric plant that supplied electricity
to a network the length of which varied between four hundred
and seven hundred miles, piped drinking water, sewers, and a
sanitation department. Each town had at least one hospital of
one hundred and fifty to two hundred beds, complete with sur-
gical capability and a staff consisting of one hundred and sixty

doctors and dentists, and eight hundred nurses. Clinics run by two doctors and half a dozen assistants were set up in each forest village, and there were seventy-two of them in 1980. Clinics were also established in all important areas of mining, farming, and industrial development. For emergencies and remote areas, an evacuation system existed, with two planes and four helicopters, ready for transportation to the hospitals in Ilha Dourada and Verdinho, the best-equipped ones, which had trauma units. The system could also provide medical flights to Belém, Rio, and even the United States, if necessary.

Education was free, and the total number of enrolled students in April 1980 was thirty-nine thousand. Teaching was conducted in Portuguese, but English was introduced in the first grade. The system then consisted of fifty-two kindergartens, seventy-six primary schools and twelve secondary schools. There were also twenty-six remedial-education centers for adults. And in Ilha Dourada and in Diamantina there were international schools where the education was conducted only in English, and where the program followed was the same as that followed in the United States, the highest grade being that of the last year of high school. The teachers received salaries that were three times that of the average Brazilian.

Each town and important center distributed food supplies through a supermarket. Being an employee of one of the one hundred and eleven companies that officially shared the territory entitled one to a card that gave access to these supermarkets, where products sold for ten per cent above cost. In 1980, the system was being extended by the installation of business centers, on a smaller scale, in the forest villages.

Each village had a bank, an ecumenical church, a library, at least two movie theaters, a police station, and, in 1975, a hotel. This last was small, visitors being rare or not admitted. Until 1970, telephone communication was available within the Kingdom, but when it came to calling outside, getting a connection was difficult. Only a few lines existed, to Belém, Manaus, and Rio. The situation improved considerably when a cable was installed that reached Georgetown, in Guyana; then a second cable went as far as Paramaribo, in Surinam. An agreement with the Brazilian company Embratel completed the system in 1976.

Transportation was the same for all, except in rare cases—and then arrangements had to be made with the forbidding Marnie Oakes. A curious color system had been created: anyone who wanted to go anywhere posted outside his home or wherever he was a flag of a particular color: green for the supermarket; yellow for the center of town, where the public buildings were; blue for sports areas; checked to call the maintenance help or repairs; and black, which was an extension of what one wore to go to church or to the cemetery and for the same purposes. Minibuses would then stop. They were in constant rotation and were free.

If the number of personal vehicles was extremely low, that of communal ones was quite high. There were three thousand three hundred and sixty miles of roads, all of which were passable year round, and fifty-six hundred miles of jungle tracks. There were seventeen hundred bridges and tunnels.

Salaries for the peons were calculated on the Brazilian average, and then raised by forty percent. An engineer in 1980 earned about three thousand dollars per month. Rent ranged between one and fifty dollars, according to given categories. Restaurants were open to all cardholders, whatever their rank. Only the price lists were different: six dollars per month for the peons, sixty for the managerial staff; and this was for three meals per day.

Recreation facilities were plentiful. In April 1980, ninety-one of one hundred and twenty-five planned swimming pools were open. Leisure centers included tennis courts, squash courts, exercise facilities, and synthetic-surfaced athletic fields. There were volleyball and basketball courts and soccer fields. Each forest village and each town was represented by at least one team in each of these three sports. In 1969, on Trajano da Silva's suggestion (he had, in his youth, played for the famous Fluminense Club), a soccer championship was organized, and Da Silva's day of glory came when a team selected by him met and held at bay, two goals to two, the great Santos Futball Club, Pele's club. His only regret was that the King, who watched the game from somewhere in the crowd, refused to be the one to hand the cup to the winning team, leaving that to one of the Brazilian directors of one of the one hundred and eleven companies.

Thirty-nine different nationalities were represented in the Kingdom. And if the Brazilians were the most numerous, former residents of the United States formed the largest foreign colony.

Settiniaz estimated that nine thousand six hundred of his fellow countrymen lived there.

Two television channels, one in English and the other in Portuguese, were on the air twenty-four hours a day, as well as four radio stations. Two daily newspapers and one bilingual weekly paper were published between June of 1968, the date of the first issue of one newspaper, and April 30, 1980.

Until May 5, 1980, the reactions of the Brazilian, Venezuelan, and Colombian governments can only be characterized as nonexistent.

7

"We have quite a few problems to solve," said Ethel Weizmann. "But those that concern us most are those caused by the *gatos*, and those occurring in that supposed town of Porto Negro."

Settiniaz didn't have the slightest idea of what *gatos* were. And as for Porto Negro . . .

"Gatos are cats. It's a nickname. And not a nice one. They deal in workers, not to say in human flesh. David, before Elias and I arrived, the companies went through private recruitment agencies. They had other problems and couldn't take the time to check on the agencies. The result was that the peons were, and are still, being exploited. Some *gatos* take up to fifty percent of the salaries of those they bring in, on credit, from the northeast."

"Have you told Reb about this?"

"Yes. And he has given us a free hand. He knew we would not have stayed otherwise. Right now, we are short-circuiting the *gatos*. We have opened a recruitment agency in Belém, one in São Luis—that's south of Belém. Two others will open, in Rio and in São Paulo, for the technicians we are training. We will put people we are sure of there, and keep a close eye on them, a very close eye, I assure you."

But the Porto Negro problem seemed insoluble. It was the existence of a shantytown, which already had fifteen thousand inhabitants and was growing rapidly.

"David, here again, we have spoken to Reb. But he doesn't want to do anything about it. He says, and he is right in this, that Porto Negro is off-limits, geographically—politically, I may say, as well as economically. He feels that it has nothing to do with his project. We have not been able to convince him. . . ."

The shantytown was formed anarchically, by miserable migrants who came from the northeast of Brazil and had been turned down by the agencies because of insufficient qualifications or other reasons. These people had piled into what could not be called houses, but primitive dwellings built on stilts, almost directly across from Ilha Dourada, but on the other side of the Negro, less than ten miles away, in the hope of one day infiltrating the new Eldorado, where there were jobs to be had.

"David, this is a leprosy that will rapidly become hideous, which it is already. We have seen many situations like this in the world; we know how fast things can happen. In three years, it will be unspeakable. But Reb will not listen. According to him, Porto Negro is the responsibility not only of the Brazilian Navy, since the area is riverine, but also of the Brazilian government. He says that if he does anything at all to help, the next day there will be one hundred thousand of them, and then a million of them, and more, all attracted by the very fact of his generosity. He says that he can't take care of all the miserable people in the world.

"David, Reb is changing; something is happening to him. His private dream is taking precedence over everything else. Do you know what we think? We think that he is not so unhappy to see this cancer growing largely and rapidly across from his own territory. Because the whole world can then see, can compare, and can judge the differences between what he has done and what others have refused to do, or cannot afford to do. . . ."

David Settiniaz saw the Weizmanns many times after 1974. Sometimes in New York, where they had a small apartment full of photographs of children of all colors, including their own two sons and three daughters and a rather surprising number of grandchildren. As far as he knew, Ethel and Elias Weizmann were the only two people in the world who, knowing Reb Klimrod and the immensity of his fortune and his genius, still maintained their objectivity toward him, and would even specifically question his infallibility.

All the other King's Men were afraid of him, deep down; yet they were fanatically devoted to him.

How else can one explain their incredible relentlessness during the 1967–80 period, that of the construction and the near- completion of the Kingdom, of which David Settiniaz was the privileged witness?

Nine billion one hundred and fifty million dollars were invested in Amazonia between 1950 and 1980. This is the figure given by David Settiniaz. He is the only one (it is not certain that Klimrod kept such precise records) capable of making such an evaluation. Six billion came from Reb himself, and the rest was self-financing, the Kingdom supplying itself from its own resources as they became available.

It is, at least, likely.

The King told Settiniaz and Tarras one day that his very first idea, the one that brought about the other developments, was the realization that the explosion of worldwide communications would necessarily bring about a shortage of paper in the nineteen-eighties, if not before. And that, therefore, forestry development, looking toward the production of cellulose, was the only solution, if it was carried out on a large scale.

He was eventually proved right and his foresight was justified.

In the nineteen-fifties, his desire to conquer the world and his desire to help the Indians to survive came into direct confrontation. He pursued these opposite objectives together. To find the forests he needed, and then the land where he could create his own world, he seized the forests and the land that were the natural habitat of the Indians he wanted to protect. How could he live with such a contradiction? It was a mystery. And the rage to create won out over the humanitarian sentiment.

Enrique Escalante, a forestry expert, began in 1953 looking for trees with rapid growth rates. The theory was a simple one. The Amazonian forest is made up of several hundreds of species which are for the most part unsuitable for the manufacture of cellulose, with which one makes paper. Besides that, these trees took half a century or more to grow. After they concluded their research, Escalante and his team chose the Caribbean pine, which can be found in Honduras, the eucalyptus *(Eucalyptus deglupta)*, and the *Gmelina arborea*, a tree from Asia with which they conducted conclusive tests in Nigeria and in Panama. The growth rates were more than satisfactory: twenty years for the eucalyptus, sixteen for the Caribbean pine, six or seven for the Gmelina. Beginning in 1954 with the clearing of about two hundred and fifty thousand acres of the area purchased by Ubaldo Rocha with the diamonds, the development reached nearly two and a half million acres a quarter of a century later, with the Gmelina occupying two-thirds of the area.

The pulp plants and the thermoelectrical plants that supplied the energy were, at first, created according to the principle of decentralization. There were fourteen of them. But by 1978, Uwe Sobieski had completed their number and then partially replaced them with the enormous installation that would, for the first time, attract the attention of the public and, to a lesser extent, that of the international press. It involved four monstrous units, a combined pulp and paper plant, which measured nearly eight hundred feet in length, one hundred and fifty in width, and up to one hundred and eighty-seven in height. It was equivalent to a twelve-story building standing on two and a half soccer fields.

Construction had been financed by three companies, headed by Soubise, Hang, and Thadeus Töpfler; it had taken place in Japan, in a naval shipyard in Kure, the one with which Georges Tarras had signed agreements in 1951. The Japanese built the monsters directly on loading platforms.

Because they could not pass through the Panama Canal, and in order to avoid the roaring forties near the Horn, Nick Petridis, who was in charge of forwarding them as far as the mouth of the Amazon, chose to have them make a three-month trip, over sixteen thousand miles, from Japan's Inland Sea, through the Philippine Sea, the Indian Ocean, around the Cape of Good Hope, and finally across the South Atlantic.

They reached the Rio Negro in drydocks especially constructed by Da Silva's teams and hoisted over more than seven thousand five hundred pillars made of *macarenduba*, an Amazonian wood that is extremely hard and almost totally resistant to rot. Since

426

the drydocks permitted emptying and filling, there was always the possibility of putting these floating plants out to sea again, and, if need be, move them anywhere else in the world.

Railroad tracks for the transportation of logs were laid in 1967, to take over what had previously been done with difficulty by trucks. The length of the system on May 1, 1980, was almost three hundred miles. The General Plan foresaw six hundred.

Transported on ships belonging to the Petridis brothers, the bales of cellulose were exported to Europe, the United States, Japan, and Venezuela. Production capacity of the plants was two thousand two hundred tons per day, or eight hundred thousand tons per year.

The first sawmills were installed in 1954. But the most modern one, using a laser, was completed in February 1979, and it alone could produce forty thousand tons of lumber and pressed wood.

The paper plant, producing two hundred and fifty thousand tons, was set up in 1976.

As for underground development, the plan for processing Kaolin, the fireproof clay used for coating by the cosmetic and pharmaceutical manufacturers, went into service in 1972, with an annual production of two hundred and fifty thousand tons, and this was from a vein evaluated at sixty million tons, with about one hundred million in reserve.

The production of bauxite briquettes, intended for blast furnaces, began the same year.

The following year saw the start of the rolled-aluminum complex, which was set up outside the Kingdom, near Belém, at a cost of three billion dollars. Involved, in addition to nine of the King's companies, which had been regrouped into a holding company, were companies in the U.S., Canada, Brazil, and São Paulo. Although it was outside the Kingdom, it processed resources from inside it, which were estimated at two hundred and sixty million tons.

To these resources must be added, as the prospecting teams of Jean Coltzesco found them, the development of phosphate, fluorine, nickel, thorium, zirconium, rare earth, and uranium. And, of course, gold, diamonds, emeralds, and semiprecious stones. But these last were the King's secret domain, and the only one to whom Coltzesco communicated the figures concerning them was Reb Klimrod.

From them, the King must have filled up what Settiniaz calls his "personal privy purse."

In the agricultural area, the eighteen companies run by Escalante and Ung Seng, each of which was headed by a Brazilian secondary trustee, who in turn was subordinate by a trust agreement to Jorge Socrates and Nelson Coëlho, Emerson's son, did remarkably well. The rice, which at first had been intended solely to supply the Kingdom, rapidly became its basic product. Its exportation began in 1965, to the Brazilian market, which was and still remains deficient in it. The General Plan foresaw cultivation of five hundred and fifty thousand flooded or floodable acres, with a return of five tons to the acre, semiannually, according to Ung's calculations, which proved correct. In May 1980, more than half of this amazing program had been carried out; one hundred and forty silos, each with a capacity of twenty thousand tons, and two decortication plants, capable of processing thirty tons per hour, completed the system.

Stock farming—one hundred and twenty thousand head of cattle in 1980—was carried out in all of the areas where the Caribbean pine trees had been planted. Farther south, near the Amazon, pigs and fowl were raised. In 1972, production was sufficient for all internal needs, and exportation started the following year.

An experimental agricultural center was created in 1966 by Escalante and a remarkable Brazilian expert named Madeira. Its principal objectives were cocoa, which, it was proved, could be cultivated in plantations of Gmelinas, and traditional heveas, Pará nuts, citrus fruits, palm oil, sugar cane, manioc, soybeans.

A research establishment appeared in 1974. The following year studies were conducted of a wood-based carbochemical fuel and a combustible substance made from a mixture of sugar cane and manioc, to obtain methanol and methane. The main idea behind this was to achieve complete self-sufficiency and a rational system of energy development.

The first quinquennial plan was established, and followed to the last detail, in 1960. In May of 1980, the fifth of these plans was in process, with sixty percent of its goals already reached.

At this time, May 1, 1980, besides Tarras, Settiniaz, the King's Men, and perhaps, at a maximum, five dozen men and women, high-ranking technicians, pilots, and communications people, no one knew who Reb Michael Klimrod really was.

No newspaper, no publication had ever so much as mentioned his name or, much less, published his picture.

8

Tudor Anghel, the Los Angeles lawyer of Rumanian origin, who had been the King's Man in many areas, but especially for matters pertaining to gold mines, died in June of 1976, of a heart attack, as he was driving his car in Santa Monica.

Shirley Tarras died nine days later, on the twenty-eighth, after having fought for over ten years a cancer that was devouring her.

David Settiniaz learned the news from the King.

Very distressed, he asked: "When did it happen?"

"Three hours ago."

Reb's voice had a strange sound, and it took Settiniaz a while to figure out the reason.

"Are you calling from a plane?"

"Yes. We left Rio two hours ago. David, I'm going directly to Boston. Will you join me there?"

This, perhaps more than anything else, touched Settiniaz's heart. The death of Shirley Tarras, whom he had known and loved almost like a mother for over thirty years, affected him strongly, although the news was not too much of a surprise. The doctors had given up hope four years ago.

The surprise was that the King himself was making this trip.

"At the time," Settiniaz remembers, "I had not seen him for over fifteen months. Following Reb's specific instructions, I handed over to Marnie Oakes documents I wanted him to see, in which I sometimes pointed out the financial difficulties I was having because of the increasingly enormous withdrawals he was making. The documents were returned to me three days later—'Strictly confidential.—To be delivered to addressee in person'—by one of Jethro's anonymous messengers. A short note said: 'I know. Do the best you can.' And I remember having imagined him then, naked, with his green snakeskin band around his forehead, his hair down to his shoulders, in the heart of this totally inhospitable jungle, feeling at home though among illiterate Indians, eating God knows what, and still capable of keeping tabs on me. Other notes said, for instance: 'The Udruzena Poljobanka of Zagreb, account number 583452 L M 67, did not make that transfer of $112,600. Why? RMK.' Or: 'Have already made demand for complete withdrawal of capital from Tosse Keckavarsi Iran in Teheran; demand not completed. Take care of it, please. RMK.'

". . . And now I learned he was reappearing with no other motive than to be with a friend for the funeral of his wife, in a tiny country cemetery in the heart of Maine . . ."

Georges Tarras also remembers, of course.

Shirley's death had occurred around nine o'clock in the morning. In a way, it had been a relief. For almost six weeks, she had been nearly unconscious, knocked out by the increasing quantities of morphine she was being given. During the last few days, she could not have weighed more than sixty-five pounds, and, through a strange detour of his memory, Tarras had seen again the ghosts of Dachau and Mauthausen.

When it was all over, he did not cry or manifest his sorrow in any way; he was beyond tears. His intention was clear and had long been set in his mind: he wouldn't tell anyone. He knew too well what would have happened: his former students and colleagues from Harvard would have come running, as would all of Shirley's innumerable friends in publishing circles. Some famous authors she had in turn passionately supported and joyously slaughtered in her reviews would have felt it their duty to come up to Maine.

Only for one person did he hesitate: David Settiniaz. Shirley thought of him as their son. He went as far as picking up the phone to call New York, but changed his mind. In spite of his depression, of the overwhelming feeling of loneliness that enveloped him—"Why, dear God? Since I knew she was going to die, and she was really dead, for months now"—he still managed to make fun of himself. Sarcastic even now, he could not imagine himself talking on the telephone: "You might just start sobbing, suddenly, Tarras, and make a fool of yourself."

In reaction, he plunged into immediate and practical things. He hired a plane, and a hearse to meet him in Bangor, took care of the formalities required for the transfer of a body from one state to another. He was in Maine by two o'clock in the afternoon, and spent two more hours making the arrangements for the burial, which was to take place the following day. At five o'clock he reached his lonely house, which, on its promontory between bays, seemed more solitary than ever. And there, he cracked a little, as he was making tea. He had a rather difficult twenty-minute period as he roamed through the empty house, during which he could not get out of his mind the pills in the medicine cabinet in the bathroom. Finally, it was his sharp sense of the ridiculous that took over. Mrs. Cavanaugh was going to be making her triweekly muffin delivery the next day, and it might truly upset her to find out that he had passed on to the next world precisely on a Wednesday, the day when the muffins were at their best, without explanation.

He went outside.

Those two stupid cormorants, Adolf and Benito, were there, perched on their crumbling dock, as sadly devoid of humor as any living creature could be. They came back every year, and spent the summer. They were probably not the original Adolf and Benito of the nineteen-forties, but they were certainly their direct descendants. What other cormorants of any other ancestry could look so stupid?

"I must say," said a slow, calm voice, "I do not remember ever seeing such stupid-looking birds."

"I have granted them an emphyteutic lease of ninety-nine years," answered Tarras, seemingly unsurprised. "Renewable by tacit agreement."

He sensed another presence besides Reb's. Turning around, he recognized David, a few feet away. Then he really cried.

431

The next day, after the burial, for which there were only the three of them present, Reb said that he would like to spend a day or two in the red house.

"Red, for lack of a better word, of course. But I am imposing myself, in a way."

"I snore; I am warning you," said Tarras.

"Not as loud as one of my friends' jaguar. And your whiskers are shorter."

After David returned to New York, the two men walked for a long time. Although it was June, the air was cool, and although it wasn't raining yet, it was visibly imminent. Reb was shivering in his white cotton T-shirt.

"Cold?"

"It's the change of climate. It will pass."

"Or malaria."

"We Shamatari are immune to malaria."

But they returned to the house and made a fire. They spoke of Montaigne, Styron, Pa Kin, Naipaul, of painting and many other things, but Tarras could see that Reb was discussing everything but what really concerned him. The very word "Amazonia" seemed to be erased from his memory.

Mrs. Cavanaugh arrived around three-thirty, by car, with the just-baked muffins. She made them tea and told them they were crazy to stay inside on such a lovely day, a little humid perhaps (it was pouring at that moment) but it reminded her of her home-land, Ireland. She offered to stay and prepare dinner, but Reb thanked her and told her that would not be necessary, he would take care of everything. The Irish woman left.

"Take care of everything! You make it sound as if I were a hundred years old!"

"You are seventy-five."

The scarlet room had no other light than that coming through the window, plus that of the fire. This semidarkness emphasized the gauntness of Reb's face. He has almost not changed since Mauthausen, Tarras thought. He will die unchanged. Shirl used to say that he was the most fascinating and distant man who ever walked the earth, and that perhaps he came from another planet.

He said aloud: "How did you learn that she had just died, Reb? Through Jethro?"

"It's not important. Unless you really want to talk about it."

"You're right: it's not important."

"Tell me about this book you're writing."

"Tell me about Amazonia."

"I did not come for that."

"I know exactly why you came. And, as it happens, I wanted to . . ."

"Tttttt," said Reb with a smile.

He put down his cup, got up, and went to find his cloth bag, from which he pulled three or four bottles.

"Do you really want this tea from China?"

"I haven't had any vodka for more than fifteen years."

"And I must have had some three times in my life."

They attacked the first bottle. Reb started to talk, this time about himself, of his buried past, of Sicily, when he had gone there with Dov Lazarus, who, in front of his eyes, had shot two men, Langen and De Groot. He told about another time with Dov, when he was shooting seagulls and exhorting him to kill for vengeance, as the two men stood near the Malabata Point lighthouse in Tangiers. He was certainly not drunk, since his lips had hardly touched the Georgian vodka, and therefore it was not the alcohol that was reviving his memories.

For Tarras, it was very clear: "He was never able to talk easily about love or friendship; he had, when it came to it, a great, almost paralyzing modesty. But I am sure that that was what he was trying to do, when he shared all these personal stories with me: he was trying to show me the friendship he felt toward me."

"Don't try to get me drunk," said Tarras, who by this time had finished three-quarters of the bottle by himself. "I am Georgian, originally—that is to say, almost Russian, or at least from the Soviet Union. I have Caucasian and Ukrainian blood mixed in with American blood. It is not your vodka, however Georgian it may be, that will . . ."

"Nessim brought it back from Tbilisi."

"It's excellent."

"I don't want to bore you with my stories."

"Don't be an ass, Master Klimrod. You know very well how much your stories interest and fascinate me. What was the name of the man in Nuremberg who wanted to exterminate three or four hundred thousand Nazis?"

"Bunim Anielewitch. He died. A day came when he could no

longer find his place in the Eastern countries. So he went to Israel. He was killed during the Six-Day War. Under another name, of course."

Night fell, and at ten o'clock Reb said he was hungry. Tarras came to the conclusion, after a few steps, that his house, and probably the entire rocky promontory it stood on, listed. He therefore decided to remain in his armchair, thinking that he had, at that moment, the wealthiest manservant in the world. The rain stopped, and the now-calm ocean could hardly be heard.

Reb returned with a bacon-and-basil omelette he had prepared. They shared it, drinking the second bottle of vodka, which Tarras had already started.

"More stories, Georges?"

"Invent them, if you need to."

"But I am inventing them, Georges. What else do you think I have been doing?"

There followed then the story of the hunt in Austria, the visit to Simon Wiesenthal, the pursuit from Salzburg and through the Dead Mountains, the death of Dov Lazarus, and the meeting with the terrified man who had four passports bearing four different names. "Eichmann, can you imagine?"

Tarras fell asleep. He woke up during the afternoon of the following day, his tongue feeling like cotton, and, in the great silence of the house, thought he was alone. He hurried downstairs and found Reb on the telephone, speaking Portuguese.

"I've made some coffee," said Reb, his hand covering the mouthpiece. "It's still warm. It's in the kitchen."

He continued phoning, in English, German, Spanish, and French.

Outside, the weather had turned fair. It was beautiful, the sky perfectly clear, with a light wind. They went out and walked along the shore.

"Did I go to bed, or did you carry me?"

"A little of both, in a way."

Adolf and Benito were at their posts, as stupid as ever.

"Reb," said Tarras suddenly, "I want to be part of it."

His eyes met the gray ones, and that same timidity he had felt in Mauthausen thirty-one years earlier came over him again. He continued:

"I am not that old. And you know exactly what I am talking

about: this battle that you are sooner or later going to wage, or have to wage. . . . This is the only point I do not know: whether you will make the first move or have it be made for you. I lean toward the first proposition."

Reb leaned over, picked up a large pebble, and threw it. The stone hit the water right between the two cormorants, who made a point of ignoring it.

"Are you quite sure they are alive?"

"Indeed they are. And so am I."

Reb took off his shoes and, barefoot, walked into the water, unconcerned with the fact that his pants were getting wet. He shook his head.

"I have not made a decision yet," he said. "For the time being, the people in Brasília are leaving me alone. As are the people in Caracas and Bogotá."

"That will not last, and you know it."

Silence.

Reb was taking off his T-shirt. He very slowly immersed himself in the ocean, up to his face, with his eyes wide open, looking somewhat like someone who had drowned. Tarras went to sit on his personal rock.

"Don't lock me out, Reb, please. Please."

Reb disappeared beneath the water, swimming, and he did not reappear for two interminable minutes. He swam back to the rocks, got completely undressed, rung out his clothes and put them back on.

"You have only been there once, Georges."

"I detest the heat. And I am not offering you my services as a woodcutter."

There was silence again. Reb was tying the laces of his sneakers. But he stopped, lost in contemplation.

"I told you that I have not come to a decision. And that is true. I could go on living this way, with things as they are."

"How many companies have you used this time?"

"One hundred and eleven."

"With nothing officially tying them together?"

"Nothing."

"Is there the slightest chance that someone, someday, will reveal the fact that you are the one and only owner?"

"I don't think so."

Tarras was thinking. He finally said:

"You're right. You could 'go on living this way,' as you put it. The worst that could happen would be that some complaint would be brought against one of your one hundred and eleven companies, but I suppose that each one of them is represented by its own team of crafty lawyers. And I believe I remember that some of your men are in the government itself. Isn't one of them the personal adviser to the Brazilian President?"

Reb smiled. "Yes."

"So the only real risk," said Tarras, "would be a Cuban-style revolution, in Brazil, Venezuela, or Colombia. It is not very likely, at least for the next twenty years. And arrangements can always be made with the heavens, even be they red. Do you still have those excellent relationships with the people in the Kremlin?"

"Yes."

"Through Paul, Nessim, that American art collector, and that other Frenchman, with the heavy accent?"

"Yes. And through others."

Tarras managed to laugh. "My God, Reb, you're a multinational organization all by yourself. What am I saying, one multinational organization? You are several multinational organizations! You could buy General Motors or Exxon, probably. Or both. Am I right?"

"I never thought of it."

They started walking again, side by side, back to the house.

"Reb, it's very simple: it's your decision. If you continue to keep quiet, to maintain your anonymity, nothing will happen, nothing serious."

They went into the house.

"But I know that things will not happen that way," said Tarras.

"No?"

"No. You said so yourself: 'I have not come to a decision.' That means you are thinking about it. And I think you will do it. I think you will be the one to start the battle. You have created a nation, and few outside its boundaries know about it. There will have to come a time when you start talking. And I can, I believe, help you, when that time will come. I have thought a great deal about it lately. I suppose you have, as well."

Reb smiled.

"Come," said Tarras.

He went to his study. Book and notes were piled up in a way that would horrify someone like Settiniaz.

"Last night," said Tarras, "before you so shamefully got me drunk, you asked me a question, which I have not yet answered. You asked me to tell you about the book I am writing. . . ."

He picked up a folder and opened it.

Inside, there was a single sheet of paper.

"This is the whole thing, Reb. I doubt whether it will ever be published. It is, however, finished. Everything is here. I can read it to you, if you like."

"I am burning with impatience," Reb answered with another smile.

"First, the title: *Of the Total Imbecility of the Legitimacy of States*, by Georges Tarras. Now for the text. This is the first chapter. There are no others, actually. The first and only chapter reads as follows:

> "The principle of the legitimacy of states is a ridiculous and perfectly inept concept. It has no legal foundation whatsoever. At the basis of each state, there is this historic fact: at a given moment, one tribe had bigger stone axes than the neighboring tribes, thanks to which it crushed those tribes. In consequence, it is perfectly clear that no actual state has the slightest legal existence."

"That's it, Reb. I find my conclusion very satisfying."

"Reb," he said, "I can teach you the course, I can . . ."

"I would like to see some books on the subject."

"*General Principles of International Law*, by Sir Gerald Fitzmaurice; *The International Society as a Legal Society*, by Mosler; the *Principes du droit international public*, by Paul Guggenheim; *La règle du droit de la paix*, by Cavaglieri; the *Traité du droit des gens*, by Redslob; the journals published by the International Academy of Law of The Hague; the *American Journal of International Law*, the *German Yearbook*, the *Journal of World Trade Law*, the *Recueil des Sentences Arbitrales de l'O.N.U.* . . . And, of course, I could add Westlake, Wheaton, Renault, Alvarez and his excellent *Droit international américain.* . . . And Tunkin, who was a Russki, Jiménez de Arechaga, who came from Montevideo, the Verdross and Simma, which just came out and which I don't have a copy of yet, but I can get hold of one. . . . Without even mentioning O'Connel, Kelsen, Von der Heydte, Schwarzenberger, Brownlie . . ."

"Catch your breath."

"You could spend years at it, Reb. Even if you read at the speed of light."

Tarras touched one pile among others, which collapsed.

"Many of them are here, but not all of them, of course. You will have to confide in someone, Reb."

"In you."

"Yes, me. Me and all the other lawyers you can assemble, of every nationality, of course. I can even get hold of an authentic Russian, with the perfect rubicund coloring, who is not even a dissident, but who nevertheless is important and has contacts in the Kremlin, even though he lives in London and Finland. He would be part of the team and keep his mouth shut, on Tarras's honor."

"And what would this team do?"

"Whatever you want it to do, Reb: try to prove that this country you have created can and must exist, that it has the right to, just as you conceived it."

The gray eyes widened.

"And I would be crazy enough to do this, Georges?"

"I think you are much crazier than that, Reb."

Tarras was thinking: There is, in the end, something of a Diego Haas in me. It is as if we were both created and put on this earth to push Reb Michael Klimrod to fulfill his destiny. . . . But, in the next few instants, he got hold of himself: that was according to himself and Diego Haas, and gave them too much importance.

He continued softly: "Reb, I know that I am seventy-five years old. I am not asking for this as an act of charity, which you would accord to me because I am now alone, and in the name of this friendship you perhaps feel for me. I really can constitute this team, and have it ready, for the moment when you decide to make your move."

Silence.

Then Reb said to him: "I would like you to go there. At least one more time. Your only visit was in 1964."

"Nineteen-sixty-five."

"Sixty-four," said Reb, "November 23, 1964. Do you want to bet?"

"Good God, no," said Tarras. "I know your memory too well. You could probably tell me what I was wearing that day."

"A white suit, green tie and handkerchief, and a Panama that amazed Jaua and his sons. They still laugh about it. Georges, I would like you to come next year. Let's say in February. It will rain less then."

"I will come. If I am still of this world, of course."

"If you were to die, I wouldn't forgive you."

There was a pause. The look in his eyes was deeper.

"Can you really develop a strong argument?"

"A state is an entity that has a territory, a population, and a government. Which, furthermore is sovereign and independent, and, as such, is not subordinate to any other state or any other entity, though subject to international law. Right there you have enough material to keep generations of lawyers fighting for five hundred years."

"I probably won't wait that long."

"Reb, even the words 'international law' have no serious foundation. It is an expression that was used for the first time by a man named Bentham, almost two hundred years ago. And Bentham must have invented it during an alcoholic crisis. It did not exist before him. Before him, the expression *jus inter gentes* was used, a Latin formula, which, in turn, was taken from another madman, named Victoria, during the fifteen-hundreds. The Frenchman d'Aguesseau, around 1720, translated *jus inter gentes* as the *right between nations*. Which was presumptuous and stupid, for anyone who knows a little Latin. Old d'Aguesseau was working at the time for his master and for France, which was right in the middle of imperialist expansion. And the Anglo-Saxon lawyers, who were anxious to justify national conquests, as well as to give them a pretext, rushed to fall into step with him. So that when good old Kant, in his project for perpetual peace . . ."

"Georges?"

". . . published in 1795, replaced the word 'nations' with 'states,' international law . . ."

"*Georges.*"

"Well, I could go on talking like that for one hundred and forty-three hours," said Tarras. "At least."

"A territory, a population, and a government."

"You have the territory and apparently the population. Name Jaua prime minister or president, whichever you or he wants. No one will be able to contest his rights as first occupant, other than to go back to the time before the formation of the Bering Strait, when America's Indians were still Asians. As for the territory, you will have to reveal to the world that these one hundred and eleven companies are but the pieces of one puzzle, designed by you alone. This will—and you have certainly thought of it before I and that is perhaps the reason for your hesitation—shed light on everything you have created, Reb, not only in Amazonia. Everything. The whole world will learn then—and will probably fall over on its ass—that there exists a Reb Michael Klimrod."

Reb had his back to him.

"A fucking price to pay, Reb. You will have to come out of the shadows. In a way, it will be a suicide. After so very many years . . ."

Reb remained quiet, and still.

"The most extraordinary thing, Reb, is that I am convinced that you will do it, at whatever price. Not because I have spoken to you about it. I don't for one second pretend to think that I could ever influence you. How long has this idea been on your mind?"

"For years," said Reb, calmly. "In a way."

He turned to Tarras.

"Do you really want to take charge of this whole matter?"

"There is probably nothing in the world that I want more," answered Tarras, with an almost ferocious determination. And he added: "But certainly not because I am alone. Reb, I want to handle this because I sincerely believe, as clearly as possible, that I am in the best position to do so. I know you a little . . ."

"Rather well," said Reb with a smile. "This proves it."

"I can do it, Reb. I have already thought of some people. Five or six. To begin with. With the idea of enlarging the group,

440

eventually, after we have squeezed our brains dry. And we will need people to do the paperwork. I know a marvelous woman who could put a team together for us. We will get hold of every existing piece of international law and go over it with a fine-tooth comb. Reb, since the beginning of time there has never existed one single state that was legitimate. Legitimacy does not exist; it is a hoax. *Ubi societas, ibi jus*: where there is society, there is law. Poppycock! Just words. In such cases, lawyers paint empty spaces in different colors and claim to have built walls. And they pretend to believe us when, like good old d'Aguesseau, we sing the King's song. Look, right behind your left shoulder is Hall's book. Take it down and open it, to page 127, I believe, and read:

> "A State can acquire a territory by a unilateral act of its own initiative, by occupation, by the transfer issued by another State or community or individual, by a gift, by the prescription resulting from the passing of time or by growth caused by an act of Nature. . . .

"I am quoting from memory. Did you hear that, Reb: 'A unilateral act of its own initiative . . .' That is nothing more than a description of theft, of a conquest by violence, or a robbery. So much for legitimacy, sovereignty, and this sinister farce of sacrosanct law; they are all of the colors used to paint wars, dominations, imposed or inflicted treaties, or those resulting from the equilibrium between two similarly fearful or exhausted adversaries. Belgium was born of the frenzied antagonism between France and the United Kingdom, these nations being the target of successive invasions; the African countries are made of haphazardly cut-up pieces, which correspond only by chance to ethnic origins; and what can you say about South America, or Central America, or even North America? What would have happened if the Spaniards, who conquered Mexico, had not been defeated after the Alamo by the descendants of British nationals who took over the United States? And what is the USSR if not the Empire of the Russians, those from the Baltic and the Ukraine, who extended their fat paws as far as the lands of the Japanese, Mongolians, Afghans, and Chinese, not to mention the Kazaks they so joyfully exterminated thirty years ago, or these swarthy Cubans who serve as their Gurkhas or their Senegalese sharpshooters? Where is the sacrosanct law of the Turks, the conquerors of the Central Asian steppes, who went as far as the Mediterranean and who solved the Armenian problem in about the same way we handled that of our own Indians? After how long an occupation does one become a native? I have met, in Mexico, in Algeria, in Vietnam, people who were indignant about having been colonized, but González in Mexico came straight from Castile or Aragon, just as Mohammed of Tizi-Ouz-ou came from Arabia in order to convert, with the help of a big stick, the Berbers who had preceded him, and who were themselves part Visigoth or Allah knows what. And Nguyen Whatever, in the Mekong Delta, joyfully stepped over the stomachs of the Hams and other Khmers who had lived there previously. I could go on forever. The sacrosanct law! Ha! Let me roar with laughter. There are millions of things to be said on the subject."

"Enough, enough," said Reb.

"Reb, no theory exists or will ever exist; there is no rule. Just this year, to give you an example, they are going to refuse to recognize the Transvaal, not without good reason, though, because there are real doubts as to its real independence vis-à-vis South Africa, but who has ever brought up the fact that the Soviet Union has three votes at the United Nations: as the USSR, as the Ukraine, and as Byelorussia? Who the hell would dare to claim that Byelorussia is independent?"

"And that being said?"

"That being said, and a million other things that remain to be said, the case can be pleaded, Reb. Provided you find a forum and commit hara-kari, or at least sacrifice this absolute incognito that is like a second skin for you. Reb?"

"Yes?"

"Could you build one or several atom bombs?"

"Yes."

"Do you really have the means to do it?"

"Yes."

"Have you thought of it?"

"Of course I would not do it, but I have thought of it. Let's say as an intellectual game, out of pure speculation."

"As you surely know, that would be the other solution. Declare war on Brazil, Colombia, and Venezuela; and if you can arrange it so that the two actual godfathers of the Great Worldwide Robbery—I am referring to the United States and the USSR—can get something out of it and hold their guns . . ."

"Another Katanga."

"That comparison is of no advantage to you. The so-called Katangans were defending a colonial acquisition, but you, you have created something from nothing. Besides, you are infinitely smarter. But you won't do it either."

"No."

"That's what I was afraid of," said Tarras, as sarcastic as ever. "Too bad: there is nothing like a good war—a lovely massacre and a great blood bath—to found an unquestionable and 'legal,' in quotes, new state."

Tarras watched Reb pick up his bag and get ready to leave. But the imminence of his departure didn't affect him, as it would have the night before, giving him the acute feeling of being so alone. He is going to say yes, he has already said yes, and I am going to wage this battle, he thought.

"You know, of course," said Reb, "the kind of file I would like you to prepare."

"The freedom to undertake and to create, the priority of the individual over the state, the inadequacy of all the actual systems, all of them, the necessity for a new example, the denunciation of all cynicisms, of all 'isms.' Out of nearly two hundred, there are not, in this world, twenty nearly free countries. And you can't be 'nearly free,' just as a woman cannot be 'nearly pregnant.' Anything else, Reb?"

"That will do for the moment."

Reb went to the door.

Tarras knew that somewhere, invisible but definitely present, Diego Haas was waiting.

"I will get started right away," he said. "No, don't start talking about money, please. With what you have given me over the years, I could hire six hundred high-flying lawyers. My banker thinks I'm a drug dealer. And for the seminars, I could rent Versailles. Reb? You have not asked me what the chances are of your being heard, when the day comes. . . ."

"I know the answer. And so do you."

"Nil," said Tarras. "Absolutely and irremediably nil. But who has ever tackled windmills of such a size?"

9

"I was in Kuala-Lumpur, in Malaysia," said Elias Weizmann. "Georges, I still cannot get over it. He had given us a quota of five thousand. One million would not have been enough."

"It's always like that," said Tarras.

"Nick Petridis, the big shipowner, put three of his ships at our disposal for three months. It's enormous and absurd. The Gulf of Siam and the South China Sea are swarming with these miserable people who are fleeing the Mekong Delta. You should see them: we came across boats on which everyone had starved to death, from wandering around; and that's when they were not massacred by local pirates. And we are in 1977!"

"There will always be pirates."

"As to having to sort through people, to choose five thousand from among them, it was one of the most horrible things I've ever been asked to do. I tried to reach him several times, to ask him to raise the quota. I couldn't convince him and I cannot even be angry with him. He is extremely wealthy, I know, or at least he has a great deal of money, but he cannot be expected to take care of all the miserable people in the world. I suppose he was the one who chartered the boats from the Greek?"

"Nick Petridis is American. Yes, I suppose you could speak of chartering. Did you also go to Thailand?"

"Thailand also," said Weizmann. He had spent two months in the camps along the Cambodian border, to collect five thousand more Khmers willing to go to Amazonia.

"I was even accused of flesh-peddling, and because of those absurd rules of silence Reb imposed on me, I could not even defend myself. Thank goodness for those foundations you told me about; they really helped me out. And that billionaire of press and television, that fellow Dunn, had the State Department and the French Minister of Foreign Affairs intervene on my behalf. Does this Dunn fellow have anything to do with Reb?"

"Not as far as I know," said Tarras, feeling ashamed of his lie. "I did not speak of Reb to anyone, I assure you."

"I don't think the mention of his name would have done you any good anyway."

"I think you're right. Ethel has a theory about Reb. Of course, she has theories about everything. She believes that he is even more important than he seems, that he is more than a foreman. She thinks that he is the managing director of a giant consortium, grouping together perhaps two hundred American or Brazilian companies."

"I really don't know Reb very well," said Tarras, feeling more and more uncomfortable.

He had been in New York for a week, and had met with Weizmann in his capacity as president of one of the foundations whose role in Southeast Asia had recently been evoked.

During this summer of 1977, Georges Tarras had put together, piece by piece, his international legal task force. The operation had been conducted with the utmost secrecy. He had rented offices on Madison Avenue, still under cover of his foundation, and had brought in thirty experts, of whom only three knew the ultimate objective: the creation of a new state.

As Reb had asked him to, he had, overcoming his abhorrence of the tropics, returned to Amazonia a second time. He had flown over the Amazon, the Negro, and the Branco rivers, but had listened only distractedly to Sobieski's presentation of his latest project: an enormous hydroelectric plant, comparable in size to the one in James Bay, in Quebec. Tarras's indifference to technical matters was complete: changing a light bulb was the ultimate of his potential in that field. But he had noticed the difficulties being faced by the lawyers of Sobieski's company: a national law, which was energetically brandished by the National Security Council of Brazil, forbade any foreign company from owning an energy source in a border zone. What was more, the projected extremely powerful plant (the number of megawatts was not the problem) challenged the monopoly of the state-owned company, Electrobras. The subject was causing great controversy in Brasília, in spite of all the contacts Klimrod had there. Even if some agreement seemed possible, Tarras saw, in this kind of difficulty, early signs pointing to the fact that sooner or later Reb was going to have to come face to face with the Brazilian state, which had remained indifferent so far.

And, therefore, that the time was getting short, for himself and his team.

To make Elias Weizmann talk was part of the plan for the preparation of his file. The Weizmanns were, with a fervor that could move mountains, in the process of traveling all over the world, filling the quotas from misery and horror. Elias was just now returning from Asia, where he had recruited South Vietnamese and Cambodians expelled by the Tonkinese annexation; before that, he had been in India, Afghanistan, Pakistan, and the Philippines. Ethel, meanwhile, was in Africa, drawing from the enormous reservoir of displaced, harassed, or martyrized people in Ruanda, Ethiopia, Guinea-Bissau, Uganda, Angola, and other countries. The choice was great, unfortunately.

The result was that, in the most extraordinarily discreet fashion, thanks to Reb's planes and ships, the parts of Amazonia where he had planned his Kingdom were beginning to look like a gigantic international refuge.

And since one had to look at things with the cold, lucid, detached gaze of a lawyer, it was a solid argument in their favor that the country they were trying to establish was the one, the only one, really, where all races, all cultures, and all hatreds could be forgotten as soon as one arrived there.

It was, of course, a dream, but on certain days, he believed in it. . . .

"You know Ethel," said Weizmann. "I don't quite know how to say this, or even who to say it to, but Ethel and I are bothered by something, an idea we have had. . . ."

"Yes," said Tarras, having already guessed what he was about to say, and feeling embarrassed in advance.

"We were wondering," continued Weizmann, not without some hesitation, "if we were not being used, and if all of these people we are recruiting and sending to Amazonia are not being used, as a pretext . . ."

He smiled timidly.

"Forgive me, but experience has shown us that generosity rarely exists without its counterpart. And in the case of Amazonia, it is so enormous that we cannot help but wonder."

"Have you told David Settiniaz about your misgivings?"

"Five months ago, right before my departure for Asia. Ethel was with me."

"And what did he say?"

Weizmann said, in a happier tone of voice: "I have always considered David Settiniaz to be the straightest man I know. . . . Speaking of that, have you noticed that one is always ready to consider as an imbecile someone who is completely devoid of agressiveness? Well, Settiniaz let us go on until the end of our remarks. After which, he exploded in a rage. That is to say, he raised one eyebrow, got up, walked around his desk, and sat down again. After which he assured us that our fears were unfounded, and he gave us his word on this."

"And you want me to give you a similar assurance," said Tarras, knowing already that whatever he could tell them would not be sufficient.

"Tarras, Ethel and I are running a kind of quasi-secret organization, through which we have, over the years, sent to Ilha Dourada, Verdinho, and Diamantina more than one hundred and fifty thousand men, women, and children. From all parts of the world. And each year we are responsible for twenty-five to thirty thousand new migrants. This is 1977, and in three years there will be in that territory more than three hundred thousand human beings, who, in one way or another, will depend on one of the hundred or more companies that, together, run—how shall I put it—the zone in question. These companies operate in a concerted, harmonious manner that is quite surprising, and proves that there is behind all of this a rather remarkable co-ordination. With the precise goal . . . No, wait, let me finish . . . At first, Ethel and I thought that they were looking for inexpensive labor. But that didn't make any sense: they could have turned to the immense Brazilian reservoir: there are millions of men looking for good work, or any work at all. And then we looked a little closer. These people we have taken the responsibility to recruit are, on their arrival, extraordinarily well received: given housing, work, a cultural environment. To a certain extent, it's the Promised Land.

"And it's too good to be true."

"There is that. It is as if someone, or, rather, some people— it does not seem possible that one man alone could have the means, financially or even intellectually, to conceive so monumental a project—that some people, then, are trying to create a country. By bringing in refugees. And by presenting Brazil and the rest of the world with a *fait accompli*, the refugees become hostages, in a way. . . . And it is not only Brazil. Some of the companies that employ us own land in Colombia, in Venezuela, and in Guyana. That is not all. We have discovered that our

447

migrants are given no other document than the famous green working card that entitles them to benefit from the advantages of the territory. Nothing else. No passport or identification papers. You know what that means: in the eyes of the Brazilian, Venezuelan, Colombian, and Guyanese authorities, our people are illegal immigrants.

"Israel was created the same way."

"My name is Weizmann; I know how Israel was founded. But the illegal immigrants of Israel were Israelites; they had religion as a bond, not to speak of a common language, traditions going back thousands of years, and a great shared dream. Our migrants have nothing else in common but the fact that they were all thrown out of their countries of origin."

"It could be worse."

"Tarras, American, Brazilian, and French journalists, among others, have come to see us, Ethel and me. They smell something. They have asked us questions, which we avoided as best we could. Because we made a pact with Reb to be discreet. But I can't promise how long we will hold out. The whole thing is taking on gigantic proportions! Just think about this. One of my colleagues, a Dane by the name of Nielssen, is actually in Beirut; he is in charge of Lebanon and Syria, where he is recruiting five thousand Palestinians, just as I have recruited South Vietnamese and Cambodians. Can you imagine the effect of a newspaper headline like 'An American Jew sends five thousand Palestinians to Amazonia?' Can you imagine?"

"They would first have to establish some connection between Nielssen and you."

"I have followed the instructions of the formidable Marnie Oakes. In principle, the secret will be kept. But the fact is, Tarras, that we are forced to act as spies. The twenty or thirty foundations that finance us, the forty shipping companies that lend us their ships, the airlines that provide planes for us, any of the companies in Singapore, Hong Kong, Bangkok, Liberia, the Cayman Islands, the Bahamas, Liechtenstein who always intervene at the right moment, the hotel chains that put us up, the banks that issue us credit on the spot—it's all too much. . . . Why do men as different as this incredibly wealthy Chinese in Hong Kong, this Roger Dunn, this Lebanese named Nessim Shahadzé, the Petridis brothers, who seem to be richer than

Niarchos, this Soubise, who was a minister in his country, these Swiss bankers in Zurich, this Argentine multimillionaire by the name of Rochas, to mention just a few—why do they all help us with such self-sacrifice, with such prodigious co-ordination? What kind of an international plot is this? It's unbelievable! Three weeks ago, I was in Hanoi, and I was contacted by a Russian from the embassy there. The Vietnamese government was causing me difficulties, making it hard for me to go to Saigon, I mean Ho Chi Minh City. Well! My high-ranking Russian, within ten seconds flat, had everything arranged. Ethel tells me that Del Hathaway, who heads seven or eight mining companies, is a personal friend of the governor of California, who will perhaps someday become president of the United States. And Ethel also tells me that Hathaway is regularly visited by planes full of senators."

The small, frail Weizmann shook his head.

"And you think we don't wonder?"

Tarras was thinking: This was bound to happen sooner or later.

He mumbled: "In other words, Settiniaz didn't convince you."

"We don't for one second doubt his honesty. But perhaps he is being manipulated, as we are."

"And as I might be, right?"

Weizmann looked upset.

"I am really sorry, but it has gone too far. A simple assurance, even coming from Settiniaz and you, would no longer be enough. I wanted to tell you myself, before Ethel. She is sometimes more excessive in her remarks."

Tarras took the time to count to ten, just to convince himself that he had taken the proper time to make his decision.

"Give me two days.

"Ethel will be in New York tomorrow morning. She called me yesterday from Nairobi. You can be sure that she will be arriving with her fists clenched, ready for a fight. She is capable of exploding in front of journalists. Once, she slapped a secretary-general of the United Nations because he kept answering 'money' and 'national sovereignty' while she was talking about children who were dying."

"Two days," said Tarras. "Can you keep her quiet until the day after tomorrow?"

449

He got the icy but very efficient Marnie Oakes on the line and said to her: "I would like to speak with him. It's urgent."

"I will transmit your message," said Marnie. "He will call you tomorrow morning at the latest."

"It's a matter of hours."

There was a short silence.

"Where are you?"

"New York, Algonquin Hotel."

"Go to East Fifty-eighth Street. No name over the telephone but you know whom I mean."

David Settiniaz.

"Yes," said Tarras. "Thank you."

He hung up. In spite of the sort of excitement he felt, knowing something important was about to take place, he was having fun, like the good old kid he was. He walked to the East Fifty-eighth Street office. By coincidence, one of the Black Dogs, Lerner, was in Settiniaz's office that day. Tarras waited outside. The offices, set up twenty-six years earlier, had grown enormously and had changed; they now took up several floors. And the most sacred thing of all, the computer, was better protected than the White House (here, there were no visits). About it Tarras only knew that, behind an incredible barrage of access codes, was the complete and exhaustive list of the King's fifteen or sixteen hundred companies. And probably also, he thought, an incredibly detailed curriculum vitae, mentioning the advent of my very first wisdom tooth. Lerner left, without a glance at Tarras.

"I didn't even know you were in New York," said David, who seemed to be in a very bad mood, which was surprising with him.

Tarras had asked Reb whether he should inform Settiniaz of the existence of the special task force on Madison Avenue. Reb had not hesitated in his answer.

"Not yet, Georges, please. I told you that I had not yet decided. Therefore, I do not know myself whether your project will have a next step. No point in preoccupying David with something that might never take place.

"I am aging a little too rapidly in Maine," answered Tarras, once again embarrassed by the lies Reb forced him to tell. And to David, of all people.

450

The telephone rang. Settiniaz answered, listened, seemed surprised. He hung up.

"It's as if the mysterious Jethro has started spying on us again," he said, bitterly. "Georges, I have just been informed that a radio communication will be transmitted here in four minutes precisely. And it's you he wishes to speak with. Only you."

Tarras desperately tried to think of some appropriate rejoinder, but he could not come up with one.

"Come," said Settiniaz. In his office, hidden behind a regular door, which had to be unlocked with a special key, was a little elevator. They entered it. It could make only two stops besides its starting point in the office: a room inside the computer-system department, which was two normal floors above, and, at the very top of the building, what appeared to be an apartment. Empty.

"Here," said Settiniaz.

He pointed to an obviously soundproof room, which was full of equipment. Tarras walked in.

"When this red light flashes, press down this lever. He will be on the line. Talk into this microphone. When your conversation is finished, reverse the lever. To get out of here, you take the elevator; everything is precoded; you can end up only in my office. However, if you wish to leave without seeing me, use the service door. Don't worry about closing it behind you; it closes by itself; the outside handles and locks are fake. It can be opened only from inside, or by electronic signals, which I'm sure you don't give a hoot about. I'll leave you now, since it's with you only that he wishes to speak."

"David, is something wrong?

"You have seventy seconds before he calls."

Settiniaz left, his face muscles tight. Tarras heard the noise of the little elevator, then nothing.

The red light started flashing.

"Reb?"

"Yes, Georges. I am listening."

Tarras thought: He's in his giant helicopter, somewhere over the jungle or over this one. He began to summarize his conversation with Elias Weizmann and to point out the possible dangers that the effervescent Ethel might present.

There was silence.

"Reb?"

451

"I heard what you said, Georges," said the voice, so calm, so distant, in every sense of that word.

"All right. I will take care of Ethel and Elias."

"Time is running out."

"I know. Thank you for calling."

Tarras hesitated, then said: "Something is wrong with David. Did you two have an argument?"

"In a way. That has nothing to do with you, Georges; you are in no way involved. Neither you nor what you might be working on. How are things going?"

"They're coming along."

"When do you expect to be ready?"

Tarras's heart did a somersault. This was the first time since June of the previous year that Reb had spoken of the work of the Madison Avenue task force as a project that was really going to see the light of day.

"A few months," said Tarras. "Six or eight."

"You have more time than that. At least two years. And you are, naturally, taking into account, in your files, the 'international refuge' aspect, without any consideration of race, religion, or political leanings?"

"That was the very reason for my meeting with Elias. As you asked me to, I am following his work and Ethel's closely, as well as the work of their respective teams. It's enormous, Reb." Tarras hesitated. "and I know . . . I know that it is not some kind of alibi."

After a pause Reb uttered this amazing, sentence, which was unbelievable because it permitted one to suspect, in the formidable mind of the King, an inconceivable fissure: "In that case, you know more than I do. . . . "

After that, only the noises of the rotors of the Sikorsky, nearly five thousand miles away, could still be heard. Had it not been for the red light, which was still on, Terras would have thought that the contact had been broken.

But Reb finally said: "There is one more element I would like included in the file: the survival of Amazonia. This is not only a Brazilian problem, or that of one of the bordering nations. Amazonia is the lung of the planet Earth, Georges, practically the only one it has left. Get part of your team to work on that, in that direction, please. Let them think of something like what

452

is being done for the Poles, for whom there has been almost international co-operation."

"Without attacking the Brazilians."

"Of course. They are doing what they can, and no other country in their position would do any better. But look into all the possibilities of . . . international independence, in the interest of the generations to come. Even if it means compensating those nations which the hazards of history of colonization have made the official—the legitimate, in your sense of the word—owners of these territories."

"I understand," said Tarras.

The kind of lassitude that could be heard in Reb's voice worried him. He said: "You mentioned two years."

"Probably a little more than that."

"You have made a decision, haven't you?"

"Almost."

"And you already have a date in mind?"

"Yes."

This time it was Tarras who waited a few moments, before asking: "Do you want me to take care of anything else? For example, of how it could take place, on the given day?"

"That will not be necessary. Thank you, Georges."

"You will need maximum exposure."

"I think I have already found it," answered Reb.

10

Settiniaz remembers:

"In the light of what happened after that, I feel bad, naturally. But this is what happened: 1977 and 1978 were the years when what you might call my opposition to Reb was at its peak. In January of 1977, I went to Amazonia, one month before Tarras, as it turned out. But I knew nothing about Georges's trip; he told me about it only much later. In fact, at the time, I did not have the slightest knowledge of what was being concocted in the Madison Avenue office, and I was under the impression that Tarras had more or less retired. His name no longer appeared in any of the operations conducted by Nick and Tony Petridis, and the only mentions of his name were in connection with these foundations into which Roger Dunn and others, such as the Californian Jubal Wynn, who was Tudor Anghel's successor, poured nearly all of the profits of their respective companies."

"As for Ethel and Elias Weizmann, I remember their visit, of course. Their questions infuriated me. But not for the reason they believed. They thought I was reacting out of indignation at the idea that they doubted Reb's sincerity. . . .

"By the way, they came back to see me about five months later and told me that they had met with Reb and that he had 'straightened everything out.' I didn't ask them anything, but just by the way they were looking at me, looking at my office, I understood that Reb had probably told them everything about himself and my organization. In any event, they never caused any more problems, until the end, and actually became King's Men at that time, sharing in the secret as much as Tarras and I did.

"But they were mistaken about the reasons for my anger. I had other reasons for being furious, far more serious ones than a simple case of indignation.

"The trip I made in January of 1977 had no other purpose than to try to set things straight between Reb and myself."

"I have all the figures, Reb. These withdrawals you have been making during the last few years are putting most of your companies in jeopardy. My assistants and I are forced to perform the most extravagant acrobatics."

"The work you are doing is remarkable in every way, David."

"I did not come here to be flattered. Nick was in my office three days ago. He does not have one single dollar left in liquid assets in the Liberian and Panamanian companies, which are in debt up to their ears. Roger Dunn told me the same thing the week before that. And Wynn, who in no way measures up to Tudor Anghel, is having serious problems in California. Nessim is not one to complain, but you just have to follow the course of his transactions in the financial markets to see that he is short of supplies. If it were not for his operations with the Soviets and the Middle Eastern countries, he would almost be out of work. Ditto for Paul Soubise and Santana, who is in a panic because of the risks you forced him to take in Dallas. Even Hang is affected: his last operation with the Chinese in Peking was concluded with a loss, and, since Hang is not fool, I assumed he did so on your instructions, with the sole purpose of furnishing you with some fresh cash. Am I wrong?"

"No."

"If it wasn't for the capital that comes from the casinos, your two hundred and some hotels would have gone bankrupt two years ago; you drew too much from them without giving them the chance to pay off. Ethel Court is not one to complain either, but she is extremely concerned and is wondering what you are up to. In any case, even the gambling money will end up not being sufficient. Within a year, or less, there won't be enough. The only banks from which you have not borrowed are your own. There are currently twelve outstanding loans, and those establishments are not going to give you anything for free."

An hour before, the huge Sikorsky had dropped Settiniaz off on the bank of a large river whose waters were almost black. The Shamatari, among whom Reb towered like a giant, didn't even look up as the giant apparatus appeared. The Indians were setting up an encampment, and Settiniaz, who was panicked by the jungle to the point of feeling physically ill, wondered how, admidst this green ocean, Ubaldo Rocha had been able to find Klimrod.

"We are going to have lunch," said Reb.

His eyes searched Settiniaz's face.

"Will you eat with us, David? Don't feel that you have to. My friends would not be shocked if you shared the pilots' sandwiches."

"What's good enough for you is good enough for me," snapped Settiniaz. "And I can offer my resignation whenever you like."

"We will discuss it later, David."

His voice had its usual courteous calm, which was sometimes so exasperating, as it was at this moment.

Settiniaz had not been paying attention to the preparations for the meal. The Indians had shaken some of the trees, and several caterpillars had fallen out, or had been directly picked out. Then the Indians opened them up with a flick of a nail or a tooth and set them to boil inside leaves.

"David, I have asked too much of you, and I hope you will find it in your heart to forgive me. These last few years, I have not made things easy for you. Let's tackle the immediate problems. Make all the arrangements to have Jaua go public. That should bring close to two billion dollars. . . . These worms are called *mana*. Taste them. They're very sweet and nourishing. You'll see.

Settiniaz was almost speechless with anger. But he recovered quickly enough, thinking: This is sheer madness. Here I am, in the heart of the jungle, discussing billion-dollar transactions with a naked man who is making me eat caterpillars?

"Sell everything?"

"If you want, David. Or just put some of the companies on the market. Whatever you need to balance the books."

"There are more than three hundred companies linked to Jaua."

"Would you like me to list them for you?" Reb asked quietly.

Settiniaz felt his anger growing, and he was not used to such violent feelings. He attributed it to the environment, which was so unfamiliar.

"Reb, you have spent more than six billion dollars . . . on this
. . ."

He gestured toward the Indians, the clearing, the Sikorsky, and the whole world created in the heart of Amazonia.

"Go on, David."

"What is your goal? You told me, one day, that you had Ubaldo Rocha buy the first pieces of land so that the Indians would be their own landowners. Do you remember?"

"I never forget anything, and you know it," said the soft voice.

"I know: you are infallible. But on this land, which you supposedly bought for your Indian friends, you ravaged the forest, tore down the trees. You have destroyed the natural habitat of these people you claim you want to protect."

The gray gaze was on him, totally inscrutable. But Settiniaz was now possessed by real rage. He went on:

"The president of the Foundation for the Indians is a certain General Bandeira de Melo, or was; I don't remember. Anyway, he is, or was, the man officially in charge of 'respecting the Indian people and their institutions, and to guarantee them,' I am still

456

quoting, 'the exclusive possession of their land and their natural resources.' Am I mistaken?"

"You are not mistaken."

"One of his statements was translated for me, and I am quoting, precisely: 'Any assistance given to the Indians cannot stand in the way of national development.' Do you remember that sentence, Reb?"

"Yes."

"You could have said it yourself. But in your mouth, the words would have been a little different. You would have said, for example: 'Any friendship or love I might have for the Indians cannot stand in the way of the development of the country that I am creating or that I have already created.' "

There was no reaction. Reb simply did not move; he was sitting on his heels, his large hands hanging down, open, and he kept looking at Settiniaz without really seeming to see him. Around the two men, the Indians were speaking, in their own language, and laughing. Some women went to swim in the river; they lay down in the low water and laughed sharply. Some of them were young and, even to Settiniaz, their bodies were beautiful, naked and smooth; the pink lips between their legs were clearly exposed. Trajano da Silva had told Settiniaz that, even in their coupling, the Indians had singular habits: having penetrated the woman, the man would remain still, refraining from the slightest thrust or back-and forth movement; the rest was up to the woman, by slow internal movements, invisible movements, taught to girls before puberty, so that the act of love, beginning at dusk, should not, ideally, end until dawn.

"I don't wish to take back anything I have said," Settiniaz said in a hollow voice.

"Since that is what you believe."

"It is."

"That is your right, David."

"Just as I believe that what you are doing here in Amazonia has no common sense. Lord, I began working for you in 1951, twenty-six years ago, without ever remembering having agreed to do so. I was carried away, and for more than a quarter of a century I have been doing nothing more than trying to keep my head above water. You are probably a genius; perhaps you see things differently from the way I do. But I am just an ordinary man. I am tired. I am fifty-four years old. To follow you in all things, one needs simple blind faith. Georges Tarras can do it. I can't. I can't do it. I need to understand. You have built an unimaginable fortune, without ever showing your face, and I have helped you do it, however much I could. I am a rich man today, richer than I ever dreamed of being. But I don't understand what is happening now or where you want to go. I have tried to like you, and at times I thought I had succeeded. Now, I don't know. I don't know whether I want to resign or not."

"I would rather you did not," said Reb very softly.

"If I did, everything would be in order. I have made arrangements so that there would be no interruptions in the work. Should I die or leave, your affairs would not be affected in any way. This monstrous machine that you have built . . . "

"We built it together, David."

"Perhaps, yes. Perhaps in a minuscule way, I did play a part in it. But it would keep running in any case. I am even convinced that it would keep running without you."

No answer. And it was this silence, which he took for indifference, that hurt Settiniaz the most. What did I expect? he thought. He is incapable of feeling any human emotion, and, as the years go by, he is becoming a little crazy.

It is true that in 1977, and even before that, he had organized his task force on East Fifty-eighth Street in such a way that it could operate without him. His natural prudence and his attention to detail, his straightforwardness and, whatever he may have thought of them, his exceptional qualities as an organizer had led him, since the beginning, in the nineteen-fifties, to take precautions such as this. He had gone as far as instituting in his own offices the system of airtight companies that had been so successfully developed by Klimrod. He had divided the King's affairs into eight departments, independent of one another, and only the computer's memory could link them together. It was he who had suggested to Reb, in 1952, the storing, in a very secure place, of all the important documents, especially the innumerable trust agreements. Reb had bought a small bank in Colorado, which offered the advantage of having a vault that was as well guarded by nature as the command post of the Strategic Air Command. And, as a backup, he had suggested that Reb follow this security measure with another one—"which even I should know nothing about, Reb." So, somewhere in the world, perhaps in Switzerland, in Töpfler's territory, or in London, under Nessim's guard, or even in Hong Kong, in Hang's domain, or even in all of these places, there existed one or several copies of the documents that were stored in the Rockies, thirteen hundred feet below ground.

During his 1977 meeting with Klimrod, Settiniaz had the announcement of his resignation at the tip of his tongue.

But he did not reach the end of his anger, or of his resentment. So he didn't say anything.

Back in New York, he set about carrying out, with his usual efficiency, Reb's orders concerning the Jaua and its incomprehensible (incomprehensible to anyone other than Reb Klimrod and himself) network of subsidiary companies.

In perfect agreement with Ernie Gozchiniak, whom Reb had contacted in the meantime, he put the group of companies into a holding company. This being done, he requested an appraisal by an auditor. For this, he chose one of the most reputable and trustworthy firms. Following the appraisal, a price for the shares of this huge limited company was decided on. The Securities Exchange Commission gave its approval, and one of New York's prestigious banks put them on the market. It was one of the big events of the fiscal year. And even though Settiniaz made sure to keep for Reb, through Gozchiniak, fifty-one percent of the shares, it still managed to net at least one billion nine hundred and forty-three million dollars.

Enough to restabilize, more or less, the majority of the King's business accounts.

Actually, it was more like a respite. The withdrawals that Klimrod kept making, the enormous repayments of outstanding bank loans, already foretold that this respite would last only a short time. This did not appease Settiniaz, whose worries were more than just financial. In his eyes, nothing was settled in the conflict that existed between him and Reb. The Amazonian affair still seemed to him like a bottomless abyss, into which, sooner or later, everything would disappear, unless Brazil and the other countries nearby called a stop and forbade these investments, discounting the excuse of helping the Indians, of whom Reb claimed to be the defender. As far as Settiniaz was concerned, there was megalomania in this, and a megalomania all the more unbearable because the King didn't make any effort to explain himself.

"Not even to me, who ran all of his affairs for so many years. Only through the press, and in 1978, did I learn about those giant paper-plant units that came all the way from Japan to the mouth of the Amazon, at the cost of an incredible round-the world trip. And I was the one who, later on, had to come face to face with the banks to pay for these follies!

"Actually, I thought that was the only reason I stayed on: the situation, month after month, was becoming so complex and difficult that I felt, rightly or wrongly, that the men I had prepared for my succession could not have handled it. Some pretext. . . ."

David Settiniaz remained in this uncertainty, about himself and about his feelings toward the King, until the spring of 1980.

11

What Diego Haas calls "the King's round of farewells," and the adventures thereof, which were eventually told to Georges Tarras, took place in 1979.

Coming as a complement to the confidences made to Tarras and Settiniaz by the King himself, it later helped the two men to piece together Reb Michael Klimrod's itinerary from the time of his birth, in Vienna, to April of 1980, with a few inevitable and understandable blank spots.

Reb did not follow any chronological order. He did not really go back through time. Apparently, he simply felt the need—at this time of his life when, according to Georges Tarras, he had made a decision about the end of his adventure—to go back to certain episodes of his past, haphazardly, wherever his memories or his travels took him.

In 1979, Henri Haardt was still alive and ran, in the French West Indies, a small company that chartered yachts and crews to tourists who wanted to cruise in the Caribbean.

He smiled at Diego and said: "This was one of my great regrets. If this sinister individual"—he was pointing at Reb—"had wanted to stay and work with me, we could have made a colossal fortune together."

"Smuggling cigarettes?" asked Reb, who was also smiling. The conversation was in French, which Diego understood better by then, but not as well as he would have liked.

"Absolutely: cigarettes. There was a tremendous amount of money to be made. And, actually, I made it. At one point I had made as much as one billion francs. Which I managed to lose soon after."

"And my presence would have changed that?"

"I am absolutely sure of it," continued Haardt, who turned to Diego. "He had what I never did: a good head on his shoulders, as young as he was. And what a head!"

"*Que sorpresa!*" said Diego. "I am *mucho mucho* surprised."

The Frenchman looked at Reb's old cotton pants and worn T-shirt.

"It's funny, you know," he said, "I would have sworn that you would become somebody, somebody well known."

"I know him," said Diego, in English. "And I know someone who knows him also. A guy who sells hamburgers in Greenwich Village. He is one of Reb's fans; he never lets us pay."

Haardt laughed. That was not what he meant, he said. He invited the two visitors to dinner. He was married and was a grandfather five times over, and his business was going all right, even though it was not marvelous. The banks hated him, for some obscure reasons having to do with mortgages and loans. But he liked the life he was leading, which was the life he had always led; he liked to live near the sea, and, thanks be to God, aside from the banks, he could see himself growing older not too unhappily. He raised his glass of Creole punch.

"Let's drink to the losers, which we are, and which we don't mind being."

Some time later, Haardt had as a client a rich French tourist named Paul Soubise, who was known as "Mr. President," from his service as a minister in Paris. Chance had it that this Soubise fellow had some interests in the bank that hated the former cigarette smuggler from Tangiers the most.

"And you will laugh, sir," said Haardt later on, to Georges Tarras, whose foundation had just signed a very juicy contract with the Frenchman's company, to take some children on a cruise. "But I even thought that there might be some connection between this Reb Klimrod, whom you say you know a little, and this Soubise fellow, who was so generous to me."

"You are right. I will laugh," answered Tarras, unruffled.

In Jerusalem, they spent three or four days in the rather modest apartment belonging to Yoël Bainish, who, although he did not wear a tie, was nevertheless a delegate to the Knesset and was about to become Secretary of State.

Bainish asked Reb: "You spent the last few days in Tangiers?"

"He dragged me into these markets that smell of mint," said Diego. "We even visited his former palace, which measures ten feet by ten, on Riad Sultan Street in the Casbah. I know now where he learned his Spanish, on es-Siaghin Street, with a hidalgo from northern Castile, who is dead today, and I even put my rounded buttocks in the chair of the Café de Paris where he once drank some tea. It really moved me, *Madre de Dios*. We even went as far as the Malabata lighthouse."

Diego knew Bainish well, or at least he claims he did, before he went to Jerusalem in 1979. But he always refused to tell Tarras the date, place, or circumstances of their supposed meeting. Settiniaz knew little about Bainish, and Tarras even less. The New Yorker is convinced that Bainish always knew what Klimrod was doing and why, where, and how he was doing it; he believes that there was a continuing relationship between the two men, in regard to, for example, Jethro's setup. Bainish, expert in such matters, could very well have helped to create it. And in the mysterious message of 1956 that alerted Reb to the imminent attack on the Suez Canal, he sees unquestionable proof of the existence of this relationship.

In Israel, Reb found some of the old traces of the 1945–46 days, and, even more surprising, an Irishman from Ulster by the name of Parnell, James Parnell, who had, thirty-three years earlier, served in the British Army in Palestine. It was Parnell now a journalist, who told Diego, in front of an amused Reb, about the attack on a police station in Yagur, on March 1, 1946. For some reason that no one bothered to explain to Diego, Parnell and Bainish had remained in contact during all these years.

"I would have recognized you even without Yoël," said Parnell.

He raised his index and middle fingers and pointed them toward his face.

"The eyes. I really believe they terrified me even more than those explosives you were supposedly carrying. Were you bluffing, or were there really forty pounds of TNT in those bags?"

"Sixty pounds," said Reb. "Very real."

"Were you really ready to blow us all up?"

"What do you think?"

Parnell met the strange gray gaze.

"In my opinion, yes, " he said.

They all went to have lunch at Saint John of Acre, on Han-el-Amdan Square. That afternoon, Reb and Diego left for Rome.

In Italy, they followed the old trail of the Franciscan monasteries, through which Erich Steyr had passed, along with other Nazis who were fleeing Europe. They spent one night in Rome. With Diego driving a rented car, they took two days to reach the Reschen Pass, during which Reb told the amazing story of the 412th Royal Transport Company, and Diego laughed.

But as soon as they reached Austria, Reb's mood changed. He locked himself in an almost total silence, coming out of it only to give road directions.

"And, in thirty-four years, you have never returned to Austria?"

"No."

"Shit, it was still your country."

No answer. Diego was thinking: A country that managed to kill his mother and his sisters and, especially, his father, and almost killed him. That sort of country can be forgotten. And, for Reb Klimrod, what is a country? But, still, thirty-four years . . .

They walked through Salzburg for an entire day, and Reb began to speak again, about the places they were seeing, although his voice was more distant than usual, as if he were only talking to himself. He told the whole story, starting from his arrival in the city to Epke's death, and Lothar's, the photographer of Hartheim Castle.

They made no stop or visit there, and they also by-passed Linz and Mauthausen.

Everything that Reb Klimrod did between the time of his first departure from the camp for displaced persons in Leonding until his departure for Palestine with Yoël Baïnish, everything concerning the eager search for this father and the discovery of what had happened to him, is known only through the combined testimonies of Settiniaz, Tarras, and Haas. The Salzburg episode comes mainly from Haas, the information about Hartheim castle from Settiniaz, who also supplied the story about the June 19, 1945, dawn visit to Johann Klimrod's home, and it was Tarras in whom Reb confided the story of the hunt for Steyr in Austria.

From Salzburg, they went straight to Vienna, to a lovely townhouse. Diego stopped.

"What do we do now?"

"Nothing."

Diego turned off the engine. Reb did not move. He was looking at the impressive entrance, but did not make the slightest gesture.

Diego asked: "The house where you were born?"

"Yes."

At that very moment some children came out, one with a radio pressed to his ear.

"You don't want to go in?"

"No."

But Reb had turned, his eyes following the children, who were walking toward the Bohemian Chancellory. There were two of them, a boy and a girl, between twelve and fifteen years of age. They could be Reb's children, thought Diego suddenly, with a flash of intuition. It distressed him greatly.

Silence. Reb turned to face the windshield.

"Start the car. We are leaving," he said in a low hoarse voice.

The next stop was a place called Reichenau, after a detour in Vienna to go through Schenkengasse—"there used to be a bookstore here." Reichenau was hardly even a village. Reb wanted to go to an isolated farm. He asked about a woman. The couple living there had only a vague recollection of her. "Emma Donin," said Reb. They said she had died a long time ago. Reb insisted.

"There were three children with her, three little boys with blond hair and blue eyes, who would be thirty-five or forty years old now."

They shook their heads; they knew nothing about Emma Donin and the children of 1945.

The same questions asked throughout the village brought the same answers: the late Emma Donin had not been very popular.

And there had been a procession of children staying with her during and after the war.

Reb returned to the car, sat down, and spread his large bony hands on his knees. He lowered his head.

"Let's go, Diego."

They made a short stop farther south, in Payerbach. There was a family there by the name of Doppler. Reb spoke of an old man with a wheelbarrow, who had been his friend, many years ago, and who had even invited him to dinner at his home.

No, none of the Dopplers remembered him. The grandfather, yes, of course, but not Reb Klimrod.

"You should have spoken with Gunther and his sister, who were here at the time. But they don't live in Austria any more. They are in Brazil, in Rio, making a fortune with a chain of Austrian pastry shops. If you are ever in Rio . . . "

And then, the last Austrian stop.

The man was in his forties and was the head of the Austrian equivalent of a law firm. His name was Keller and, as they had agreed over the telephone, he waited for them at Bad-Ischl. He climbed into the car driven by Diego and they drove away.

He stared at Reb curiously.

"My father told me that he had met you once, in 1947 or 1948. . . ."

"Nineteen-forty-seven," said Reb. "March 24, 1947."

Keller smiled.

"My memory must be going. Or my father's. I was only four years old at the time. But my father remembered you very well. When he died, six years ago, he made a point of telling me to satisfy any demands that might come from you scrupulously. I must admit, you intrigue me. A thirty-two-year relationship, that is really something."

Reb smiled, his only answer.

They reached Altaussee and stopped in front of the Parkhotel. Keller got out.

"This will take about two hours," said Reb. "Of course, you will be my guest for lunch. It means a great deal to me, please."

"Take your time and do not worry about me," answered Keller.

The car drove off, this time in the direction of the little village of Grundlsee. They could see a lake among the dark mountains that bore the somber name Dead Mountains.

"We're going on foot now, Diego."

465

"A dream come true."

They did more than walk; they climbed. There came a time when the little Argentine, who hated nothing more than physical exercise, and especially mountain climbing, collapsed, out of breath, and out of energy. He watched Reb continue to climb, in his Indian manner, stopping every so often, as if he were trying to locate an old trail, then going on again, helped by his prodigious memory. He reached a kind of rock overhang. There, he got down on his knees and began searching the rocky ground. He finally stood up, and remained still, looking at the black lake almost vertically below him.

Ten minutes later, he rejoined Diego. He seemed to be holding something in his hand, and guessed his companion's curiosity. He opened it, revealing, on his palm, rusted cartridges of a Colt .45.

"And what is the name of this charming place?" asked Diego.
"Toplitz."

They were back in Altaussee in time to have lunch with Keller. He was, in his spare time, a collector of clocks and spoke about them during the entire meal. It was only afterward that they went to the cemetery. The grave, covered with fresh flowers, was off to the side. The markers, of black marble, had no cross or other sign, and bore no inscription but the letters *D. L.*

"I suppose," said Keller rather timidly, "that there would no point in asking you the name of this individual you have been watching over, from a distance, for thirty-two years?"

He was of average height. The gray eyes fell down on him, opened wide and full of poignant sadness.

"What for?" answered Klimrod. "I am the only one who remembers him."

Before returning to South America, they went to Aix-en-Provence, where Reb visited another grave, that of Suzanne Settiniaz; then to Paris, where they met with a Frenchman by the name of Jacques Mayziel, who, from what Diego could understand, had known Reb in Lyon, a long time ago. Reb and Mayziel spoke of a certain Bunim Anielewitch, whom Diego remembered as the sadeyed man he had questioned as to his fluency in Lapp in a café on the Place de la Nation in 1951, just before Reb left to go share some zakuska with Joseph Stalin.

466

Only then did they take a plane that would carry them to the other hemisphere.

They went to Argentina, to Buenos Aires, where Mamita, whose name was Maria-Ignacia Haas de Carbajal, had died ten years before, in despair at never having had any official grandchildren, "and poor Mamita never wanted to recognize the existence of my nine natural children, from my so-called morganatic marriages. When I wanted to have her meet three or four of them, to make her happy, she slammed the door in our faces."

In Buenos Aires, they went to Calle Florida, to the Almeiras Gallery. Old Arcadio had also died, a long time ago, but his granddaughter looked at the Kandinsky with complete amazement.

"You want to what?"

"To give it to you," said Diego, in his most charming manner. "And I am only a messenger, so don't thank me. You see, thirty years ago, or more, your grandfather behaved like a real hidalgo. And the person whom I represent is one of those rare people who never forget anything. And by the way, are you free for dinner?"

She was.

He asked Reb: "And now?"

"Zbi, in Florida, a few others in New York, Chicago, Montreal, and the Anghels, in California, and that will be it."

An icy shiver went throught Diego.

"And then, Reb?"

"The end, Diego."

This was in November of 1979.

12

"My name is Arnold Balm," said the man to Georges Tarras. "It was I who called you this morning from New York, and two hours ago from Bangor."

467

He looked around and said: "You like red, don't you?"

"The bathrooms are white," answered Tarras, thinking: We must sound like two spys exchanging idiotic code sentences.

He asked his visitor: "Would you like some tea? I also have some muffins, which were just baked, since it's Friday. I have my mufffins delivered Mondays, Wednesdays and Fridays."

"With pleasure," answered Balm. "To tell you the truth, I am completely frozen."

Through the narrow window of the study, he glanced out at the Atlantic, beyond Blue Hill Bay, and shuddered.

"Where I come from," he said, "if the sea turned that color, we would all get into bed and stay there until spring."

"Where do you come from?"

"Cayman Brac. But really I come from Little Cayman."

The atlas Tarras had consulted in haste after receiving Balm's telephone call had been disappointingly concise.

"It's my turn to be truthful," said Tarras, "I know remarkably little about the Cayman Islands."

"Don't excuse yourself. That is normal. We have been a crown colony since 1670, but when I appeared at the Foreign Office in London, for the first time, the official in charge looked at me suspiciously and asked: 'Are you absolutely sure that it exists and that it belongs to us?' We were, I should mention in passing, discovered by Christopher Columbus in person, in 1503."

"How impressive," said Tarras.

Balm smiled.

"Isn't it, though? To find us is rather simple. Picture Cuba to the north, the Yucatan Peninsula to the west, Honduras to the south, and Jamaica to the east. In the middle, there is a large stretch of Caribbean Sea that looks deserted. But don't believe it; we are there, right in the center. We consist of three islands: Grand Cayman, Cayman Brac and Little Cayman. Our capital is Georgetown, on Grand Cayman. There are seven thousand six hundred and seventy-seven inhabitants in Georgetown, according to last year's census, and sixteen thousand six hundred and seventy-seven in all for the three islands. The problem is that Grand Cayman is eighty-nine miles away from Little Cayman, which in turn is five miles from Cayman Brac. . . . Excellent; these muffins are truly exceptional. . . . This of course prohibits us from taking the bus into town to do some shopping.

Luckily, I have my own plane, as many do. I am a banker. Almost everyone is; we have, in our territory, five hundred and forty-two banks. Or nearly one bank for every thirty inhabitants, including small children. Our main resources are banks and turtles, fresh or dried, which we export for soup. Is there anything else you would like to know?"

"I think that was quite thorough," said Tarras, somewhat astonished.

"Oh, yes! The flag. Francisco Santana, who gave me your name and your address, told me that we had to have a national flag. This created quite a problem. We do not actually have a national flag, other than the Union Jack—or at least we did not have one last week. Very conveniently, my sister, who is, if you will, our Minister of Foreign Affairs, had an idea: she thought of taking down the thing that we have hanging in the front of our Parliament. My sister's cook copied it on her sewing machine. Here it is."

He placed a little suitcase on Tarras's desk and took from it a small piece of cloth, which he spread out.

"In heaven's name!" exclaimed Tarras. "What is that?"

"That" was a turtle in a pirate's costume, with a black eye patch and a wooden leg.

"Our national emblem," said Balm, smiling pleasantly.

"Yes, I know it seems a little peculiar, but my sister put it to the Legislative Assembly, and they all felt that this national emblem was as good as any other. Everyone except Chip Fitzsimmons. But Chip always votes 'nay,' for any reason, for any project. What's more, he is my brother-in-law, and he and my sister are probably going to get divorced."

Tarras sat down. He was torn between the imminent danger of bursting out into laughter and the foreboding, infinitely more serious, than his visitor, as pleasant and funny as he was, was going to trigger a major event, which would possibly have a tragic ending. For his next question, he nevertheless maintained the British tone of a mundane conversation.

"Some milk in your tea?"

"A spot."

But the question Tarras asked a little later was of a very different nature.

"And what exactly did you decide with Francisco Santana?"

"Mr. Santana, who is an old friend, has convinced us and assured us that you, Mr. Tarras, will help us in all matters concerning our admission, as a free and independent state, into the United Nations. All the financial problems have been taken care of, and we have no worry in that area, really no worry at all. A company for which Mr. Santana is the legal counsel, and whose headquarters are in our country, has graciously put at our disposal an entire floor of offices in Manhattan. We do not really need that much space: I will be heading the delegation, but this delegation will have no other member but myself. My schedule will not be much affected by this responsibility, since I come to New York regularly on business. Can you take care of all the necessary steps, Mr. Tarras?"

"Certainly."

"Do you think this entire procedure could possibly be ready by this coming May?"

The excitement reached Tarras.

"Yes," he said. "It's quite possible. Did Santana suggest any special date?"

"He feels very strongly about May 5, 1980," said Balm.

He was drinking his tea calmly, looking around with curiosity, his gaze lingering on the impressive stacks of books. Tarras's cup, on the other hand, was shaking so much that he had to put it down. May 5, 1980, he thought, Thirty-five years later, to the day.

He asked: "And what will take place on May 5, 1980?"

"The General Assembly will be in session that day. Representatives of some one hundred and sixty nations will probably be there, as well as observers from twenty others, including Switzerland, Rhodesia, the two Koreas, to mention the most important ones. As the representative of a new member state, I will be given time to address the floor, and also the right to propose a motion to all the delegates, who will honor me by listening to me. I will propose this motion, and then turn over part of my time to a man about whom, quite frankly, I know almost nothing."

"But you know his name, at least," remarked Tarras, his heart beating wildly.

"At least that, yes."

13

Paul Soubise had his first warning at the end of the winter of 1979–80. For some time now, he had managed to stop smoking, and was doing some exercise—without, however, going as far as masquerading about in an outfit and shoes designed for jogging through the Bois de Boulogne. But he had started walking again, which he had not done since the long-ago days when he was a French boy scout, using the absurd pseudonym "Tatou Trique-Madame," which he had chosen himself, not without some bitter discusssions with his scoutmaster, whom he had finally convinced that the Trique-Madame was just another name for white stone-crops, or houseleeks, a common plant that could be found near country urinals.

The warning had come when, deciding to build up an athlete's body, he ran up the stairs of his house in Paris's Sixteenth Arrondissement. Immediately, the pain was brutal and paroxysmic. It started below his sternum, spread to his left shoulder, toward the inside of his left arm, down through the last two fingers of his left hand. At that instant, the pain was so intense he thought he would die right then and there, on the steps, like an ass, simply for having scorned the elevator that had cost him a fortune.

His private physician, who naturally belonged to the Academy, easily diagnosed angina pectoris. He adopted a grave tone.

"It could have killed you, Paul. It is a first crisis, apparently. It stopped the way it began, and that good feeling you experienced when it was over will not happen next time. Don't ever be without Trinitrin. And you must have absolute rest."

"Can I travel?"

"You can sign up for the New York marathon, but you will be dead before you reach the midpoint of the Verrazano Bridge. Yes, you can travel. But it depends where and how."

Soubise stayed in bed for a few days and was bored to tears. He kept lifting the sheets of his bed, hoping to discover the body of a woman someone had placed there by accident. He had called, along with the members of his own task force, David Settiniaz, momentarily. He had also called Nick Petridis, in New York, and Nessim in London.

So when in April 1980, his private telephone rang, his secret phone, near his bed, whose number was known only to David, Nick, and Nessim, he was sure it would be one of them.

"Paul?"

The voice, which he had not heard for three years, the calm, soft voice, was instantly familiar to him.

"Paul," said Reb, "I just learned what happened to you. I am sincerely sorry. I'm told it was just a warning, thank goodness, and that you are in good hands. I've also been told that you can travel, though with certain precautions. Therefore, I will not ask you to travel all over the world. Since you are in France, we will see each other in France. It will be in ten days, and I would like you to be there. Will you be able to meet me?"

"Wherever you want and whenever you want."

"A plane will be waiting for you at Toussus-le-Noble, on the twenty-first of this month, at eight-thirty in the morning. Come alone, please, and without too much of a fuss."

Soubise was as French as they come. If he wasn't lacking in light-heartedness, if he would not have hesitated to imperil an old friendship for a witty remark, he had nonetheless, a quick intelligence and the knack for making rapid connections.

He affirms that he knew a world would soon tumble.

Thadeus Töpfler was in Zürich when he received the call. What's more, he was sitting in the same office where, twenty years earlier, nearly to the day, he had come to face Aloïs Knapp, after having told Brockman, with a nervous laugh: "There is downstairs, a man wearing loafers and no jacket who is presenting us a check in the amount of one billion dollars." Of that whole episode, he had a memory tainted with a bitter and sad tenderness. But there was no doubt about it: as far as he was concerned, the consequences could not have been better. His personal ascension within the hierachy of the bank, although he had always worked hard, began then. And when the time came to name a successor to Knapp, it was as if the order had fallen from the sky and into his lap.

Three men, among whom was his old enemy, now his subordinate, Othmar Brockman, were present in his office when the

472

light on his ultraprivate line began to flicker. He waited until he was alone to say, simply, after having picked up the receiver: "I am listening. I was not alone."

He listened.

He decided to make the trip by car. He was more and more afraid of flying. And the train was not sufficiently discreet.

On April 11, David Settiniaz left his office to have dinner, with the intention of returning quickly to resume his work, and probably spend a good part of the night at it. The fabulous gold operation was coming to an end, perhaps, but the fantastic windfall profits had to be closely evaluated and apportioned among the six hundred or so companies that needed cash.

The order—in every way similar to the one that had established the public offering of Jaua Food and its subsidiaries—had come almost seven months earlier. Reb had established radio contact and said: "David, I know you are once again faced with serious financial problems. I did not wait without a good reason. Put everything in place to be operational during the first days of January 1980. Same system as last time: regroup all the gold-mining companies into a holding company and get ready to put them on the market."

On several occasions, Settiniaz had expected to see Reb liquidate or make a public offering of his shares in the gold mines in the Rockies, or simply give Nessim the authorization to sell the enormous stock of gold held by the Lebanese in the King's name. In September 1969, for example, when, from thirty-five dollars an ounce, gold had jumped to forty-one. When asked, Reb had said no. He had said no again in December 1974, when, on the London market, gold had reached the amazing price of one hundred ninety-seven fifty. "No, David, we will wait." For good reason, since four years after that, in October 1978, the price went to two hundred fifty-four dollars. "We are not selling, David." "We need fresh money." "We are not selling." The vertiginous climb had continued: three hundred seventeen, seventy-five in August 1979, four hundred thirty-seven on October 2 of the same year, five hundred eight, seventy-five on December 27!

And on that date everything had been ready for two months for the holding company that had been put together. "Reb, we are ready when you are." "We are not selling, David." "In spite of the problems I am facing? They are enormous, Reb."

"Sorry, David. You will have to wait a little longer. But not much longer . . ."

And on January 18, 1980. Radio contact: "David? The time has come. Go!"

Settiniaz wanted to hear confirmed the orders he had already received, which seemed so amazing to him. It would be the first time the King relinquished part of his own holdings. "Reb, is it absolutely clear that I will be putting *every single* share on the market? You do not want to keep anything?" "Nothing, David. We are in agreement. We are selling all the gold, wherever it may be. Inform Nessim, Hang, Paul, Thadeus, Jubal in San Francisco, Jaime in Buenos Aires. Within the hour, please."

Settiniaz says: "During the thirty years I had worked for him, this was the first time he was completely, without holding on to the slightest interest, getting rid of a company he had created. Just that should have alerted me. But I was immersed in big problems. . . ."

Settiniaz's inextricable financial problems were miraculously solved on January 21 when the price of an ounce of gold reached the history-making, unbelievable level of *eight hundred and fifty* dollars.

The operation resulted in a net profit of four billion three hundred and forty-five million dollars. The King's fortune thus reached its highest peak—at the end of January 1980. Taking into account the Amazonian investments, which were by this time showing a profit (in turn being reinvested elsewhere), Settiniaz estimated the figure at seventeen billion three hundred and fifty million dollars.

Leaving his office, he stopped for a few seconds in the lobby to exchange some words with one of his assistants. Then he took just three steps.

"Settiniaz."

Someone touched his arm. He recognized Diego Haas.

"He wants to speak with you," said Diego. "Now."

Their eyes met. Diego smiled.

"Orders, Settiniaz."

Outside, double-parked, a car was waiting. Diego yelled something in Spanish to a nearby policeman, who burst out laughing. Then sat down behind the wheel and drove off, with a cold look in his eyes.

"Where is he?"

The Argentine simply nodded and pointed a finger toward the arch. He left, disappearing rapidly in the traffic.

Settiniaz began to walk down a path. He soon discovered Reb, sitting on a bench and sharing a sandwich with the curious black squirrels. He was wearing jeans and a rough cotton shirt; his jacket and his cloth bag were at his side. His hair was longer than it had been during any of his previous trips to New York, but it didn't quite reach his shoulders. Settiniaz saw him from behind, and a bizarre emotion overtook him suddenly. "He gave off such a feeling of solitude," he said later. "And he was staring at the ground, a few feet in front of him, his eyes full of dreams. . . . I don't know what came over me. . . ."

Settiniaz came closer, and stood there. Only after a few seconds did Reb realize he was there. He smiled.

"I didn't want to come up to Fifty-eighth Street," he said "Forgive me; I had my reasons. Serious ones. Are you expected anywhere?"

"I was on my way home to have dinner."

"And after that you were going to return to the office?"

"Yes."

Reb moved the bag and the jacket, and Settiniaz sat down. The squirrels, who had scrambled away at the arrival of this intruder, returned. Reb threw whatever bread he had left to them. He said very softly: "David, over three years ago you offered me your resignation."

"My offer still stands," Settiniaz said, and in the same instant regretted it, sensing that it was clearly inappropriate.

Reb shook his head.

"That is not the problem, or at least I was not referring to that kind of resignation. David, things are going to change, in a . . . spectacular way. Everything you have done for thirty years will be affected by it. You are the first one I am talking to about this. And that is only right."

Settiniaz's pulse began racing. And, as he asked the question, he had the same feeling of having said the wrong thing, of missing the point.

"Not even to Georges Tarras?"

"Georges is aware of what is about to happen, but I needed him. I could not have done it any other way. David, there has been a shadow between us, and I would like to see it disappear. Lately, I have had a very difficult decision to make, and I have depended on you for many, far too many things. Forgive me."

An incomprehensible emotion came over Settiniaz. He was looking at the thin face and was not far from admitting to himself that, after all, and in spite of everything, he had for this man an unsuspected amount of affection.

"And this difficult decision had been made now?"

"Yes, Everything's set. It is about this that I wanted to speak to you, David."

He told him then what was going to happen, and how and especially why he felt he had to do such a thing. He spoke in his usual slow, calm voice, without one word pronounced in a higher tone than another, in that polished, almost precious English he always used.

"It's suicide," said Settiniaz in a hollow voice, after an interminable silence.

"That is not the question. The question is you."

"You are destroying everything we built over thirty years," said Settiniaz, in dismay.

"The question is you. I have asked too much of you to accept the idea that you might be placed in an embarrasing situation, in the most embarrassing situation, because of me. You can retire now, go on a trip, disappear for a while, until things quiet down. I think you should do it. After May 5, you will be hounded; they won't leave you alone for one second; you will be right in the center of the spotlight, with all the unpleasantness that entails. Real unpleasantness, David. You protected me for too long; they won't forgive you for that, not in this country."

Settiniaz closed his eyes.

"Leave the sinking ship."

"In a way."

Reb started speaking again, about all the things that Settiniaz could do to avoid exposure.

Settiniaz was barely listening. He felt as if he had been knocked out. And then suddenly, his decision having been made without his even realizing he had made it, he said, sure of himself for once in his life: "I would like to go to France, Reb."

Reb looked at him.

"You are not a man to make snap decisions."

"That is true."

Silence. Reb shook his head slowly.

"Do you think madness is contagious?"

His eyes were laughing.

Settiniaz let himself go completely. He smiled.

"According to Tarras, it's the only reasonable thing."

They left for France on the twentieth and landed directly at Marseilles. The big country house that had belonged to Suzanne Settiniaz was twelve and a half miles from Aix-en-Provence, on six acres of land. There was even a little river, rich in trout.

"I was not aware that you had bought it when my grandmother died. In fact, I reproached myself for having let it be sold."

"It is not in my name, but in the name of your youngest daughter, Susan."

Stunned, Settiniaz could not find anything to say. He suddenly remembered a letter Suzanne Settiniaz had written him, some thirty-one years before: "I met the most disconcerting boy, the strangest and yet also the most extraordinarily intelligent boy. . . . If there is anything you can do . . . for Reb Michael Klimrod . . ."

"My grandmother was infinitely more perceptive than I. She loved you very much, though she hardly knew you. She often asked me questions about you. . . ."

They were walking down a path lined with giant two-hundred-year-old plane trees. Suddenly the way one often becomes aware of the most evident things, even though he has walked by them day after day but without seeing them, Settiniaz understood Reb Klimrod's unbelievable solitude. A powerful emotion seized him, nearly tore him apart, in this garden of which he himself had so many memories of a happy childhood and adolescence, the picture of his entire life, so ordered and so peaceful.

"Reb, if there is anything that I can do for you . . ."

"You have done so much."

"I would like to do more. If you wish, I will continue to take care of your affairs—what if I have a few problems!—to take care of them for as long as I can."

He wanted to say more, and say something else. For example, to offer the peace of his own family circle, which Klimrod had never entered, and to offer his friendship, which, he could see now, he had measured out sparingly, when he had not simply refused it. "I was never anything more than an accountant, in his eyes, and it was my fault," he remembers. All it would have taken was one word, at one moment. . . . That is the most painful regret I have: that I never tried to go beyond courtesy. With him, I was always stupidly on my guard, out of short-sightedness and an instinctive refusal to accept greatness, out of an idiotic self-esteem, and maybe also out of the ridiculous fear of being oppressed by his personality. I envy Georges Tarras, who was content to love him without looking any further, and who, seeing him far less often, knew him so much better than I."

During the evening of the twentieth, they had dinner on the large square in town, where there is a large fountain. It was an April night that announced summer. And it was that evening that Reb Klimrod told the story of the visit to his father's house, which had been completely emptied except for the wheelchair, forgotten in the small elevator hidden behind a tabernacle panel that came from the Tyrol or Bohemia.

And the next day, arriving one by one from all over the world, answering the call that had come from Reb, they all appeared, amazed to find themselves so numerous, astounded by the incredible power that, grouped together for the first time in thirty years, they, the King's Men, represented.

To Hang and Nessim Shahadzé, to Paul Soubise, Jorge Socrates, Ethel Court, Nelson Coëlho, Thadeus Töpfler, Nick and Tony Petridis, Jubal Wynn, Francisco Santana, Philip Vandenbergh, Ernie Gozchiniak, Jamie Rochas, Henry Chance, Roger Dunn, Kim Foysie, the least important amoung them handling for the King a fortune of one hundred million dollars at a minimum—to all of them Reb Klimrod announced what he was about to do. He pointed out at the start that nothing would be changed as far as they were concerned, and that, unless they decided to end their collaboration with him on the spot and leave, they could continue to take care of their respective fiefs.

Except that, from this point on, it would be known that they were operating in his name.

He told them that he was going to reveal his face, reveal who he was and the extent of his fabulous fortune. Certainly not out of pride for his accomplishments, but because he would have to explain how he had created this kingdom in the heart of Amazonia, which he now wanted to proclaim as a state, and demand that its existence be recognized by what is commonly referred to as a "league" of nations, though so disparate in reality.

He told them that he did not have the slightest illusion about his chances of being heard and followed when he announced the official birth of the new state, with the most complete indifference toward laws and their pretended application, which he was, in fact, questioning and denying by this very gesture. He did not doubt that they would make fun of his folly, and of him, because he supposedly rejected any notion of legitimacy, of sovereignty, and of sacrosanct law and other such nonsense whose first consequences was to justify the crushing of the individual and of his liberty.

And, finally, smiling, and looking at them, one after the other, he pointed out that if there were any of them who did not completely understand his reasons, they could always consider the gesture he was about to make as a challenge to the whole world.

14

At around two in the morning, during the night of May 4, 1980, Georges Taras reached the definitive centainty that he would not be able to sleep. He put the light on for the sixth time since he had gone to bed, and foraging through the piles of books cluttering his suite at the Plaza, found his dear old Montaigne, the very edition he had lent to a miraculous young survivor of the Mauthausen camp in Austria.

We have come full circle, he thought.

He looked out of one of the windows and saw Central Park, black under the moon, its business and paths probably far more dangerous at this hour than the Amazonian jungle. He opened the Montaigne at random. Book III, chapter two:

Je propose une vie basse et sans lustre, c'est tout un. . . . On attache aussi bien toute la philosophie morale à une vie populaire et privée qu'à une vie de plus riche étoffe; chaque homme porte la forme entière de l'humaine condition. . . .

(I propose a humble life devoid of luster, it is all one. . . . All moral philosophy can as well be applied to a common and private life as it can to a richer one; each man carrries within himself all of the human condition. . . .)

He went back a few lines.

. . . Le monde n'est qu'une branloire perenne. Toutes choses y branlent sans cesse: la Terre, les rochers du Caucase, les pyramides d'Egypte, et du branle public et du leur. La constance même n'est autre chose qu'un branle un peu plus languissant. Je ne puis assurer mon objet. Il va trouble et chancelant d'une ivresse naturelle . . .

(The world itself is in perpetual motion. All things therein move incessantly: the earth, the rocks of Caucasus, the pyramids of Egypt, all move in public motion and by themselves. Constancy itself is but a slower motion. I cannot secure my object. It stumbles and staggers with a natural drunkenness. . . .)

How many times did he read this book, he thought, during all the years he kept it with him, before coming to give it back to me.

Returning to the center of the room, Tarras noticed that the red button on his telephone was flashing, meaning that a call had come for him while they thought he was asleep. He called the operator. He was told that a Mr. David Settiniaz had called a few minutes earlier, but that, upon learning that Tarras might be asleep, simply left a message that he had called.

"Call him, please," Tarras asked the operator.

Settiniaz answered.

"I cannot sleep, Georges. I am going round in circles."

"By a strange coincidence, Master Settiniaz, I am in the same predicament. Perhaps it's spring. I have some glasses and some ice cubes, and if you could provide the bottle . . ."

"Twenty minutes."

It took him less than fifteen. They drank, not excessively, reassured by each other's presence in the heart of the night. But they nevertheless finished the bottle, as the hours went by, and they saw the sun light up the springtime foliage of the park. They spoke little, not having anything to say but what they already knew, of each other and of Reb, having long since passed the time when, overshadowed by the King's secret, they would keep things from each other.

They did not even wonder where he might be. They did not know. Tarras, a week before, had prepared for him an exhaustive exegesis of his own work of legal compilation, with the help of the Madison Avenue task force. Since then, no news. And Settiniaz knew even less; he had not seen him since Aix-en-Provence.

Neither of them was surprised, or affected by it. They discovered, after making the calculations, by adding up all the time spent with him, that in thirty-five years (they were exactly twelve hours away from it) they had not looked into his eyes for more than one hundred or perhaps one hundred and twenty hours. If they could still be surprised by anything when it came to him, it was that, and the influence he had nevertheless had on both their lives. Not only on their lives, but on those of hundreds of thousands of men and women, whose destiny he had changed. They agreed on this.

And there was another thing on which they agreed: were he to disappear completely, maybe within the next ten or twelve hours, the monstrous machine he had built would still keep turning, producing perfectly useless riches, since he did not care about them.

In fact, it was perfectly conceivable, the mechanics being what they were, that the seventeen billion dollars of this year of 1980 might become within the next ten years, thirty or forty billion; and even more by the end of the century. It was mad, but very possible, maybe probable.

As long as the system that had permitted such a blossoming lasted until then.

"And here we go philosophizing," said Tarras. "This is not the time for that. It is time to get ourselves showered and dressed, Master Settiniaz. Or else we will be in quite a state when the time comes. . . ."

"We are in quite a state," said Tarras. "If you are half as nervous as I am, I sincerely pity you."

He, at least, had the strength or power to seek refuge in sarcasm and irony. That was not the case for Settiniaz, who was pale as a ghost.

The taxi dropped them off on First Avenue. The entrance to

the United Nations was animated, but no more or less than usual. Cars bearing flags lined up in the circular driveway, dropping off delegates.

The first person Settiniaz saw was Diego Haas.

The small Argentine was standing near the Dag Hammarskjöld Library, and he was alone, leaning against the wall, looking at the crowd that was beginning to arrive with his sparkling yellow eyes full of contemptuous mockery. Settiniaz almost went over to him, putting aside for the moment his feelings of antipathy, to find out whatever he might know. "But he would not have told me anything," he said later. "Had he had a message for me or for Georges, he would already have delivered it. He certainly saw us arrive, and was pretending not to see us. . . ."

May 5 seemed like a summer day, in spite of the light fog over the East River. Tarras and Settiniaz walked to the entrance of the thirty-nine-story-glass-and-steel tower designed by Le Corbusier.

But they did not go inside. They waited in front of the Liberty Bell.

"When is this Arnold Balm supposed to arrive?"

"He should be here in twenty minutes. My God, David, look!"

Settiniaz's glance searched through the thickening crowd in the direction Tarras had indicated. He made out Paul Soubise's elegant thin figure among the bright costumes of some African delegates. Soubise was smiling, but without any joy, almost embarrassed, which was surprising for him.

And he was not alone. Nessim Shahadźe and the Petridis brothers appeared together. In the next minute, all the King's Men were there, forming a group, as if to create a front, all of them adopting a polite, tense expression of false indifference.

Settiniaz, his throat tight, said: "I did not know you were coming. . . ."

Soubise nodded.

"We did not know ourselves, David."

The sparkling intelligence that usually lit up his eyes was for once covered with a kind of timidity.

"To the devil with ridicule."

And then, emerging from the crowd, without acknowledging each other and known only to Settiniaz, the Black Dogs also appeared, Lerner and Bercovici first, looking impassive and somber, strangely similar to their fanatically secret ways, as if they were hesitant to be seen in broad daylight. The emotion wracking Settiniaz became more pronounced as he thought: He notified them also, to tell them the end of the story. Perhaps he brought them all together, or, more probably, contacted them one by one. The second explanation seemed more likely, since, besides Bercovici and Lerner, all these men and women, whom Settiniaz had for years seen coming in and out of his office, passing without knowing each other, now remained scattered, looking around furtively. They did not form a group, although there were nearly thirty of them, some having come from Europe, Asia, or Africa.

"Here is Balm," said Tarras. "Right on time."

It was exactly nine-thirty, and the delegates of some one hundred and sixty nations began to enter the large and beautiful domed building where the General Assembly met.

"I will accompany Balm and wait for you over there," said Tarras.

Settiniaz nodded, incapable of uttering a word, managing just barely to control the shaking of his hands.

Tarras walked away with the man who had come from the Caribbean and who was carrying, like a salesman, his fantastic flag, packed in a long black case.

At almost the same time, there was some commotion near the library. Settiniaz was surprised that he had not thought of them sooner: the delegation was led by Marnie Oakes and Trajana da Silva, followed by MacKenzie, Coltzesco, Escalante, Ung Seng, Sobieski, Hathaway, the Weizmanns, Everett, and many more whose names Settiniaz remembers more or less. They had undoubtedly come from Amazonia.

The crowd was growing, now that the beginning of the session was approaching. Settiniaz looked for Diego Haas, but the little Argentine had gone, or, at least, was no longer in the same place. His excitement and near-anguish increased. Any minute now, he thought. To his right Soubise was talking, in French, quickly, simply in reaction.

A car appeared.

Then another.

Both bore a green flag and the light-blue sticker of the United Nations.

Four Yanomani got out of the first car, two more and Reb

from the second. Settiniaz recognized Jaua. The group started walking, Reb at the front and the only one wearing shoes; his companions had remained barefoot, although they had donned pants and shirts.

Something happened then, something inexplicable: a double row formed, spontaneously, in absolute silence, a double row through which Reb and the Indians walked with impassive faces. The small group headed for the General Asembly building and, having presented the necessary documents to the guards, went inside.

"Let's go," said Soubise.

He moved and all the others followed.

Settiniaz remained alone, incapable of moving, trying desperating to measure what he felt, with his never-ending need to understand. He discovered, in the end, that it was pride, an extraordinary pride, which overshadowed everything else.

The crowd had left.

Settiniaz waited a few more minutes. He felt uncertain. He was not sure he wanted to witness what was bound to be—he was sure of it—bitter and painful, and which would stay with him for the rest of his days. He did not have the courage. He finally made up his mind. Reb had said: "I don't speak Russian or Chinese, and not enough Arabic. But I will speak in English, in French, and in German, which are the three other official languages. This is perhaps childish, David, but if there was a language that had no nationality, that is the one I would use."

Settiniaz went in and reached the rooms reserved for simultaneous translations.

Tarras opened the door to the little room, and said: "I thought you would never come. It's almost time. Arnold Balm has almost finished his formalities, and then it will be his turn."

"I am not going to stay," said Settiniaz.

From behind his glasses, Tarras's sharp eyes looked at him, amicably.

"I didn't know you to be this sentimental, David."

"I didn't know it myself," answered Settiniaz in a hoarse voice.

He remained on the threshold. There were two translators, a man and a woman, and facing them, beyond the glass window, the immense room appeared bathed in a yellowish light. Settiniaz

484

was directly across from the podium, which was lit by several spotlights and was surrrounded by electronic boards on which appeared the names of the represented countries.

"*Now*," said Tarras . . .

. . . at the instant when, in the room below, Arnold Balm concluded his brief speech.

Tarras leaned over, with a new and added tension in his whole body and, in his eyes, something of the avid ferocity of Diego Haas.

They waited in the outer hall. Settiniaz leaned against a wall, which caused one of the guards to ask, "You look pale. Are you all right?"

"Yes."

He started walking again. He went down to the cafeteria and asked for a glass of water. Overtaken by nausea, he hardly touched it. After a few minutes, he went outside.

No longer blocked by the great steel-and-glass tower, the May sun shone down.

May 5.

Thirty-five years ago on this day he arrived at Mauthausen. *On this day!* He shivered. The coincidence was too great to attribute to chance.

He sat on the steps, indifferent to the questioning glances of people passing by.

He sensed someone beside him. Diego Haas.

"What's happening?"

"They said he couldn't represent the Cayman Islands. They said Balm's request was refused. They said he is not an official representative and only official delegates can speak."

Haas was smiling, almost a mocking smile.

"How is he taking it?"

"He told them he'd give them half a billion dollars if they'd let him speak for half an hour."

Settiniaz said, "They'll never believe him about the money. Will they let him speak?"

Diego Haas shrugged. He held out the palms of his hands. "Who knows?" Then he started back to the building.

Settiniaz got to his feet and followed.

They came upon Reb standing outside of the huge doors, waiting for them to open. And, as the two men came close to him, the doors did open.

A small dapper-looking man, a look-alike for David Niven, strolled out of the large hall directly to Reb.

"Mr. Klimrod?"

"Yes."

The Security Council has considered your request."

"Will they allow me to speak?"

"It isn't possible."

"Why?"

"It just isn't possible."

"Why?"

"You are not official. You do not represent any member nation in the United Nations."

"I represent Amazonia. That's what I've come to speak about. If I can be heard, perhaps some solution to the threat of a world-wide nuclear holocaust—"

"I'm sorry."

Klimrod stared at him. Then slowly, as if his strength was ebbing with each word, he said, "You allowed Arafat to speak! Why not me?"

"It isn't possible. We have rules. It's against our rules." The dapper man leaned forward as if sharing a confidence: "Frankly, Mr. Klimrod, it's against our interest. Boundaries and nation-alities and tribalism—that's what we're all about. If they would disappear, we would disappear. There would be no need for us, then, would there?" He winked.

Klimrod stared at him but the man avoided eye contact. Instead he surveyed Klimrod from his headband to his sandals.

"I'm sorry," the little man said. For the first time his eyes met those of Reb, but only for seconds. Then he whirled about like a ballet dancer doing a pirouette and hurried back into the hall. The guards closed the large doors behind him.

There was a stillness, broken when a newspaper reporter hur-ried up to Reb's side. "Mr. Klinerode, is it true that you were trying to buy time before the United Nations? They say you are a billionaire. They say—"

Ignoring him, Reb Michael Klimrod began slowly to walk to-ward the exit. The reporter started to follow, but changed his mind. "Frankly, pal," he called, "you don't look like you have bus fare to the Bronx!"

Georges Tarras was crying.

Haas stared, as if mesmerized.

Diego raced passed Reb on the way to the underground parking lot.

At the entrance, Reb paused and turned around. He stared at the high cellings and the far walls. Then his eyes turned to those he knew.

"Reb, come with me. I'll get my car—"

"No," he said. "I will go with Diego."

Settiniaz hurried after him and then stopped, frozen in place when Reb's eyes met his. He heard him mutter a single word: *Mauthausen*.

And then the tall thin figure was gone.

From a page in a journal kept by David Settiniaz:
I never saw him again. Nor have I heard from him.

The Black Dogs have also disappeared from my life. I get no messages. I receive no instructions. No courier from Reb has ever again visited my Fifty-eighth Street office.

I have done what needed to be done. I've taken care of my succession for the day when I retire or die. All the King's Men have done the same. The machine will keep functioning, smoothly and efficiently. It could go on for centuries if, indeed, human beings go on for centuries.

Amazonia is there still, a Kingdom without a King. It is without direction and the project has begun to decay.

More than three years have passed since May 5, 1980.

I miss him. I've done everything I could to find him. Georges Tarras went with me to visit the woman painter in Brooklyn Heights who looked so much like Charmian Page. She hadn't seen or heard from him either.

Our agents in Rio checked Diego's house near Ipanema Beach. It's occupied by a family who never heard the names of Klimrod or Haas.

Ubaldo Rocha was difficult to reach. I personally went all the way to the Carcarai Falls to confront him. He and Jaua both said they knew nothing of Reb's whereabouts. They seemed much too sad to be lying.

I would have ventured the guess that he'd go away with Georges Tarras. Instead, he chose Diego. Crazy Diego. And he hasn't been seen again since that day.

Tarras is sure Reb is alive, but Georges believes what he wants to believe.

Actually, I don't even know if he's still alive. I hope he is. It would be difficult for me to face the possibility that I will never see him again. I cannot face the thought that we had all those years together and never once did I look into his gray eyes, lonely and full of dreams, and tell him how much I admired him and that I loved him.